THE LIVES OF THE SAINTS

THE
LIVES OF THE
SAINTS

by Omer Englebert

Translated by Christopher and
Anne Fremantle

BARNES
&NOBLE
BOOKS
NEW YORK

NIHIL OBSTAT

Edgar Hardwick, Ph.D.,

Censor Deputatus

IMPRIMATUR

✠ *Leo*

Episcopus Northantoniensis

Northantoniae, die 26a Februarii 1951

This edition published by Barnes & Noble, Inc.

1994 Barnes & Noble Books

ISBN 1-56619-516-0 (casebound)
ISBN 1-56619-836-4 (paperback)

Printed and bound in the United States of America

MC 9 8 7 6 5 4 3 2
MP 9 8 7 6 5 4 3 2 1

CONTENTS

ILLUSTRATIONS

SOURCES OF ILLUSTRATIONS

St. Anthony, St. Agatha, St. Benedict, St. George, St. Margaret, St. Justina, St. Francis, St. Catherine: Jacobus de Voragine 'Legende doree en françoys', Lyon, 1483; St. Urban, Sts. Peter and Paul, St. Augustine: Jacobus de Voragine 'Legenda aurea de Sanctis', Augsburg, 1472; St. Nicholas: Jacobus de Voragine 'Legenda aurea de Sanctis', Lyon, 1486

Initials: 'Catalogum Sanctorum'. Jacques Saccon, Lyon, 1514

Illustration on Title Page: 'Saint Augustin—Sermons', Paris, 1498

INTRODUCTORY NOTE

THERE is generally too much and too little in Lives of the Saints—too much pious exegesis, too little factual information about the saint. Father Omer Englebert has sought to remedy this excess and this lack, and he is uniquely qualified to do so. For he is not only an historian of impeccable authenticity—his life of Saint Francis is the only Catholic one that can be set beside the great scholarly tome of Paul Sabatier, the most erudite of Protestants—but he is also the editor of a new edition of Migne's *Patrologia*, which is the great source for all our knowledge of the Apostolic and the Desert Fathers.

Omer Englebert was born in the Ardennes, on March 31st, 1893. His father, a local landowner, belonged to a family settled at Ollomont-Nadrin for many centuries. His mother, also of local land-owning stock, had Rhenish and Spanish blood. Until the age of eleven, he lived in a little village hidden in the mountains, chiefly occupied with his two pet goats, his dog and his tame crow. He studied at the Ecclesiastical College of Bastogne. A bad pupil, he cared only for music and history.

He wished to become a Franciscan, but his health would not permit it. So he became a secular priest, being ordained *propter beneficia*, and thus being under the jurisdiction of no bishop. This suited his itinerant temperament, and his travels have taken him over all Europe except Russia, and to both North and South America.

In 1919 he founded a monthly, *La Terre Wallonne*. Ordained in 1924 by Cardinal Mercier, he was made by him literary editor of *Vingtième Siècle*. His first book, *La Sagesse du Curé Pecquet*, appeared in 1927, and was an immediate and lasting success. It has been translated into most of the European languages, and was followed by two later volumes, *Le Curé Pecquet Continue* and *Le Curé Pecquet Vit Encore*. Of this character, Henri Clouard writes in his *Histoire de la Littérature Française*: "Essentially true to type, this Father Pecquet is one of the few real priests in modern literature. He gives to orthodoxy the savour of paradox, and defends divine government with all the brilliance usually reserved to the opposition. Moreover the remarks of this saintly individual reflect a wisdom which is marvellously, fully, and sweetly profane."

Henri Clouard sums up the author of the Curé Pequet books, of *Vie et Conversion d'Ève Lavallière, Le Père Damien Apôtre des Lépreux, Vie de Saint Martin, Vie de Saint Pascal Baylon,* and numerous other books by saying, "What distinguishes him is a robust and realistic spirit exacting in substantial values, and therefore opposed to all that is confused, and superficial, in psychology, morals and politics."

ANNE FREMANTLE

PREFACE TO ENGLISH EDITION

SINCE *The Golden Legend*, "lives of the saints, according to the ecclesiastical calendar," have been plentiful in every country. The work of Jacobus de Voragine (d. 1288) has been done over a hundred times, has been abridged, completed, improved upon, spoiled, and still more often, alas, imitated. For, indeed, in other days the custom of reading the life of the day's saint was very widespread.

Our contemporaries have no less need than earlier generations to know the mortal events of the lives of those saints of whom we speak and to whom we pray; those saints who furnish writers and artists with the subjects of their masterpieces; whose names are borne by our cities, towns, and villages and by ourselves. But where can we inquire? Who has time to go to the libraries and examine the sixty volumes of the *Acta Sanctorum*, the dictionaries of Migne, Baudrillart, and Leclercq, or recent hagiographical compilations in a dozen or a score of volumes?

As for the one-volume collections at present on sale, those without religion, and even many good Christians, find them generally uninteresting, for they are either prepared in dictionary style or the little information that they contain is drowned in floods of eloquence and words of edification. Henry Clouard, the best contemporary French critic, writes on this subject: "Why does the hagiographical style so often discourage us? Because it is in the hands of manufacturers of homilies and learned bug-hunters. So in it inanities flourish, neglect struts, and pedantry dilapidates."[1]

What most readers want are the interesting and colourful facts and historical settings of these lives, and they would like these given without solemnity and subjective reflections. It is mainly for this public that the present work has been written. Biographies and not homilies will be found in it. This not because the admiration and respectful friendship due to the saints is denied them here; but on the sole occasion when the author meets them and has a page to devote to them, he has chosen to speak of *them* rather than of anything else; he has preferred to show them at work, tell about their lives, and record their words, rather than digress, comment, harangue, and moralize about them.

The omissions of this work are gladly acknowledged. Some arise from having to cover in fifty or fifteen lines lives at times extremely full. But this fault comes from the style adopted, and it has to be remedied by packing the limited framework to the utmost. If the reader has a mind to know more,

[1] *L'Activité Littéraire*, 1949, No. 41.

he can always acquire a fuller biography of the saint in whom he is interested.

Another omission is due to insufficient emphasis on the virtues of our heroes, as we often fail to point out in what their sanctity consisted or why they have been placed on the altars. But we have feared monotony, which leads to sleep and boredom, let alone that there would then have been no room to say in what respect the life of each saint was different from that of others. This defect is moreover easily reparable, and we shall so far as is possible repair it once and for all. Let the reader kindly round out any notices which seem to him incomplete with the following lines:

"Finally let us add that our saint loved God with all his heart, and his neighbour as himself; that he cherished Our Lord Jesus Christ, meditating his words in the Gospel, feeding on His Body at the altar, and counting on His merits to be saved; and that in addition he lived in the fellowship of the Holy Spirit whose inspiration directed his conduct. He was humble about himself, seeking the last place, and to be scorned; he obeyed his superiors; he was merciful; he practised mortification and patience; prayed without ceasing; restrained his passions; followed the narrow way; esteemed himself unworthy of graces received; believed that he could never do enough in response to the divine goodness, or to merit heaven. Far from seeking in his supernatural virtues a pretext to elude the natural law, he avoided lying, double-dealing, deceit, stealing, and flattery of his neighbour; he was always straightforward and regarded all his brethren as having been created for God and not for himself."

To this supplement, everywhere indispensable, it will be convenient, in those cases where the biography has provoked some surprise, to add here and there the following:

"If this saint did things which do not have your entire approval, reader, reflect that the customs of his time were not those of our own; that his character was not by any means yours; that the Creator, bestowing His gifts unequally, gives some of His creatures more originality than others, and He often gives special inspirations to His special friends; that indeed is doubtless His right, as it is your duty to avoid judging too hastily or believing your judgments to be infallible. And if, seized with a desire of emulation, you decide to attempt holiness for yourself, you can always begin by imitating the example of the saints who please you, before following in the steps of the ones who put you off."

Of the twenty thousand of the elect mentioned in the martyrologies, the breviaries, missals, calendars, dictionaries, and hagiographical collections, we have only retained around two thousand three hundred, and have given space to a bare thousand. This privileged thousand are those who left their mark on history, or under whose patronage men and women of today continue to be placed. The others receive but a few lines.

It will be noticed that our biographies are by no means of equal length or typographical composition. At first sight this may seem somewhat arbitrary. But in view of the space at our disposal, to have done otherwise would have been to sacrifice those saints whose names are most widely known, and many readers would have complained at seeing their patrons neglected. It will be seen, however, that not one of the great names of hagiographical history has been omitted.

Among the twenty or thirty thousand facts, dates, names of persons and places which this work includes, we do not flatter ourselves that no errors will be found. Some arise from the typists, typographers, paleographers, and geographers who have lent us their co-operation; the rest should be imputed to us; all, we hope, can be corrected in due course.

The Church generally fixes the feast of the saint on the date, known or presumed, of his death. When this date is already taken, another date is chosen for the feast. This is the reason that a certain number of saints are mentioned twice in the Roman martyrology: first, on the date of their decease, a second time on the day the Church wishes to mention them in its liturgy. This is the case with St. John Chrysostom, St. Cecilia, St. Francis de Sales, St. John Fisher, and certain others. In this work we have almost always placed the notice of the saints on the actual date that their liturgical feast is celebrated by the Church.

How far can the reader trust what we have recorded about the saints? If he will read with attention, and frequently between the lines, he will not often risk being mistaken. For the saints who are well known, we have drawn our information from the sources or from works of criticism. For the less known saints we have said about them no more than we know, or than is known to scholars. Qualifying expressions then warn that, historically speaking, we are no longer on firm ground.

And there are the saints who are only known through their legends. These are sometimes the most honoured, those who seem best to recompense the faith of those who invoke their aid, those who have left the greatest mark on the speech of the people and on works of art. Are we then to pass by in silence those who were worthy to become a legend? On the contrary, we have retold their legends with pleasure, certain that, among poets and persons of taste, none will complain.

O. E.

THE SAINTS OF JANUARY

January 1st

ST. ODILO (d. 1046)

NATIVE of Auvergne, Odilo was the son of Bérald de Mercœur, of whom it was said that his word was his bond, and his mother was Gerberga, who died as a nun of St. John at Autun.

Cured in his childhood by Our Lady, he always cherished a tender devotion to his heavenly guardian. One day when he was singing in choir the verse of the *Te Deum* where it is said, "When thou didst take upon thee to deliver man, thou didst not abhor the Virgin's womb," he was carried away in ecstasy and fell unconscious. From that time there arose among the Benedictines the custom, which still exists, of making a low bow at the recitation of these same words. At the age of twenty-nine, Odilo entered Cluny, and three years later succeeded St. Mayeul. He was abbot for fifty-six years, until his death on January 1st, 1046.

It was St. Odilo who first instituted a day of prayer for the faithful departed. He set it for Cluny on the day following All Saints; due to him, this feast found its place in the Roman liturgy.

The institution of the Truce of God is also due to him; by it princes and lords bound themselves to respect from Wednesday evening till Monday morning the life and possessions of their neighbour. The authority and virtue of the abbot of Cluny must have been extraordinary for his contemporaries to agree to such a restraint upon their native ferocity for four days and five nights a week.

Moreover, the saint's goodness was extended to all. During the fearful famine of 1006, he sold the sacred vessels and precious ornaments of his church to buy bread for the unfortunate. As humble as he was charitable, Odilo refused to occupy the archiepiscopal see of Lyons when elected to it in 1036.

CIRCUMCISION OF OUR LORD

Established in the East about the middle of the 4th century, this feast was only adopted by Rome three or four centuries later.

St. FULGENTIUS (468–533)

By origin a Carthaginian, Fulgentius became a monk, founded monasteries, became bishop of Ruspe (district of Tunis), was exiled to Sardinia and returned to die in his church at Ruspe. He is the author of various treatises on theology and apologetics, Augustinian in tendency.

St. FELIX

Bishop of Bourges, died about 580.

St. CLARUS

Abbot of St. Marcellus at Vienne in Dauphiny (d. about 660).

Blessed WILLIAM

Abbot of St. Benignus at Dijon (961–1031).

Blessed HUGOLINUS

Augustinian hermit of Gualdo in Umbria (d. 1260).

Blessed GUISEPPE MARIA TOMMASI

Theatine monk, born in Sicily in 1649; author of works of piety and learning; died, a cardinal, in 1713.

St. VICENZO MARIA STRAMBI

Passionist, bishop of Tolentino (1745–1824).

St. TELEMACHUS

Martyred in Rome about the year 400.

January 2nd
ST. MACARIUS THE YOUNGER (d. about 408)

MACARIUS, called the Younger, to distinguish him from other solitaries of the same name who lived, as he did, in the Egyptian desert, was born at Alexandria at the beginning of the 4th century and died aged almost a hundred, about the year 408.

He began by being a sugar-plum merchant, a fact remembered by pastry cooks and confectioners who have taken him as patron. At the age of forty, he withdrew into Nitria where thousands of men were living a life of contemplation, devoted to manual work and to penance. Macarius, who was a priest, was very soon held up as a model of piety and a master of spiritual knowledge. Many were the vexations he suffered from the devil and the persecutions he endured at the hands of Lucius, Arian patriarch of Alexandria.

This austere man seems to have been a poet, and, like St. Francis of Assisi later, to have enjoyed the friendship of the wild animals. His friend Pallas reports that a hyena one day came to place before him her newborn cub which was blind. Macarius stroked it and restored its sight. The next day he saw the hyena coming back with a magnificent sheepskin in her mouth, a token of thanks from the grateful mother. Macarius accepted it, and made it into a tunic which he wore until his death.

The *Lausiac History* further relates that, crossing the Nile in a boat, Macarius, whose face was always joyful, was questioned by an officer who said to him: "How can you be so happy when you live in such poverty?" The anchorite replied: "It is because I despise this world, of which you are the slave, as much as it deserves." This reply so struck the officer that he too became a hermit in order to enjoy thenceforth the same happiness.

THE HOLY NAME OF JESUS
Originally confined to the Franciscan order, this feast was extended to the universal Church by Innocent XIII in 1721.

Sts. NARCISSUS, MARCELLINUS, and ARGEUS
Martyrs of Tomi in Pontia (4th century).

St. MARTINIAN
Bishop of Milan (d. about 435).

St. ASPASIUS
Is supposed to have evangelized Melun (d. about 560).

St. FROBERT

Abbot of Moutier-la-Celle in the Troyes country (d. 673).

St. VINCENTIANUS

Hermit of Limousin (d. about 672).

St. ADELARD

Grandson of Charles Martel, abbot of Corbie; honoured and persecuted in turn by the Carolingian kings; one of the great monks of his time (d. 827).

Blessed GERARD CAGNOLI

Franciscan lay brother, died at Palermo in 1345.·

Blessed STEPHANA QUINZANÌ

Dominican tertiary of the Brescia country (d. 1530).

January 3rd

ST. GENEVIEVE (d. about 500)

BORN at Nanterre about 420, Genevieve lived during the last convulsions of the Roman Empire and during the establishment of the Frankish monarchy from which the nation of France evolved. She died at Paris about 500.

When barely seven, she promised St. Germain of Auxerre to embrace the religious life, and she was not more than fifteen when she made her vow of virginity before Villicus, bishop of Paris. Two years later, her parents being dead, she left Nanterre and came to Paris to live with her godmother. She lived there in partial seclusion, favoured with extraordinary graces, notably of the gift of reading consciences and calming the possessed.

Her virtues and her miracles gave her an immense authority; people even went so far as to attribute the defeat of Attila to her prayers. What in fact she did bring about was the prevention of a general exodus of the inhabitants of Paris when, in 451, Attila swept down upon Gaul. "The women let themselves be persuaded easily enough," wrote the author of the *Vita sanctae Genovefae.* "As for the husbands, she repeated to them that they had nothing to gain by flight; the places where they were counting on refuge were surely devastated, while Paris would certainly be preserved." Events justified her prediction. Abandoning the Paris road, the Huns turned toward Orléans and were defeated by the Romans and the Franks on the Catalonian fields. Later, when the Franks attempted to starve Paris, it was again Genevieve who by her calm and ingenuity ensured the revictualling of the town and prevented the whole population from dying of hunger.

These are only a few of the exploits which can be added to the score of this good, able, and heroic woman. Furthermore, all her contemporaries, including Childeric and Clovis, venerated her; and the city of Paris regards her as its particular patroness.

St. FLORENTIUS

Bishop of Vienne, whose life some place in the 3rd, some in the 4th century.

St. BERTILIA

A widow, died as a recluse at Marœil in Artois, in 687.

January 4th
ST. RIGOBERT or ROBERT (d. about 750)

IT is known how the mayors of the palace reduced the Merovingian sovereigns to the role of "do-nothing kings" and ended by supplanting them. It was on the eve of this change of dynasty that Rigobert lived. Having been the Benedictine abbot of Orbais, he became archbishop of Rheims, and was persecuted by the mayor of the palace, Charles Martel. As brave and able as he was ambitious, the latter, who was the actual ruler of Austrasia, also planned to conquer Neustria. He achieved this when, in 717, he won the victory of Vincy against Rainfroy, mayor of Neustria. As soon as he was victorious, Charles exiled Rigobert, whose sole crime had been to remain neutral in these conflicts, to far-off Gascony, and gave his temporal power to Bishop Milo, who already possessed that of Trier.

Later an arrangement was made between Milo and Rigobert, which allowed the exile to return and live on his little property of Gernicourt, near Rheims. He lived in retreat and in prayer, patiently bearing his humiliation, rancorous toward none. One of his greatest joys was sometimes to reappear in his old cathedral, where the usurper Milo authorized him to perform certain ecclesiastical functions.

St. Rigobert died a little before 751, the year in which Pepin the Short, son of Charles Martel, proclaimed himself king of the Franks, thus founding the Carolingian dynasty which reigned for two centuries over France.

St. Titus

Disciple, companion, and correspondent of St. Paul, died on the island of Crete about the year 96.

St. Benedicta

Martyred at Rome about 362.

St. Pharailde

Sister of St. Gudula and niece of St. Gertrude of Nivelles, was long married to a man who ill-treated her. Widowed, she devoted herself to good works in Belgium, and died aged ninety (8th century).

Blessed Roger of Ellant (d. 1160)

Cistercian of English origin who founded the abbey of Ellant (Ardennes).

Blessed Angela of Foligno (d. 1309)

Born at Foligno of a wealthy family, Angela married young, had several children, lived in sin, even committing sacrilege; she was converted, became a Franciscan tertiary, and passed the rest of her life in seclusion, only broken by several pilgrimages to Assisi. The surpassing graces with which she was enriched are recorded in her *Book of the Experiences of the True Faithful*. Angela is one of the great Catholic mystics. Some call her "saint".

January 5th
ST. SIMEON STYLITES (d. 459)

STYLITES comes from a Greek word, *stulos*, signifying column. It was in fact upon a column that St. Simeon passed the greater part of his strange existence.

He was born on the borders of Cilicia and Syria; at the age of thirteen he was watching his father's sheep when he heard this verse of the Gospel: "Woe upon you who laugh now; you shall mourn and weep" (Luke vi, 25). He asked an old man the meaning of these words, and it was explained to him that eternal happiness is obtained by suffering, and that it is in solitude it is most surely gained.

The young boy at once joined some hermits of the district, with whom he lived for two years. Then he lived for some ten years at the monastery of Teleda where his unusual mortifications finally caused his dismissal. Then, reaching Tellnesin, near Antioch, he settled in a cell where they walled up the door on Ash Wednesday and in which he remained confined until Easter morning without food.

Importuned by increasingly indiscreet visitors and admirers, Simeon resolved to escape their importunities by living thenceforth on a column. He stood upright, without shelter, exposed to the intemperate climate, almost continually absorbed in prayer. On feast days, after nones, he addressed two exhortations to the people, and at all times replied in a friendly way to those who had recourse to his arbitration and advice. Numerous were the spiritual and bodily cures which he accomplished. Moreover, homage meant nothing to him, and he remained perfectly humble.

He died in 459 in his sixty-ninth year, as he was bowing in beginning his first prayer. There are still remains, at Gata'at Sema'an, of the immense basilica raised upon his place of penance.

St. Telesphorus

Pope for ten years, martyred at Rome in 126.

St. Emiliana

Roman virgin, aunt of Pope St. Gregory (d. 6th century).

St. Amata

Abbess of a convent in the Thebaid (d. 5th century).

St. Gerlach (d. about 1170)

Born about 1100 in the country of Fauquemont (Holland), Gerlach was first a soldier and even a brigand. The loss of his wife made him reflect upon his ways. He left for Rome, confessed to Pope Eugene III, who ordered him to care for the sick in Jerusalem for seven years. This penance accomplished, he returned to settle near Maestricht, where he led a hermit's life until his death. Although he was much slandered, St. Hildegard had a great esteem and spiritual friendship for Gerlach.

January 6th

ST. GUARINUS or GUÉRIN (d. 1150)

A NATIVE of Pont Musson in Lorraine, Guarinus was first a Benedictine monk at Molesme in Burgundy. He was about twenty-five when he was sent with two or three companions to the diocese of Geneva to found a new abbey. Established in the valley of Aulps, it quickly prospered and about 1121 was extended to Lake Bourget to a place later named Hautecombe.

When the Cistercian reform was inaugurated, the abbot of Aulps wished to join it. It was Guarinus, elected abbot about 1110, who obtained from Pope Callistus II permission to pass with his monks under the Cistercian obedience. From that time they all gave up the brown habit for the white tunic and their fervour became such that in 1136 St. Bernard wrote to Guarinus to congratulate them.

Two years later, the clergy and the faithful of Sion in Valais elected the abbot of Aulps as bishop; he at first refused the honour, and it took nothing less than the insistence of Pope Innocent II to overcome his unwillingness. Nevertheless, every year Guarinus left Sion to spend some time in retreat in his beloved abbey. His last visit there was in August 1150; on the 27th of that month he again left for Sion, but his strength gave out on the way and, retracing his steps, he returned to die in his monk's cell.

The characteristic virtues of St. Guarinus seem to have been wisdom and severity united with gentleness. His relics were venerated at the abbey of Aulps until 1793 when they were profaned by two members of the Directoire sent to seek the abbey treasure. Some parts of them were saved, and were afterwards said to have preserved many soldiers from death on the battlefields.

EPIPHANY OF OUR LORD

Epiphany comes from a Greek word signifying manifestation or apparition. From the 4th century on, the Greeks commemorated at this feast the baptism of Our Saviour, when it was revealed that He was the son of God ("Thou art my beloved Son, in Thee I am well pleased."—Luke iii, 22) and the marriage of Cana, when Jesus for the first time publicly manifested his miraculous power. The Latins recall in addition upon this day the appearance of the star in the East and the journey of the Magi to Bethlehem.

Sts. MELCHIOR and GASPAR

The two wise kings to whom a white face has been given by popular tradition. The third, St. Balthasar, whose feast is January 11th, the same tradition holds to have been a negro.

St. GERTRUDE VAN DER OOSTEN (d. 1358)

Dutch mystic who received the stigmata and died in 1358, at the almshouse of Delft. Her surname came from her habit of singing a song of her country *Het daghet in den Oosten* (Day breaketh in the East), applying these words to Our Lord. Some only give her a title of Blessed.

St. PETER THOMAS (d. 1366)

Carmelite monk, a great preacher, a fiery defender of the doctrine of the Immaculate Conception, bishop, archbishop, patriarch, universal legate of the Holy See in the East, Peter Thomas worked for the reunion of the Greek and Latin Churches and directed a crusade against the Turk, which, however, failed. He died at Famagusta (Cyprus).

January 7th
ST. VITALIS (d. 1122)

VITALIS was born at Tierceville in the Bayeux diocese. In his student days he was nicknamed "the little vicar" by his fellow disciples, so much virtue and piety did they see in him. The Count of Mortain wanted to make him his chaplain but, in 1188, Vitalis went to the wilderness of Mantilly, in the diocese of Séez, to lead the eremitic life. With Raoul de la Futaye and Bernard of Abbeville, he came under the influence of the celebrated preacher Robert d'Arbrissel, founder of Fontevrault, and for some time shared his apostolate.

Becoming a master in his turn, Vitalis had many disciples who came to him. He built in the forest of Savigny, in Normandy, a monastery where the Benedictine rule was followed and reinforced with most rigorous rules. This monastery increased greatly and spread to England and Ireland.

Vitalis died in choir, in the darkness of the night, as he was reciting the Little Hours of the Blessed Virgin with his community. The monk whose duty it was to read the lesson at matins had turned towards him to ask him to give the ritual benediction; Vitalis gave it to him saying: "May the inter-cession of the Blessed Virgin Mary grant that we are reunited in the assembly of angels." Then, suddenly, he expired while a supernatural brightness and a celestial perfume filled the church.

St. LUCIAN OF ANTIOCH

Professor of exegesis, translator of the Old Testament, martyred at Nicomedia in 312.

St. VALENTINE

Missionary bishop in Rhaetia (d. 440?).

St. TYLLO (d. 702)

A missionary of Saxon origin; died as a recluse at Solignac in Limousin.

Blessed WIDUKIND

Duke of Westphalia; enemy, then friend and godson of Charlemagne, died fighting against the Suevi in 804.

St. CANUTE

Duke of Schleswig, put to death by political enemies in 1130.

St. ALDRIC

Of German origin, was bishop of Le Mans for twenty-three years (d. 856).

St. RAINOLD (d. 960?)

The youngest, it is said, of the four sons of Aymon. It is told how, having become a monk at St. Pantaleon in Cologne, he was killed by some stone-masons whose work he was inspecting.

St. CEDD

English bishop and missionary, died of the plague at the monastery of Lestingay in 664.

In addition, today the Roman martyrology mentions the RETURN FROM EGYPT of the Child Jesus.

January 8th
ST. SEVERINUS (d. 482)

IT is not known whence Severinus came when, in 454, he appeared at Astura on the Danube, preaching penance and prophesying the imminent arrival of the barbarians. None listened to him and the barbarians completely sacked the town. Then he went to Commagana, then to Favianes, where his words were heard and where his intervention resulted in these towns being spared.

For thirty years Severinus displayed prodigious activity, evangelizing Bavaria and Austria, building churches, founding monasteries. He prescribed that his disciples should model themselves upon the early Fathers; by his discourses and his example he inculcated scorn of the world and the fear of God.

Himself so merciful to the poor and to sinners, he led a life of extreme austerity. For a bed he had only a haircloth spread on the ground; he went barefoot in all weathers, had but one tunic, in obedience to the Gospel; he fasted every day until sundown; in Lent he only partook of one meal a week. It is still questionable whether he was a priest. The fact is that he refused to become a bishop, as much in humility as to preserve his freedom of action.

On the feast of the Epiphany in 482, he announced his approaching death. Two days later he gave his monks his last counsels, blessed them, and after receiving the Viaticum gave up the ghost as he was singing the psalm *Laudate Dominum in sanctis ejus* with them. Six years later an invasion of barbarians forced his disciples to take flight. They exhumed the body of Severinus, which they found to be incorrupt, put it on a cart, crossed the Alps, and carried it to Luculanum, near Naples.

Sts. LUCIAN, MAXIMINUS and JULIAN (d. 290?)

A Roman priest, Lucian displayed his zeal in Beauvaisis. Arrested under Diocletian with Maximinus and Julian, he refused, as they did also, to apostasize, and like them was beheaded four miles from Beauvais.

St. APOLLINARIS CLAUDIUS

Bishop of Hieropolis in Phrygia, author of apologetic and polemic works no longer extant (d. after 175).

St. PATIENS

Bishop of Metz (2nd century).

St. FELIX

Bishop of Nantes (d. 582).

St. GUDULA

Virgin, great niece of Pepin of Landen, goddaughter and disciple of St. Gertrude of Nivelles, patroness of the town of Brussels (d. 712?).

St. PEGA

Virgin, hermit, sister of St. Guthlac; like him, passed her life on the island of Croyland (England) and died in the course of a pilgrimage to Rome in 719.

January 9th

ST. ADRIAN (d. 710)

A NATIVE of Africa, Adrian was abbot of Nerida, near Naples, when Pope Vitalian offered him the see of Canterbury, occupied at that moment by Bishop Urphard, whom Rome refused to recognize. Too mistrustful of himself to face such a mission, Adrian told the pope that Theodore of Tarsus was better fitted to fill the post. However, he agreed to accompany and help him with all his power. This arrangement was agreed to by the Roman pontiff, and the two envoys set off for England, going by way of France. There, suspected of being a political agent of the Eastern emperor, Adrian was arrested by Ebroin, mayor of Neustria, and Theodore alone was able to proceed on his way.

When, later, Adrian arrived in Great Britain, he found Theodore there, confirmed to his see, and was named by him abbot of the monastery of Sts. Peter and Paul at Canterbury. For more than thirty years he edified his abbey and the neighbouring country by his teaching and saintliness. He him-self undertook the teaching of Greek and Latin to his monks so that they might more easily understand and draw profit from the Scriptures.

His body was preserved from corruption for some centuries, and his tomb has reappeared during recent excavations.

St. MARCIANNA

Virgin and martyr, delivered to the wild beasts at Caesarea in Maure-tania, about 303.

St. PETER OF SEBASTE

Bishop, brother of St. Basil and St. Gregory of Nyssa (d. shortly after 391).

St. MARCELLINUS

Thought to have been bishop of Ancona between 550 and 568.

St. WANINGUS

Counsellor of Queen St. Bathilde, friend of St. Ouen and St. Wandrille; founder of the abbey of Fécamp, where he wished to finish his life as a servant (d. about 699).

Blessed HONORATUS OF BUZENÇAIS

Tradition has it that he pursued the profession of cattle merchant, and was assassinated by two knaves at Thénezay in Poitou (d. 1250). He was beatified by Eugene IV in 1444.

Blessed PHILIP BERRUYER

Bishop of Orléans, later archbishop of Bourges (d. 1261).

January 10th
ST. GONZALVO (d. 1259)

BORN about 1187, Gonzalvo was ordained priest and provided with a rich benefice by the archbishop of Braga, then confiding this benefice to one of his nephews, he set out on a pilgrimage. His absence lasted fourteen years in the course of which he visited the Holy Land and the Roman sanctuaries. When he returned to Portugal, he found that his return was no longer expected. Desirous of keeping the prebend for himself, his nephew had, in fact, told everyone that he was dead.

Gonzalvo submitted to the loss of his possessions and retired to Amaranthus to live a hermit's life. Entering the newly founded Order of Preachers, he accomplished his year as a novice, then begged to be permitted to resume his hermitage. He passed the rest of his long life in prayers and good works.

Among the miracles which the Dominican chronicle attributes to him, two took place while he was building the bridge over the Tamega, where at that time many people had been drowned. One day when provisions were lacking, through his prayers the fishes allowed themselves to be taken so that his fellow workers were able to appease their hunger. Another time he made an excellent wine spring from a rock so that the same workmen could quench their thirst.

The saint learned the time of his death through a revelation, and the Blessed Virgin appeared to him at the last to lead him to paradise.

Blessed GREGORY X (1270–1276)

The Holy See had been vacant three years when Teobaldo Visconti became pope in 1271. He took the name of Gregory X, came to Lyons in 1274 to open the 14th œcumenical council, and died at Arezzo as he was returning to Rome.

St. WILLIAM

In succession canon of Soissons and of Paris, monk of Pontivy, abbot of Châlis, and archbishop of Bourges (d. 1209).

St. Peter Urseolus

Former doge of Venice, who died a hermit in Rousillon (928-987).

St. Agatho

Pope (d. 681).

St. Domitian

Bishop of Melitene in Armenia (d. about 602).

St. Marcian

Priest, who lived and died at Constantinople (d. about 471).

St. Petronius

Monk of Lérins and bishop of Dié (d. about 463).

January 11th

ST. THEODOSIUS THE CENOBITE (d. 529)

THUS called to distinguish him from his namesake, Theodosius of Antioch, and to mark the kind of religious life which he advocated, Theodosius the Cenobite was born at Garissus in Cappadocia. It was at Jerusalem that, at first hesitant between the eremitic life and the cenobitic, he finally opted for life in a community. With a few companions he retired into the caves in the environs of the Holy City. The first thing which he advised his followers was to think ceaselessly of death. For this purpose a grave in the ground, freshly dug, remained always open, beside which each in turn came to meditate. Theodosius set them an example of austerity by eating only vegetables and fruits. He passed thirty years, writes his biographer, without eating a morsel of bread.

His disciples becoming more and more numerous, he moved to Cathismus not far from Bethlehem and raised an immense monastery which finally sheltered a host of cenobites. It contained notably three great infirmaries for different classes of ailments, and four churches reserved respectively for the Greeks, Armenians, and Slavs who could all pray in their own tongue. The fourth received penitents who were not yet "reconciled".

Theodosius was about ninety when, because of his loyalty to the Catholic faith, he was exiled by the Emperor Anastasius, protector of the Eutychians. But the death of this ruler soon put an end to his exile, and he returned to pass the last eleven years of his life in the midst of his monks. He died at the age of a hundred and five, full of infirmities from which he would never pray God to deliver him.

St. BALTHASAR

One of the three Magi.

St. HYGINUS

Pope (d. 142).

St. PALEMON

Hermit, teacher of St. Pacomius (d. about 330).

St. ANASTASIUS

Monk of Mount Soracte (d. about 570).

St. VITALIS

Monk of Gaza, who, from his sixtieth year, consecrated himself to the conversion of women of evil life (d. about 625).

St. PAULINUS

Patriarch of Aquileia, polemist and poet, friend of Alcuin (d. 804).

January 12th
ST. VICTORIAN (d. about 558)

VICTORIAN lived successively in Italy, France, and Spain. In Italy, of which he seems to have been a native, he devoted himself to the building of monasteries and hospitals. Then he is found at Asana in Aragon, directing a small community of cenobites. Several of his disciples became bishops, notable among them St. Gaudiosus of Tarrazona.

The Spaniards attributed one of their victories against the Moors to St. Victorian, and even in our day they venerate his remains at the monastery of Montaragon.

ST. AELRED (d. about 1167)

HE is one of the most lovable saints. Of noble birth, Aelred first lived at the court of David, king of Scotland. There they thought him happy. He wrote: "Nevertheless the wound in my heart caused me unspeakable torments and I could not bear the intolerable burden of my sins." Breaking the closest ties, he resolved to leave the world. "It was then, O my God," he went on, "that I began to taste the comfort, the joy, and profound peace which is found in seeking after You and in serving You."

In 1135, at the age of twenty-six, Aelred entered the Cistercian abbey of Rievaulx. Ten years later he became its abbot, which he remained until his death in 1167. This monastery, where a great fervour and charity reigned, counted more than three hundred monks. Aelred who only sought "to love and to be loved", tasted pure happiness there whilst making others happy.

Among the writings of St. Aelred there is one in which the charms of spiritual friendship are extolled in an incomparable manner.

St. ARCADIUS

Martyred, it is thought, about 304 at Caesarea in Mauretania.

St. JOHN (d. 494)

Bishop of Ravenna, he appeared clad in his pontifical adornments before Attila, begging him to spare the town. The king of the Huns agreed to pass through it without inflicting damage.

St. CAESARIA

Abbess, sister of St. Caesarius of Arles (d. about 529).

St. BENEDICT BISCOP

Founder of several monasteries in England (d. 690).

Blessed BERNARD OF CORLEONE (1607-1667)

A former soldier and brigand, Bernard became a Capuchin lay brother at the monastery of Caltanisetta (Sicily) and one of the greatest contemplatives of his century.

St. STEPHEN

Abbot of St. Lawrence at Liége (d. 1059).

St. NAZARIUS

Supposed to have succeeded St. Victorian as abbot of Asana (d. 6th century).

St. FERREOLUS

Said to have been thirteenth bishop of Grenoble (d. 670).

January 13th
BLESSED YVETTE (d. 1228)

OF the seventy years she lived, Yvette passed forty in the midst of the world, and thirty in a walled cell close by the church of Huy.

Born in that town in 1158, married very young and against her will, and being widowed with two children at the age of eighteen, she had refused to be remarried, and dedicated herself to the education of her sons. One of them became abbot of Orval in Luxemburg; the other, at one time led astray, ended by returning to God. Yvette also had the happiness of converting her father, who became a monk at Villers in Brabant. It may be added that before her retirement, Blessed Yvette had nursed lepers in a lazaretto for ten years.

ST. LEONTIUS (d. about 337)

ONLY a few reliable facts are known of the life of St. Leontius, bishop of Caesarea in Cappadocia.

In 302, he evangelized Armenia, converted King Tiridates, and conferred episcopal consecration on Gregory the Illuminator. In 314, present at the Councils of Ancyra and Neocaesarea, where a ruling was made on the question of the penance to be imposed on apostates, Leontius ranged himself on the side of the moderates. Then, taking part in 325 in the Council of Nicaea, he revealed himself as one of the most determined opponents of Arius.

Blessed GODFREY OF KAPPENBERG (d. 1127)

Descendant of Charlemagne through his father, and of the dukes of Swabia through his mother, Godfrey was twenty-five when, in 1122, he offered his estate of Kappenberg for a Premonstratensian monastery. He and his young wife entered the new order in 1224. He died at the age of thirty at the abbey of Ilbenstadt.

Blessed BERNO

Benedictine reformer and founder of Cluny (d. 927).

Blessed HILDEMAR (d. 1097)

Native of Tournai, he followed William of Normandy to England. Returning to France after the Conqueror's death, he wished, with a few companions, to establish a religious community between Bapaume and Corbie, in the forest of Arrouaise. This place was a brigands' hideout, and Hildemar hoped to convert them. One of them donned clerical garb and feigned conversion in order to get rid of Hildemar, and he stabbed him to death.

St. VERONICA OF BINASCO (1455–1497)

Born in a very poor family, Veronica enjoyed from childhood the gift of contemplation. Having become an Augustinian nun at Milan, she was favoured with innumerable ecstasies and visions. On Our Lord's behalf, she brought a secret message to Alexander VI, who received it with respect. The *Revelations* which Veronica left are of the same kind as those of Catherine Emmerich and Maria d'Agreda.

January 14th

ST. HILARY (d. about 367)

THE time of St. Hilary is that during which divers errors concerning the Trinity were being propagated among the Christians. Among them the Arian heresy was widely spread, and under the guise of appeasement certain emperors attempted to impose it upon the entire Church. We know that the Arians denied that the Word participated in the divine substance. St. Hilary made himself champion of orthodoxy against them, and his zeal was the cause of his being exiled to Phrygia by the Emperor Constantius. Apart from this exile of about four years, he passed his life in Aquitaine, where he had been born of a pagan patrician family, between 310 and 320.

He has himself told of the interior drama which led him at about the age of thirty-five to embrace the Catholic faith. "I said to myself," he writes, "that if the present life is not given us to set us on the road to eternal life, then it is not a benefit from God." It was in reading the sublime texts in which Scripture evokes the divine attributes that he found the grace of conversion.

Although married and the father of a young girl, his knowledge, his social standing, and his piety commended him to the suffrage of the people who elected him bishop of Poitiers. But his influence was not confined to his diocese, and he was instrumental by his perseverance and moderation in purging all Gaul of heresy.

His wife and daughter were also devoted to the service of God. They went before him to the grave; and it is believed that he placed their bodies in an oratory dedicated to the holy martyrs Paul and John.

Honour is given to St. Hilary for having softened Latin, making it more readily adaptable to Greek thought, and for exact definition of the mysteries of our faith.

St. FULGENTIUS

Born at Seville, died bishop of Ecija in Spain (d. about 632).

St. FELIX OF NOLA

A priest of Campania (d. about 260).

St. SABBAS

First monk of Mount Athos, then metropolitan of Serbia (d. 1237).

Blessed ENGELMER

Hermit in Bavaria, put to death by a thief who believed that he was the possessor of treasure (d. about 1096).

Blessed ODO OF NOVARA (d. about 1200)

Prior of the charterhouse of Geyrach in Slavonia, Odo resigned in order to avoid further friction with the local bishop; then he went to live a hermit's life near a convent at Tagliacozzo.

Blessed ODORIC OF PORDENONE (d. 1331)

A Franciscan missionary and a prodigious explorer, he traversed and preached in Greater Armenia, Persia, Chaldea, India, the islands of Ceylon, Java, Sumatra, the Philippines; it is believed he even penetrated into Japan; he preached in the principal cities of China, and stayed at Lhasa, capital of Tibet. He died at Udine (Italy) after dictating in Latin the story of his travels.

January 15th
ST. MAURUS (d. 584)

BORN at Rome of a family of senators, Maurus was confided to the care of St. Benedict at the age of twelve. He responded so well to the affection and solicitude of his master that he was soon held out as a model to the other monks. St. Gregory extols him as having excelled in the love of prayer and of silence, and he tells that, after the example of St. Peter, his obedience was rewarded by being able to walk on the waters.

One day a youth named Placidus fell into the lake of the abbey. St. Benedict learned of it by revelation and calling his young disciple said: "Brother Maurus, go quickly and find Placidus who is drowning." Armed with the blessing of his father Benedict, Maurus fled to the rescue of Placidus and, seizing him by the hair, brought him back to the shore. He had not even noticed that he had left the dry land, and when he recognized the miracle he attributed it to the merits of St. Benedict.

The course of his religious life did not disappoint these promises. Maurus so well realized the monastic ideal that all saw in him the perfect spiritual heir of St. Benedict, and his eventual successor. Therefore, when the saint left Subiaco he unhesitatingly charged Maurus with the administration, as prior, of the monastery of Monte Cassino.

St. PAUL

First hermit, who lived, says St. Jerome, to be one hundred and thirteen, and passed ninety years in the desert without speaking to anyone (d. 342).

St. ALEXANDER THE ACEMETE

Anchorite, missionary, and founder of monasteries. He is given, with his followers, the name of "acemete" (in Greek: *akoïmètos*) because the uninterrupted and alternate recitation of the Holy Office by these monks made it appear that they never slept (d. about 430).

St. IDA or ITA

Irish virgin and great contemplative (d. about 570).

Blessed GEOFFREY OF PERONNE

Met St. Bernard at Liége, became prior of Clairvaux, refused out of humility the bishopric of Tournai, and died in 1147.

Blessed PIERRE DE CASTELNAU

Cistercian and apostolic legate, was assassinated during the crusade against the Albigenses (d. 1209).

St. ISIDORE OF ALEXANDRIA

Priest, hospital administrator, and travelling companion of St. Athanasius (d. about 403).

January 16th
ST. MARCELLUS (d. 309)

POPE ST. MARCELLINUS having died in 304, the Christians of Rome waited until 308 to appoint a successor. Their choice fell upon the priest Marcellus whose singularly thorny task it was to repair the evils caused by the recent persecutions of Diocletian. Many religious buildings had been destroyed, the greater part of the cemeteries confiscated, and many of the faithful had apostasized.

Marcellus reopened several churches for worship. He attempted to impose rules of penance upon the repentant apostates, but some judged them to be too harsh, and raised a revolt against the pontiff. Public troubles ensued which the Emperor Maxentius suppressed and for which he held Marcellus responsible. He was exiled and died far from Rome in 309.

ST. HENRY (d. 1127)

WHEN he came of age, Henry was inspired to leave Denmark and to set sail for England to embrace the religious life. He went to the priory of Tynemouth whose superior allowed him to settle in the island of Cocket. There he built himself a hut and an oratory and lived as a hermit, working with his hands and practising rigorous austerities.

Upon discovering his retreat, his friends invited him to return to his native land where, they said, his kind of life would certainly edify. Henry, swayed by love of his country, was almost convinced. But after having passed a night in prayer, he determined not to leave his hermitage. And it was there that he died, after sufferings of every kind, on January 16th, 1127.

St. PRISCILLA
Established the oldest of the Roman catacombs (d. about 98).

St. MELAS
Bishop of Rhinocolura in Egypt, exiled for his defence of the Nicene Creed (d. about 390).

St. HONORATUS
Founded the abbey of Lérins and died bishop of Arles (d. 429).

St. Fursey

Irish monk, founder of the abbey of Lagny, died at Mézerolles in Picardy (648).

Sts. Berard, Otho, Accursius, and Adjutus

Franciscans, martyred in Morocco in 1221, during St. Francis' lifetime. The two first were priests, the other two lay brothers. Carried away by desire to shed their blood for Christ, all went out to meet danger, preaching in mosques, treating Mohammed as an impostor, and, as it were, obliging the prophet's followers to kill them.

January 17th
ST. ANTHONY OF THE DESERT (d. 356)

BORN in 250, near Heracleus in Upper Egypt, Anthony lost his parents at the age of about twenty. His first action was to complete his sister's education; then he sold the house, furniture, and hundred acres of land which he possessed, giving the proceeds to the poor, and joined the anchorites who lived in the neighbourhood. He retired into an empty sepulchre, where at once began those struggles with the demon which he had to support throughout his life.

At the age of thirty-five he plunged into the desert alone. For twenty years he lived in an abandoned fort, the entrance to which he had barricaded, but his admirers finally broke in. Anthony then miraculously cured several sick people and consented to give spiritual counsel to some souls. His special recommendation to them was to base their rule of life on the Gospel. Little by little so many disciples came that he was able to found two monasteries, one on the right bank of the Nile at Pispir, the other on the left bank beside Arsinoe.

Anthony appeared for a few days at Alexandria in 311, to fight the Arian heresy and to comfort the victims of Maximinus' persecution. Before his death he had the joy of seeing his sister once more. She also had grown old in the search for perfection and directed a community of dedicated virgins. Filled with serenity, he ended his existence at the age of a hundred and five in a cave on Mount Colzim.

This great ascetic was always perfectly modest and courteous. He has been called the "father of cenobites", because it was in great part due to him that the monastic life spread in the East and later in the West. In addition, he inspired innumerable souls by his example and maxims. His *Life*, written by St. Athanasius, had an immense influence both on art and hagiography.

St. SABINUS

Bishop of Piacenza (d. 420).

St. RICMIR

Superior of a monastery in Touraine (d. about 715).

St. ROSELINE

Prioress of the Carthusian convent of Celle-Robaud in Provence (d. 1329).

St. AMELBERT (d. about 800)

Born in Bavaria of a wealthy family, Amelbert was very much opposed by his parents in his religious aspirations. To punish him because he would not carry arms, they obliged him to look after the cows. They sent him a light of love whom he put to flight with a firebrand. When his father died, Amelbert was ordained priest, made a pilgrimage to Rome, then settled on his lands and there led the life of a pastor filled with zeal and charity.

January 18th
BLESSED BEATRIX D'ESTE (d. 1262 or 1270)

BEATRIX D'ESTE, daughter of the marquis of Ferrara, belonged to the family which later reigned over Hanover, and today still reigns over England. She appeared from her youth to be preparing for the religious life, but her father promised her in marriage to the noble Galeas Manfredi, and the ceremony was set to take place at Milan. She had just arrived in that city when news came of the death of Galeas from wounds received in battle.

Beatrix did not wish to return to the world, and her parents were obliged to let her follow her vocation. She founded a convent of Benedictines at Ferrara, where she herself took the veil in 1254 and where she lived until her death.

ST. LEOBARDUS (d. about 593)

HAVING allowed himself to be persuaded by his parents to marry, Leobardus was about to obey them when their unexpected death reopened the question. He set off on a pilgrimage to the tomb of St. Martin, in order to receive guidance. There his calling became clear. Foregoing return to his native Auvergne, Leobardus settled near Marmoutier in a cell which he hewed in the rock.

Gregory of Tours, his bishop, sometimes came to visit him. It is he who tells how the hermit, in argument with a brother, thought of betaking himself elsewhere. The bishop dissuaded him and to facilitate his spiritual progress gave him the lives of the Fathers and some other good books to read. Leobardus himself made some parchments on which he transcribed the most beautiful passages from the psalms and from Holy Scripture.

He lived for twenty-two years in his Touraine retreat. When he felt death approaching, he had Gregory of Tours asked to bring him the eulogies, as they then were called, that is, the last sacraments. Then having dismissed all, he rendered his soul to God without witnesses.

St. PRISCA

Virgin martyred at Rome in the 1st or 3rd century.

St. VENERANDUS

Bishop of Clermont in Auvergne (d. about 423).

St. VOLUSIANUS

Bishop of Tours, driven from his see by the Goths (d. about 496).

St. WILFRID

English missionary who evangelized Sweden where he was martyred (d. 1029).

St. DEICOLUS (d. about 625)

Born in Ireland, he accompanied St. Columbanus into France and, like him, fled from Luxeuil in 610 to escape from Queen Brunehaut. Columbanus was able to reach Italy; but, aged and infirm, Deicolus had to stop only a few miles from his abbey, in a place where he later built a monastery which gave birth to the town of Lure (Haute-Saône).

January 19th
STS. MARTHA AND MARIS (d. about 270)

MARTHA and Maris belonged, it is said, to the Persian nobility, and came with their sons Audifax and Abachum on a pilgrimage to the tombs of the apostles at a time when a terrible persecution was raging in Rome. They set about helping the confessors of the faith and gathering together the ashes of the martyrs. Arrested in their turn, and refusing to sacrifice to the gods, they suffered cruel torments, and finally Maris and his sons were beheaded, while Martha was drowned in a pond.

ST. CANUTE (d. 1086)

SUENO II, king of Denmark, had died without legitimate heirs, leaving several illegitimate children. Among them Harold, called the Idle, was chosen to succeed him while Canute or Knut retired to Sweden. When Harold died Canute ascended the throne.

The beginning of his reign of six years was marked by victories and timely reforms. In addition the king gave an example of all the private virtues and of great zeal for the conversion of his subjects.

Canute suffered his first setback when he attempted to press his rights over England where William the Conqueror had just established himself. His expedition proved disastrous and a goodly number of his subjects then gave signs of rebellion. They refused to pay taxes, especially ecclesiastical tithes. Assisted by his brother Benedict, Canute wished to bring them to reason, but he was ill-informed and ill-advised. Instead of marching against them, he tarried in the town of Odense and was surprised by a rebel attack.

While hearing Mass in the Church of St. Alban he learned he was lost. Having received Communion and forgiven his enemies, he prostrated himself in the form of a cross before the altar and awaited death. Soon the conspirators invaded the church and fearful butchery took place in which the king, his brother Benedict, and seventeen of their companions were massacred.

St. PONTIAN

Martyred at Spoleto in 160.

St. BASSIANUS

Bishop of Lodi, friend of St. Ambrose (d. 413).

St. LOMER

Abbot of Moutier-au-Perche, in the diocese of Chartres (d. 593).

St. WOLSTAN

Bishop of Worcester (d. 1095).

St. HENRY

Of English origin, he evangelized Scandinavia in company with Nicholas Breakspear, the future Pope Adrian IV. The latter consecrated him bishop of Upsala in 1152. Two years later Henry undertook the religious conquest of Finland. In 1157 he was stoned to death by a sinner he was exhorting to repent.

Blessed BEATRIX OF LENS

Daughter of a noble of Lens, founded a Cistercian monastery in the neighbourhood of Mons where she died about 1216.

Blessed ANDREA OF PESCHIERA

A Dominican of Greek origin, preached the Gospel for forty-five years in the district of Vatellina.

St. SULPITIUS THE PIOUS (d. 647)

Bishop of Bourges, Sulpitius enjoyed high standing with the Merovingian kings with the result that they used great moderation towards his flock. He worked hard for the conversion of the Jews. After seventeen years of a fruitful episcopate he placed his duties in the hands of a coadjutor so that he might devote himself exclusively to the poor.

January 20th
ST. SEBASTIAN (d. 288)

A NATIVE of Milan, Sebastian set out for Rome and enlisted in the army, not that he had any definite inclination for a career of arms, but he wished to be of use to the persecuted Christians without arousing too much suspicion.

The first to benefit from his devotion were the brothers Marcus and Marcellinus, recently condemned to death. At the request of their parents, a respite of three days had been granted to allow them to reflect and possibly to apostasize. Sebastian went to the house of Nicostratus, clerk to the prefecture, who, with the help of the jailer Claudius, was charged with their surveillance. Before them all he spoke so wondrously of Christ that not only the parents of the condemned but also the clerk Nicostratus, the jailer Claudius, and sixteen prisoners confided to their guard asked to be baptized. These conversions also led to that of Agrestius Chromatius, governor of Rome, who released the converted prisoners. Sebastian, for his part, continued to show himself such a good soldier that Diocletian named him captain of the Pretorian guard.

Nevertheless, a recrudescence of persecution took place in 286, and several of those mentioned above were victims: Nicostratus and his wife were drowned in the Tiber, Marcus and Marcellinus were shot with arrows, and the son of Chromatius was beheaded. These events provided the centurion with many new opportunities to exercise his zeal.

But finally his role was discovered. Diocletian reproached him with ingratitude. Vainly did Sebastian protest that he had always meticulously fulfilled his military duties; the emperor delivered him to the archers, who, having shot him through with arrows, left him for dead. However, he recovered from his wounds, and was urged to hide himself. But burning to be martyred in his turn, Sebastian deliberately set himself in Diocletian's path and said to him: "Know that you will have no peace until you cease from shedding innocent blood!" Overcome with surprise and rage, the emperor ordered him to be cudgelled to death and his body thrown into the sewer.

St. FABIAN

He was pope for fourteen years and died a victim of the persecution of Decius in 250.

St. EUTHYMIUS THE GREAT

Celebrated anchorite in Palestine, defender of the Council of Calcedon, organizer of the Greek liturgy, one of the most illustrious saints of the Eastern Church. When the Empress Eudocia, who had first taken a fancy to Eutyches, decided to abandon heresy, she asked St. Simeon Stylites to receive her. He replied: "Why go to draw water from so far when there is a better well at her door? Let her go and see Euthymius and follow his advice." The empress went, expecting a long interview with Euthymius. He told her in two words to return to the communion of the orthodox bishop of Jerusalem, gave her his blessing, promised to pray for her, and withdrew (d. 473).

Blessed DESIDERIUS (d. 1194)

Of Flemish origin, Desiderius was bishop of Thérouanne for a score of years. Three years before his death he resigned and donned the Cistercian habit at the abbey of Cambron.

January 21st

ST. AGNES (d. middle or end of the 3rd century)

WE possess little reliable data on this very celebrated saint. Some place her martyrdom about 254; others under Diocletian, about 304.

Agnes was twelve when she was faced with sacrificing to the gods and renouncing her virginity. Neither threats nor promises could turn her. She was tortured. Those watching her torment wept. She, on the contrary, continued to appear happy. Several young men presented themselves, who wished to marry her. "It is an insult to my heavenly Spouse," she said, "to try to please me. He shall have me for His own, who first chose me. Why, executioner, all this delay? May this body perish rather than delight the eyes of those that I refuse."

According to the Latin tradition, Agnes was beheaded. According to the Greek tradition she was first sent into a house of ill repute, where her virtue was miraculously preserved; then she was thrown on to a pyre.

ST. MEINRAD (d. 861)

BORN about 797 in Swabia, Meinrad was related to the Hohenzollern princes. He became a priest in 821, and monk at the abbey of Reichenau the following year; there he taught literature and the Holy Scripture, a duty which he afterwards fulfilled at the monastery of Bollingen.

Feeling himself drawn rather to the eremitic life, the young monk obtained permission to go and live on one of the peaks of Mount Etzel, near the Lake of Zurich. He stayed there seven years, cared for by a pious widow of the village of Altendorf, after which he buried himself in the forest to the south, near Sihl. The exquisite place where he settled, and which he believed to be inaccessible, is where Our Lady of Einsiedeln, also called Our Lady of the Hermits, is still venerated.

This celebrated shrine, moreover, owes its origin to an image of the Virgin which Meinrad placed in his chapel and before which he prayed during the last twenty-five years of his life. He was assassinated by bandits who believed he was in possession of a hidden treasure.

St. PATROCLUS

Hermit, native of Troyes, martyred between 259 and 273.

St. Epiphanius (438–496)

Bishop of Pavia when the Roman Empire was crumbling, he had occasion many times to intervene between the barbarian chiefs who were quarrelling over the fragments and he almost always succeeded in his efforts. He has been called "Epiphanius the Peace-maker"; he is also called the "light of the bishops" and the "glory of Italy".

St. Avitus

Bishop of Clermont, died about 689.

Blessed Inez

Spanish Augustinian, celebrated for the demoniacal persecutions she endured and for her prophetic spirit (1625–1696).

January 22nd

ST. VINCENT (d. 304)

This martyr is one of the most universally honoured of the Latin Church. He was born at Huesca and had been ordained deacon by Valerius, bishop of Saragossa, who, old and tongue-tied, could not preach. Vincent substituted for him in his preaching ministry.

These duties brought him into the limelight; and he was among the first to be arrested, with his bishop, when the persecutions of Diocletian began. They took him in chains to Valencia to appear before Dacian, governor of the province. He interrogated Valerius, endeavouring to intimidate him. The old man expressed himself with difficulty and at one moment stopped short.

Dacian was already triumphant, seeing in his silence the promise of apostasy. But Vincent, for whom it was simply the usual effect of the prelate's infirmity, asked to speak for him. "My son," replied the bishop, "I commit to you the charge of testifying to our faith as you have that of preaching the Gospel." Then Vincent protested eloquently that nothing whatsoever should triumph over their common fidelity to Christ.

Furious at this interference, Dacian momentarily forgot about the bishop and had the deacon put to torture. The latter seemed to think nothing of it. Dacian ordered that his flesh be torn with iron hooks, that he should be roasted over a slow fire, and he urged the torturers to redouble their savagery. It was of no avail; the victim was only the more firm and joyful in confessing his faith. The governor thought that he would finally give signs of weakness or at least die in fearful anguish. But here again his hope was in vain, for his victim prayed and sang psalms until the end, and it was in the full joy of the spirit that he drew his last breath.

St. Vincent is here and there taken as patron by the wine-growers, but unless we accept that it is because of a pun on the first syllable of his name, the reason for this patronage is unknown.

St. Gaudentius

Bishop of Novara in Italy (d. about 418).

St. Anastasius

Son of a Magus and a Magus himself, he became a monk and was martyred in Assyria (d. 628).

St. Dominic of Sora

Hermit, founder of monasteries, died at Sora in Campania (d. 1031).

Blessed Gauthier of Bruges (1307)

This learned Franciscan was named bishop of Poitiers against his will. As such, he had to excommunicate Bertrand de Got, bishop of Bordeaux, who had disobeyed pontifical orders and remained obdurate. When the latter became pope under the name of Clement V, he deposed Gauthier, who humbly submitted and committed himself at his death to the judgement of God. Clement V repented of his conduct after the death of the servant of God, and had a tomb built for him in the church of the friars minor at Poitiers.

January 23rd
ST. ILDEPHONSUS (d. 667)

ILDEPHONSUS was born at Toledo, of royal blood, on December 8th, 606. His parents attributed his birth to the intercession of the Blessed Virgin.

He became a monk, then abbot of the Benedictine monastery of Agalia. Later he was chosen as bishop by the church of Toledo; he hid himself, was found and dragged by force to the consecration. During the ten years that he occupied the bishopric he showed himself a model shepherd, watching over his flock with solicitude, and combined preaching with the writing of several books. The most celebrated of them is *The Perpetual Virginity of Mary against Jovinianus, Helvidius, and a Jew*.

Ildephonsus was also an ardent protagonist of the feast of December 18th, called *Expectatio partus* or "the Expectation of the Blessed Virgin Mary". Two miracles which Our Lady accomplished in his favour are reported. One year, on the eve of December 18th, as he was entering the church with his clergy for matins, he found the Virgin seated on the bishop's throne surrounded with angels. Beckoning to him, she put on him a splendid chasuble and said: "Here is a present my Son sends you to wear when in future you celebrate the offices in my honour." The tenth Council of Toledo instituted a liturgical feast in order to perpetuate the memory of this apparition.

The other miracle took place when, in company with King Recesvint, the pious bishop was praying one day in the Church of St. Leocadia. The patroness of Toledo, whose relics were believed lost, appeared to him and pointed out to him the place where the relics lay; then she said to him: "Praiseworthy art thou, Ildephonsus, for having so well defended the honour of Our Queen."

St. RAYMOND OF PENAFORT

Catalan Dominican, minister general of his order; a former professor of law, he was ordered by his superiors to write a *Summa* of cases of conscience and by Gregory IX to compile the *Decretales* (d. 1275).

St. EMERENTIANA

Roman martyr, foster sister of St. Agnes (d. about 305).

St. JOHN THE ALMSGIVER (d. about 616)

Born in the island of Cyprus, of which his father was governor, John married in obedience to his parents. Having become patriarch of Alexandria, he named the poor his "lords and masters" and every day gave help to seven thousand five hundred of them. When his close friends observed that certain fake beggars were exploiting him, he only replied that they themselves were much too inquisitive. One day some of the faithful having gone out before the end of the service, John also left the choir and went out and sat down in the midst of them. "My children," he said, "the pastor should be with his sheep; that is why you should come back into church with me, if you don't want me to stay with you in the public square." From that time all awaited the end of the office before withdrawing.

St. BERNARD

Of Lyonnaise origin, a Benedictine monk, bishop of Vienne in Dauphiny (d. 841).

January 24th
ST. TIMOTHY

THERE is no one to whom Paul gave higher praise than to Timothy. He was born in Lycaonia, of a Greek father and a Jewish mother named Eunice. When Paul came to Lystra for the first time, he converted Eunice and doubtless baptized her son too. On returning, he found Timothy grown so virtuous, courageous, and selfless that he made him his close companion and lifelong friend.

From the spring of the year 50 to the fall of the year 52, the latter accompanied his master to Ephesus, to Jerusalem, and to Rome; with him he traversed Phrygia, Galatia, and Macedonia; he also assisted him in evangelizing the Thessalonians and Corinthians. In the beginning of the year 53, Timothy was at Ephesus with Paul, when the latter entrusted him with a mission to the churches of Macedonia and Corinth. We know that on this occasion the Corinthians did not give a warm welcome to the missionary. In the years following, we find him at Paul's side in Macedonia, in the Peloponnesos and at Troas. It seems that he rejoined him at Rome between 61 and 63.

Twice St. Paul wrote to him during his second captivity in Rome. We know the moving phrases in which he took leave of him: "I have fought the good fight; I have finished the race; I have redeemed my pledge; I look forward to the prize that is waiting for me, the prize I have earned. The Lord, that judge whose award never goes amiss, will grant it to me when that day comes" (II Tim. iv, 7–8).

It is believed that Timothy survived his master by some thirty years, presiding as bishop over the destinies of the church of Ephesus. He was, it is said, stoned to death during a pagan feast which he was trying to prevent his flock from attending.

St. FELICIANUS

Was bishop of Foligno for fifty-six years and died during the persecution of Decius, aged ninety-four (d. 251).

St. BABILAS

Bishop of Antioch, died in prison during the same persecution and wished to be buried with his chains (d. 250).

St. ARTEMIUS

Diplomat converted by Bishop Nepotianus, whom he succeeded in the see of Clermont (d. about 396).

St. MACEDONIUS (d. about 430)

This anchorite spent forty-five years in an unsheltered ditch near Antioch, and then twenty-five in a covered retreat. The people of Antioch having broken the statues of the emperor to show their discontent, Macedonius reasoned in the following terms with Theodosius, who was inclined to take a serious view of the offence: "Your subjects were evidently wrong to throw down the statues which are the image of your majesty; but you would be still more wrong to put to death the culprits who are the living images of the most high God. Think, besides, of the irreparable harm you would do; for, although you are emperor, you cannot restore to life those whom you have killed, while your subjects, with metal which is plentiful, will easily replace the statues they have broken." Theodosius allowed himself to be mollified by these words.

St. CADOC

Welsh prince, was at first a governor of his country, then became an anchorite. He died about 577.

Blessed PAULA GAMBARA (1473-1515)

Born at Brescia and married against her will to Count Costa de Benasco, Paula became a mother at fifteen. She heroically supported the conduct of her debauched husband, who imposed on her the presence of an insolent and cruel mistress in her home. Paula cared for this creature in her last illness and brought a priest to her bedside. She then converted her husband, who allowed her to wear the habit of the Franciscan third order of which she was a member.

January 25th

ST. ANANIAS (d. about 70)

In his discourse to the Jews of Jerusalem, St. Paul recalled how he was thunderstruck and lost his sight on the road to Damascus, then he spoke to them of the visit he had received from Ananias:

"There a certain Ananias," he said, "a man well known among his Jewish neighbours for his pious observance of the law, came and stood beside me, and said, Brother Saul, look up and see. And at that instant I looked up into his face. Then he said to me, The God of our fathers has made choice of thee to know his will, to have sight of him who is Just, and hear speech from his lips; and what thou hast seen and heard, thou shalt testify before all men. Come then, why art thou wasting time? Rise up, and receive baptism, washing away thy sins at the invocation of his name" (Acts xxii, 12–16).

In another place the Acts of the Apostles reports the vision in which God had ordered Ananias to restore sight and administer baptism to the former persecutor of the Christians:

"And the Lord said to him, Rise up and go to the road called Straight Street; and enquire at the house of Judas for a man of Tarsus, named Saul. Even now he is at his prayers: and he has had a vision of a man called Ananias coming in and laying hands on him, to cure him of his blindness.

"At this, Ananias answered, Lord, many have told me about this man, and all the hurt he has done to thy saints at Jerusalem; and he has come here with authority from the chief priests to imprison all those who call upon thy name.

"But the Lord said to him, Go on thy errand; this is a man I have chosen to be the instrument for bringing my name before the heathen and their rulers, and before the people of Israel too. I have yet to tell him how much suffering he will have to undergo for my name's sake" (Acts ix, 11–17).

That is all the Holy Scripture tells us on the subject of Ananias. For the rest, it is believed that he was bishop of Damascus and that he died by stoning, not far from his episcopal city.

The CONVERSION OF ST. PAUL

St. ARTEMAS

Martyred at Pozzuoli, near Capua, about 304.

Sts. MAXIMINUS and JUVENTINUS

Officers of the guard of Julian the Apostate, beheaded at Antioch for having criticized their master's edicts of persecution (d. 363).

St. PRAEJECTUS

Bishop of Clermont, died tragically, the innocent victim of a sentimental and financial intrigue in 676.

St. POPPO (978–1048)

Ex-soldier, former pilgrim to Rome and Jerusalem, Benedictine monk and reformer of several abbeys in the Flemish, Rhine, and Walloon country, Poppo was many times the object of criminal attacks on the part of those he wished to convert; he reconciled the emperor of Germany with Henry I, king of France; he let it be falsely believed that he was illegitimate by birth, so as not to have to become bishop of Strasburg; he died at the abbey of Marchiennes (Hainaut), after having made this prayer: "Lord show me that I am truly converted, by calling me to you on the day of the conversion of St. Paul."

January 26th
ST. PAULA (d. 404)

BORN at Rome, May 5th, 347, Paula was related through her father to the family of the famous general Paulus Aemilius and through her husband to the Julii, who, as we know, flattered themselves that they were descended from Aeneas and who in any case had produced Julius Caesar.

At the age of thirty-two she lost her husband Toxotius, and shortly afterwards the eldest of her five children. These bereavements, from which she suffered grievously, determined her to consecrate herself entirely to God. Meanwhile St. Paulinus, St. Epiphanius, and St. Jerome arrived in Rome and urged her to leave all to go and live in the desert. Three years later she distributed her fortune to her family and, accompanied by her daughter Eustochium, left for the East.

At Antioch she again met St. Jerome, who henceforth became her spiritual director. With him she crossed Syria and stayed for a long while in Palestine. She then visited the anchorites of the Egyptian deserts, and even thought at one time of remaining among them. But it was at Bethlehem that she finally decided to stay. She built there, near the birthplace of Our Lord, two monasteries, one for Jerome and his friends, the other for herself and her companions. There she passed the last twenty years of her life, in deep study of the Holy Scripture, working with her hands, giving alms abundantly, practising the most severe austerities, going six times a day to the church to sing the psalms which each of her nuns had to learn entirely by heart.

This great patrician lady, whose virtue was recognized by the Church, was the object of the most odious slanders. She also suffered the loss, in succession, of all her children, except her daughter Eustochium, who cared for her in her infirmity and closed her eyes in death.

She was buried opposite the cave where St. Jerome had spent his years of penance and study.

St. POLYCARP (d. about 156)

Bishop of Smyrna, he had been a disciple of the apostle St. John and of "those who had seen the Lord". Invited to deny Christ he replied: "For the eighty-six years I have served Him, He has never done me any ill; how can I blaspheme my Saviour and my King?" He was condemned to death and they wished to bind him with iron chains to the stake. "Leave me as I am," he said. "He who has given me chance to suffer for Him will give me strength; He will soften the violence of the fire and will make me able to bear its heat." Then he said this prayer: "God of Angels, who hast destroyed sin and will one day destroy death, I bless you that you have judged me worthy to approach the cup of your passion with my lips. My sacrifice then is almost consummated; before day is done I shall see the fulfilment of your promises. May your adorable name be ever glorified through Jesus Christ, eternal priest, in the unity of the Holy Ghost. Amen." The flames licked the old man without burning him; so they had to stab him on the pyre.

St. ALBERIC

Abbot of Cîteaux (d. 1109).

St. MARGARET OF HUNGARY

Daughter of King Béla IV, died a Dominican nun at the age of twenty-eight in 1270.

January 27th
ST. JULIAN (d. about 250)

IN the story of the first bishop of Le Mans, what is authentic has not yet been disentangled from what is legend.

Some identify him with Simon the Leper at whose house Our Lord was received; others say that he was of Roman origin and place his life in the 2nd century. These say he was made a bishop in Rome and came from there with Thuribius and Pavatius to evangelize the Cenomanni.

Having appeared before their capital, he was refused entry and began to preach in the vicinity. Some inhabitants of the town having come to hear him, he learned from them that water was lacking in that place. Before their eyes, Julian made an abundant spring gush forth by planting his stick in the ground. This marvel was no sooner known than the city opened its gates to him and received him in triumph. He was given the greater part of a palace to turn into a church; this was the first cathedral of Le Mans.

Julian then undertook the conversion of the country lying between the Loire and the left bank of the Seine. In this region the Druids still ruled, and the fame of their wisdom and persistent opposition to the Roman conquerors rendered them very popular with the people and very dangerous to the new apostles. But by force of his zeal and because of the numerous miracles he accomplished, Julian triumphed over Druidism as he had over the Roman gods.

When he felt his strength declining, he entrusted to Thuribius the continuance of his task and retired to the Sarthe, to the place where today we find the village of Saint-Marceaux. And it is said to be there that he died.

St. John Chrysostom

John, surnamed Chrysostom, that is to say, "golden-mouthed", by reason of his remarkable eloquence, was born about 344 at Antioch in Syria. In 374 he entered a monastery where he spent four years; he then led a hermit's life for two years; then returned to Antioch, where he was ordained deacon in 380, and priest in 386. Having become bishop of Constantinople in 397, he alienated by the intransigence of his apostolic teaching the court and the nobles, who had him deposed in 403. Four years later he died in exile.

St. Marius or Mary

Abbot in the diocese of Sisteron (d. about 550).

St. Lupus (d. about 610)

Born of a noble Burgundian family, Lupus became bishop of Châlon-sur-Saône. He was always noted for his love of the unfortunate. Even at the point of death he had a judge called to his bedside in order to obtain the deliverance of several prisoners. When he knew that his last hour had come, he gave himself Holy Communion. On the day of his funeral, at the moment when his coffin passed before the prison of those condemned to death, the door of their dungeon opened and they all recovered their liberty.

St. Thierry II

Bishop of Orléans (d. 1022).

January 28th
ST. VALERIUS (d. about 315)

WHAT is most certain concerning St. Valerius, bishop of Saragossa, we have told almost in its entirety on January 22nd in the life of St. Vincent.

We have seen that he was old, that he spoke with difficulty and that the prefect Dacian had him taken to Valencia in chains. Questioned and counselled to renounce Christ, for a moment he hesitated, then he ordered his deacon to answer in his place. By this Vincent momentarily distracted the attention of the judge, who condemned him to fearful torments.

As for the sentence later pronounced upon the old bishop, it was a little less harsh, for it only sent him into exile. And that is all that the *Passio sancti Vincentii levitae* tells of him. For the rest, it is thought that it was to Anet in Aragon that Valerius was exiled, and that his death took place in 315.

ST. CHARLEMAGNE (d. 814)

THE present French calendars generally carry St. Charlemagne on the date of January 28th. Formerly all the hagiographical collections devoted a long commentary to him. As late as 1867, the Abbé Guérin wrote (*Petits bollandistes*, vol. ii, p. 117):

"Although the canonization of Charlemagne may not have been carried out in the ordinary forms of the Roman Church, nevertheless the cult which he is shown in France and Germany, either in consecrating churches in his honour or in giving him an office in the breviaries, which the Holy See has not forbidden, obliges me to give him a place in this collection to please the piety of those people who hold his memory in such veneration."

Charlemagne was canonized in 1165 by the anti-Pope Pascal III. "This decree has acquired the force of law," writes Abbé Godescard (*Life of the Fathers*, vol. ii, p. 208, Lille, 1834), "and has had no opposition on the part of the legitimate popes. The University of Paris chose him as patron in 1661. His feast takes place at Aix-la-Chapelle with double rites of the first class."

St. FLAVIAN

Prefect of Rome, martyred, says the Roman martyrology, under Diocletian.

St. JULIAN

Bishop of Cuenca in Spain (d. 1208).

St. JOHN OF RÉOMÉ (d. 545)

Born in the diocese of Langres, he was before St. Benedict one of the principal initiators of monastic life in the West, and he founded the abbey of Réomé, which was afterwards called Moutier-Saint-Jean (Côte d'Or).

St. JAMES THE PALESTINIAN

After a misspent youth, James was converted and led a hermit's life for fifteen years. He then succumbed to a fearful temptation and committed a triple crime. A saintly anchorite prevented him from despairing of the divine mercy. James set himself once more to penance and prayer in an abandoned sepulchre, after which he died as one of the elect.

January 29th

ST. FRANCIS DE SALES (d. 1622)

FRANCIS DE SALES was born of an old family of Savoy at the Château of Thorens in 1566 or 1567. He began his studies at La Roche and Annecy; he continued them from 1581 to 1588 at Clermont College in Paris; he completed them at the University of Padua in 1591.

In obedience to his father he became, in 1591, an advocate in the senate of Savoy. The following year, free at last to follow his true vocation, he became a priest, and at once began the ministry of preaching and spiritual direction in which he was to display such mastery. From 1594 to 1598 he strove to convert the Protestants of the Chablais and met with success.

He was appointed bishop of Geneva in 1603. From then on his renown travelled beyond the frontiers of the Duchy of Savoy. At Paris, where he preached with success, he became friends with St. Vincent de Paul and directed Madame Acarie and Mother Angélique Arnauld. Henry IV said: "The bishop of Geneva has all the virtues and not a single fault." He proposed to give him a fine and famous French bishopric, but Francis refused. "Sire," he replied, "I am married; my wife is a poor woman, I cannot leave her for a richer one."

In the course of preaching Lent at Dijon, in 1603, he met Madame de Chantal, with whom seven years later he founded the Order of the Visitation.

St. Francis de Sales was a great correspondent. His *Introduction to the Devout Life* is only a compilation of the notes and letters addressed by him to Madame de Charmoisy. When this work appeared, the general of the Carthusians begged him never again to publish anything, fearing that he might be disappointed. But when, in 1614, there appeared the *Treatise on the Love of God*, the same adviser begged him never to stop writing.

Francis died in his fifty-sixth year with the calm which he had always shown. He was counselled to repeat the words of St. Martin: "Lord, if I am still necessary to your people, I do not refuse the labour." He replied: "I, necessary! No, no, I am but a useless servant!" And he thrice repeated the word "useless".

St. Constantius

Bishop of Perugia, martyred about 178.

St. Sulpicius Severus

Disciple, friend, and biographer of St. Martin (d. between 406 and 432).

St. Gildas the Wise

Abbot, born in Scotland, died in Brittany in 570.

St. Arnoul or Arnult

Young nobleman born at Cyrsoing, killed near Lille, about 742, in an attempt to save his godfather's life.

Blessed Imaine

Abbess of Salzinnes (Namur), friend of St. Juliana of Cornillon (d. 1270).

Blessed Gelasius II

John of Gaeta, monk of Monte Cassino, was chancellor of the Roman Church for forty years and then pope for one year. Driven from Rome by his enemies, he came to die at Cluny (d. 1119).

January 30th

ST. BATHILDE (d. 680)

NOTHING is known about the first years of St. Bathilde except that she was born in England, captured by corsairs and sold as a slave to Erchinoald, mayor of Neustria. A widower, he wished to marry her, but the maiden declined the old man's proposal.

She was destined to ascend the throne of France through her marriage with Clovis II, son and successor of King Dagobert. She gave him three sons: Clotaire III, Childeric II, and Thierry III. In 657, Clovis II, who had become mad, died at twenty-three, worn out with his excesses.

As regent, Bathilde was free to give course to her love of the poor and her religious zeal. With the advice of the bishops St. Eleutherius, St. Ouen, St. Leodegar, St. Desiderius, St. Erembert, and St. Genesius, she suppressed simony and the slave trade, made the taxes equitable, and favoured the development of monastic life. The abbeys of Jumièges, Fontenelle, Luxeuil, Jouarre, and Corbie owed much to her.

Bathilde dreamed of unifying the three kingdoms of Neustria, Burgundy, and Austrasia. To help her in this plan, she appointed as mayor of the palace one Ebroin, presented to her by the great nobles. This person committed political crimes the consequences of which were disastrous for the queen. In 665 or 666 the partisans of Ebroin came to order her to retire to the convent of Chelles, six leagues from Meaux. There she spent the last fourteen years of her life, forgiving her persecutors, undertaking the meanest tasks, devoting herself by preference to the care of the sick.

Bathilde was to die at the age of forty-five. As her last hour approached, she had in a dream the vision of a ladder which stood on the altar of the Virgin and reached up to heaven; and up it she climbed with the angels.

St. MARTINA

Virgin and Roman martyr (d. about 226).

St. ALDEGUNDIS

Sister of St. Wandru. She was abbess of Maubeuge and died of cancer in 684.

St. ADELELM

Born in Poitou, first a monk at La Chaise-Dieu, then founder of the abbey of St. John at Burgos (d. 1097).

St. HYACINTHA MARISCOTTI

Franciscan nun at Viterbo. Having entered the religious life against her inclination, for ten years she remained unenthusiastic, then was converted and became a great saint (d. 1640).

Blessed SEBASTIAN VALFRÉ (1629–1710)

Born of poor parents in Piedmont, Sebastian entered the Congregation of the Oratory, became its superior general, and was considered a worthy successor of St. Philip Neri. An excellent director of souls and indefatigable missionary, he always appeared joyful and full of spirit, although he had horrible interior sufferings to bear.

January 31st

ST. MARCELLA (d. 410)

BORN of a very powerful family, and having lost her husband after seven months of marriage, Marcella refused to marry again in spite of the insistence of her mother and the consul Cerealis.

She was the first young patrician in the city of Rome to live in the world a life wholly inspired by the Gospel precepts and modelled upon that of the Egyptian anchoresses. She fasted regularly, was strict in her abstinence, wore clothing of an austere and outmoded form, and divided her time between prayer and the care of the poor.

This mode of existence had been revealed and recommended to her by some priests who came from Alexandria, and in particular by St. Athanasius, at that time in exile in the West. It was, moreover, soon adopted by other great Roman women such as Paula and Eustochium, with whom Marcella was on friendly terms.

She also was in touch with St. Jerome, who taught her to interpret the Scriptures correctly. Also, when Jerome had returned to the East, she became the figurehead of orthodoxy against the Origenists and others who distorted God's word.

At the end of her life Marcella witnessed the sack of Rome by Alaric's Goths. They beat her with whips to make her reveal where her riches were. She finally made them understand that long ago they had become the riches of the poor. Then they took her and her spiritual daughter

Principia to the Church of St. Paul, designated by Alaric as a place of asylum.

Marcella died a few days afterwards, giving thanks to God for all things and manifesting a great joy at leaving this earth.

Blessed LOUISE ALBERTONI

Widow, Franciscan tertiary, died at Rome in 1533, having edified the city for twenty-seven years.

St. JOHN BOSCO

Born in the diocese of Turin, founded two congregations, one of men (Salesians), the other of women (Sisters of Mary Auxiliatrix), for rescue work among abandoned children (1815-1888).

St. PETER NOLASCO

Born in Languedoc, founded the Order of Our Lady of Mercy for the redemption of captives, lived and died in Spain (d. 1258).

St. JULIUS

Greek priest, died near Milan about 399.

St. CYRUS

Alexandrian doctor who led for a time the eremitic life then was martyred at Canopus in Egypt in 303.

THE SAINTS OF FEBRUARY
February 1st

ST. IGNATIUS (1st century)

NDER Trajan, Ignatius, Bishop of Antioch, was dragged from his episcopal throne and taken to Rome to be thrown to the wild beasts. In the course of a journey lasting many months he addressed seven letters to the churches which had shown their sympathy.

He himself tells us of his treatment. "From Syria," he writes, "by land and sea, day and night, I have already fought with beasts, chained as I was to ten leopards: I am speaking of the soldiers who guarded me—the more kindness one showed to them, the worse they became."

From Smyrna he wrote to the churches in Magnesia, Tralles, and Ephesus: "In your prayers remember me, that I may come to God; I have need of your charity and of the divine mercy, having more than ever to fear. I desire to suffer; but know not if I am worthy of it. Even though in chains, and knowing the ranks of angels and principalities, am I for that a true disciple of Christ? . . . Pray also for the Syrian Church, which has from henceforth

45

God alone for shepherd. I salute you in the Father and in Christ Jesus, our common hope."

He was afire to shed his blood for Christ, and he begged the faithful of the Roman Church to do nothing to prevent this. "I fear that your charity may harm me . . . never will so fine an opportunity be given me to go to God, and you cannot do better than to keep quiet. The only thing I ask of you is to allow me to offer the libation of my blood to God. I am the wheat of the Lord; may I be milled by the teeth of the beasts to become the immaculate bread of Christ? Caress then, these beasts, that they may be my tomb; and let nothing be left of my body; thus my funeral will be a burden to none."

They arrived in Rome for the last day of the public games. Eighty thousand spectators crowded on to the steps of the Coliseum when Ignatius underwent martyrdom. It was brief. Two lions threw themselves upon him and devoured him in a moment, leaving on the sand only the largest of his bones.

St. BRIGID OF KILDARE (d. 525)

Born in Ulster, founded several convents in Ireland. She is one of the patrons of this country in which many parishes bear her name.

St. SEVERUS

Bishop of Ravenna (d. 389).

St. URSUS (6th century)

Native of Ireland, combated Arianism in the districts which today comprise the diocese of Digne and the country around Aosta.

St. SIGEBERT

King of Austrasia, had as teacher Blessed Pepin of Landen, and died in the prime of life, about 656.

St. JOHN OF THE GRATING (d. 1163)

Bishop of St. Malo. His surname came from an iron railing which had to be placed around his tomb to protect it from indiscreet pilgrims.

Blessed ANDREA DE SEGNI (d. 1302)

Franciscan monk and one of the first theologians of his time. Popes Alexander IV, his uncle, and Boniface VIII, his nephew, could not persuade him to accept the cardinalate.

February 2nd

ST. CORNELIUS (d. 1st century)

THE conversion of the centurion Cornelius marks the break between the primitive Church and the Synagogue and testifies to the universality with which Jesus has stamped His work.

This Roman officer commanded a cohort at Caesarea and was a pious man who worshipped the true God, like all his household. On a certain day, about three in the afternoon, an angel appeared to him and said: "Thy prayers and almsdeeds are recorded on high in God's sight. And now he would have thee send men to Joppa, to bring here one Simon, who is surnamed Peter; he lodges with a tanner called Simon, whose house is close to the sea." The centurion obeyed, sent two servants and a soldier to seek for Simon Peter.

Meanwhile the apostle, who was hungry, had an ecstasy in which he saw descending from heaven a great cloth covered with every kind of animal and bird. "Rise up, Peter," a voice said to him, "lay about thee and eat." "It cannot be, Lord," answered Peter, "never in my life have I eaten anything profane, anything unclean." "It is not for thee to call anything profane, which God has made clean," replied the voice. By this the Lord indicated that the ritual observances of the Old Covenant had ended.

The next day Peter set out with some of the faithful, and the following day arrived at Caesarea. Cornelius was awaiting him there with his kinsmen and friends. He wished to prostrate himself before his guest, but the latter said to him: "Stand up, I am a man like thyself." "You know well enough," he told them, "that a Jew is contaminated if he consorts with one of another race, or visits him; but God has been showing me that we ought not to speak of any man as profane or unclean; and so, when I was sent for, I came without demur. Tell me then, why have you sent for me?" Cornelius told of his vision. "I see clearly enough," said Peter, "that God . . . welcomes anybody, whatever his race, who fears him and does what piety demands." He summarized for him the whole Gospel from the baptism of John to the crucifixion, the resurrection, and ascension of Our Lord; and ended by saying: "Everyone who has faith in him is to find remission of sins through his name."

While he was speaking, the Holy Spirit descended on all who heard him, and they began to praise God in divers tongues. The Jews present were astonished at the grace given to these pagans. But Peter replied: "Who will grudge us the water for baptizing these men, that have received the Holy

Spirit just as we did?" And he commanded that they be baptized in the name of Christ (Acts x).

And that is all that we know of St. Cornelius.

The PURIFICATION OF THE BLESSED VIRGIN

This feast seems to have been instituted in the East in the 4th century and in the West in the 5th.

St. CATHERINE DE RICCI (1522–1589)

Tuscan Dominican, friend of St. Philip Neri, favoured with visions and ecstasies.

St. JEANNE DE LESTONAC (1556–1640)

Born at Bordeaux, niece of Michel de Montaigne, who said of her: "Nature had made of her a masterpiece, allying a lovely soul with a beautiful body, and lodging a princess in a splendid palace." She married the baron de Landiras and had seven children. Widowed at the age of forty-one, she was for five months a novice at the Feuillantines of Toulouse, then founded, with the help of two Jesuits, the Institute of the Daughters of Our Lady.

Blessed JOHN THEOPHANE VÉNARD (1829–1861)

Native of Saint-Loup-sur-Thouet (Deux-Sèvres), he went from the great seminary of Poitiers to that of the Foreign Missions, sailed for China in 1852 and died there, by the sword, on February 2nd, 1861.

February 3rd

ST. BLAISE (d. about 316)

THIS is what is told of the great healer in his *Acts* of martyrdom which, however, are somewhat legendary:

Blaise was born in Armenia and devoted himself to medicine until his election to the episcopal see of Sebaste. This dignity, however, did not prevent him from withdrawing to a cave on Mount Argeus, which he made his habitual residence. There, as is shown in the window in Notre Dame at Chartres, the sick came in crowds to consult him, and not only men but animals as well. He cured them and sent them away with his blessing. A strange thing was that the animals never disturbed him at prayer, however great their need.

Under the Emperor Licinius, Agricola, governor of Cappadocia, came to Sebaste and persecuted the Christians. In quest of wild beasts for the games in the arena, they sent hunters out to beat through the neighbouring woods. These hunters, passing near the cave on Mount Argeus, saw wolves, tigers, bears, and lions waiting for Blaise to finish his prayers. The saint was thus discovered. Agricola ordered his arrest and attempted to make him apostasize. Several such attempts on his part brought only humiliating replies from the saint.

Between interrogations Blaise was returned to prison. Here the unfortunate still managed to reach him. He gave a poor woman back her pig which a wolf had stolen. He also cured a little girl who, in eating fish, had swallowed a bone and was choking. From this came the habit of invoking St. Blaise for maladies of the throat. There also came to him those who, as though choked in the confessional, did not dare to confess their sins. He is also considered as the protector and healer of animals.

After enduring various torments, Blaise was thrown into a lake. He walked upon the water and invited his persecutors to join him there. They could thus show, he said, the power of the gods they were urging him to honour. The pagans took up the challenge and were drowned to the last man. Blaise was then told by an angel to return to dry land to receive martyrdom, and he was beheaded on the shore.

St. ANATOLE (4th or 5th century)

Lived as a hermit on a crag which dominates the town of Salins (Jura).

St. THEODORE (d. about 594)

Bishop of Marseilles.

St. HADELIN (d. 696)

An Aquitaine noble, he became a disciple of St. Remaculus, and followed him to Solignac, Maestricht, and Stavelot. He finally settled on the banks of the Lesse and, with the help of Pepin of Heristal and of his wife, Plectrude, founded the abbey of Celles near Dinant (Belgium).

St. ANSCHAR (801–865)

Studied at Corbie, evangelized the Scandinavian countries and died bishop of Bremen.

Blessed ELINAND

Was born in the diocese of Beauvais, became a celebrated poet and found favour with Philip Augustus, was converted, entered the Cistercian abbey of Froidmont, and died about 1237, leaving many writings.

Blessed JOHN NELSON (1534-1578)

An English priest who accepted death "for affirming," as he declared, "the unity of the Catholic Church".

February 4th

ST. GILBERT OF SEMPRINGHAM (d. 1190)

BORN in England at the end of the reign of William the Conqueror, Gilbert was the son of a valiant Norman named Jocelin, who had received the estate of Sempringham as a reward for his services. Seeing that his son could not be made into a soldier, Jocelin showed his displeasure by sending him to study in Paris. Gilbert returned with the diploma of master of arts and opened a school at Sempringham. There he instructed the children of the poor, paying special attention to the inculcation of piety.

Soon his father provided him with two livings belonging to his estate. Gilbert distributed almost all their revenue to the destitute. Edified by his virtues, the bishop of Lincoln ordained him priest, a little against his will, and made him penitentiary of the diocese. When in 1130 the death of his parents made him lord of Sempringham, he left the bishop's palace and began to spend his inheritance. He founded two monasteries upon his domain: one of nuns under the Benedictine rule, the other of canons regular, who later called themselves Gilbertines and continued in existence until the schism of Henry VIII.

Our saint had his share of trials. He was denounced by his lay brothers to Pope Alexander III, who at first believed their slanders but afterwards admitted he had been mistaken. Another time he was accused of having given help to Thomas Becket, then in exile. This was false, but rather than appear to retract an act so charitable and meritorious by self-defence, Gilbert allowed himself to be put in prison.

As soon as he could, he renounced the direction of his order, happy to do nothing but obey and live the communal life. One of his habits was to place by his side at table what he called "the plate of the Lord Jesus" in which he put the tastiest morsels; this was the portion of the poor; what was left was for himself.

Gilbert died aged over a hundred, after having pledged his order to give abundant alms to the poor.

St. John de Britto (1647-1693)

A native of Portugal who joined the Society of Jesus and went as missionary to the Far East, even joining the Brahmin caste in trying to make converts. He was martyred at Oreiour in India.

St. Veronica or Berenice

Wiped the Saviour's face on the road to Calvary with the veil with which she covered her head.

St. Isidore of Pelusium

Hermit and theologian, born at Alexandria; has left more than two thousand letters (d. about 538).

St. Theophilus the Penitent (d. about 538)

Dignitary of the church of Adana in Cilicia, he is said to have signed a pact with the demon to avenge himself on his bishop. By invoking the Blessed Virgin, he regained possession of this document, did penance and died in the odour of sanctity. The story of Theophilus has been told in verse by Roswitha and by Rutebeuf.

Blessed Rabanus Maurus (d. 856)

Born at Mainz, he became bishop of that town, after having been a disciple of Alcuin at Tours and having made his religious profession at Fulda.

St. Andrew Corsini (1302-1373)

Florentine Carmelite, bishop of Fiesole.

St. Jeanne de Valois (1464-1505)

Deformed daughter of King Louis XI; married to the future Louis XII, she was repudiated by her husband, and founded the Franciscan order of the Annunciation at Bourges.

St. Joseph of Leonessa (1556-1612)

Capuchin missionary in Turkey; returned to die in his native Umbria.

February 5th

ST. AGATHA (d. 251)

We do not possess any entirely reliable information about this martyr, who has been honoured since the most ancient times and whose name has been included in the canon of the Mass.

Two cities in Sicily, Catania and Palermo, dispute the honour of her birth. Young, beautiful, and rich, Agatha lived from childhood a life entirely consecrated to God.

In betrayal of the duties of his office, a greedy and shameless magistrate named Quinctianus profited by Decius' edicts of persecution to attempt to abuse the virgin and to steal her fortune. He first delivered her to a matron charged with perverting her, who, however, failed. Then he made her appear before him on three occasions. The first time she was slapped in the face for having repelled the judge's solicitations and affirmed her faith. The second, Quinctianus had her stretched on a wooden horse; the executioner ripped her flesh with iron hooks and was ordered to cut off her breasts. Agatha then said to the brutal magistrate: "Cruel man, have you forgotten your mother and the breast that nourished you, that you dare to mutilate me in such a way?"

The third interrogation had no more success in changing her constancy. Fresh tortures were inflicted on her by rolling her, naked, on burning coals. Then a violent earthquake shook the town of Catania; a piece of wall broke off, crushing the judge's assessor who was his friend; the judge himself fled, terrified. As for Agatha, having thanked God for his help, she gave a great cry and expired.

The Patriarch JACOB

St. ADELAIDE or ALICE OF GUELDERS (d. about 1015)

Was at the same time abbess of the convent of Villich near Bonn, and of that of Our Lady of the Capitol at Cologne.

St. PETER BAPTIST AND HIS TWENTY-FIVE COMPANIONS

Put to death in Japan in 1597. Of these martyrs, six were Franciscans; seventeen were Franciscan tertiaries; two belonged to the Society of Jesus; and one was a catechist with the Jesuits.

February 6th

ST. VAAST or GASTON (d. 540)

VAAST or Gaston are two forms of the name Vedastus, borne by the catechist of Clovis. He was a priest of the church of Toul when the victor of Tolbiac asked for an enlightened man who could accompany him to Rheims. Vaast instructed him as they went, and the king was so pleased with him that he warmly commended him to St. Remigius. This latter made Vaast bishop of Arras and Cambrai, dioceses which had almost returned to paganism after the invasion of Attila. In them Vaast displayed his zeal for forty years, accomplishing numerous miracles and bringing innumerable souls back to Christianity. On one fine winter's night the inhabitants of Arras saw a luminous cloud ascending from the bishop's house towards the stars. Some hours later they learned that the soul of their bishop had gone to heaven.

ST. AMANDUS (d. 679 or 684)

AMANDUS was born in the country of Nantes, and at about the age of twenty became a monk on the island of Yeu, near the island of Ré. To escape the threats as well as the affectionate demonstrations of his parents, he left his monastery and reached the town of Tours. There, at the tomb of St. Martin, he was inspired to go to Bourges, where he lived for fifteen years in a cell built on the city rampart. After a voyage to Rome he came back to Bourges where he was practically forced to receive consecration as bishop. This by no means prevented him from following his vocation, which was to travel about ceaselessly preaching the Gospel.

He passed through Flanders, Brabant, Tournaisis, Beauvaisis, and even went as far as Karinthia. He was tireless and exposed himself to the worst dangers. In the region of the Scheldt, at that time occupied by brutal and superstitious people, he was beaten till the blood ran and was thrown into the river. About 646, Amandus became bishop of Maestricht, but only for a few years. He was a great founder of monasteries, and established them at Ghent, in Rouergue, and in the Laon country. The one which he founded at Elnon, three leagues from Tournai, and where he died a nonagenarian, later became the town of Saint-Amand.

St. DOROTHEA

Today is celebrated the feast of two virgins of this name about whom information is almost entirely lacking. One was beheaded at Caesarea in Cappadocia, under Diocletian; the other, Dorothea of Alexandria, virtuously shunned the advances of the Emperor Maximinus Caius (d. about 320).

St. GUARINUS

Cardinal, bishop of Palestrina (d. 1159).

St. SILVANUS

Bishop of Emesa in Phoenicia, martyred about 311.

Blessed ANGELUS OF FURCI

Augustinian hermit, studied at Paris, taught theology at Naples, and died there in 1327.

Blessed FRANCESCA OF GUBBIO

Franciscan tertiary, died in 1360.

February 7th
ST. THEODORE (d. 319)

BORN in the East, Theodore was one of the legion which, under Maxi‑mianus, had its winter quarters in Cappadocia. Denounced as a Christian, he appeared before two officers, who, after urging him to reflect, gave him his liberty. Theodore took this opportunity to set fire to the temple at Amasia, dedicated to the mother of the gods. Again arrested, he was exhorted to renounce his act and to recognize the religion of the Empire. Far from agreeing, Theodore expressed himself in the most scornful terms regarding this religion. As they tore his flesh to make him recant, he only praised God and recited the most beautiful of the psalms. He remained uncompromising and was condemned to suffer by fire.

ST. ROMUALD (d. 1027)

THE founder of the Camaldolese belonged to the family of the Onesti, dukes of Ravenna. After a wild youth, he was converted the day when his father, for whom he was acting as second, killed his opponent in a duel. Romuald forthwith entered the monastery of Classe, near Ravenna. Obliged to leave because of the spite of certain monks, he went to a spot near Vaise to place himself under the guidance of a hermit named Marinus, who disciplined him harshly for the slightest negligence. With Marinus and Peter Urseolus, Romuald then came to Rousillon, where he lived for three years in a wilderness. He learned in 994 that his father, who had become a monk at Saint Severus in Ravenna, now thought of re‑entering the world. Romuald went back to Italy and succeeded in dissuading him from his purpose. He himself again entered the monastery of Classe; but again he left it, after having tried in vain for two years to bring about its reform.

Romuald founded several abbeys in Italy, Istria, and Germany. These foundations, however, did not measure up to the ideal he had set himself. One day he was beaten with rods by his monks; another time, at Sasso Ferrato, they excommunicated him and prevented him for some time from celebrating Mass.

It was at Camaldoli, near Florence, that Romuald established the kind of monastic life of which he dreamed. The monks there were of two sorts: one kind lived as hermits and only met in church; the others were recluses who never left their cells.

This great ascetic died at Val di Castro, in the Marches of Ancona, alone, very old, shut up in a cell where for months he had lived in silence.

St. FIDELIS
Bishop of Mérida, in Spain (d. about 570).

St. RICHARD
Ancient Saxon king, died at Lucca in 722, when on a pilgrimage to Rome.

Blessed ANTHONY OF STRONCONE (1391–1461)
Franciscan lay brother, for thirty years fulfilled the duties of mendicant at the Carceri near Assisi.

Blessed THOMAS SHERWOOD (1551–1578)
Merchant draper's assistant, born in London. For having said that he considered Queen Elizabeth as excommunicated, he was declared guilty of high treason and condemned "to be dragged through the city streets, hung, then cut down, to have his bowels drawn, his head cut off, his body quartered, and the pieces exposed in such places as it should please the Queen to designate".

Blessed JACQUES SALES and GUILLAUME SALTEMOUCHE
Jesuits, put to death by the Huguenots at Aubenas in 1593.

February 8th
BLESSED JACOBA OR JACQUELINE (d. about 1273)

JACOBA DI SETTESOLI was, with St. Clare, the greatest friend of St. Francis. He probably made her acquaintance in 1212. Jacoba, who was then about twenty-two, belonged to the highest Roman nobility. Having become the widow of Gratian Frangipini, she would undoubtedly have embraced the religious life if the care of her two sons and the protection of their inheritance had not prevented her. Instead she entered the third order. She was a masterful woman and one who well deserved, because of her virile energy, the name of "Brother Jacoba", by which Francis has handed her down to posterity.

The Poverello was often her guest during his visits to the Eternal City, and at her house he ate an excellent cream called *mortairol*, composed of sugar, almonds, and other ingredients pounded in a mortar. In recognition of her affectionate attentions he made her a present of a lamb, which, says St. Bonaventure, "seemed to have been educated by him in the spiritual life". It followed its mistress to church, remained near her while she was praying, and came home with her. If, in the morning, Jacoba did not awaken, the lamb came to butt her gently and bleat in her ear, to make her go to her devotions.

A few days before leaving the world, the Poverello had his brothers write to Jacoba: "Set out then as soon as possible, if you wish to see me once more. Bring with you what is necessary for my burial, and some of the good things which you gave me to eat when I was sick in Rome." Jacoba arrived armed with what was needed to bury the Poverello: a veil to cover his face, the cushion on which his head would rest on the bier, the sheet of haircloth which was to cover his body, and all the wax needed for the watching and the funeral ceremonies. She also brought the sweetmeat made of almonds which he desired, but he could only taste it.

In addition to many other sufferings, Jacoba had that of surviving those she loved, her two sons and all her grandchildren. She passed her last years at Assisi in order to be near those who had known St. Francis. She was buried not far from him in the great Umbrian basilica, and on her tomb was written: HIC REQUIESCAT JACOBA SANCTA NOBILISQUE ROMANA.

St. MEINGOLD (d. 892)

Lord of the Liége country, put to death by former political enemies as he was returning from a pilgrimage.

St. STEPHEN OF MURET (1048–1124)

Founder of the order of Grandmont in the forest of Muret, in Limousin.

St. JOHN OF MATHA (1160–1223)

Provençal noble; founder, with Felix of Valois, of the Trinitarian order for the redemption of captives. In France the Trinitarians were called

Mathurins, because they were established at Paris near a chapel dedicated to St. Mathurin.

Blessed ISAIAS BONER

Born at Cracow, became an Augustinian hermit, and was professor of Holy Scripture in his order (d. 1471).

February 9th
ST. APOLLONIA (d. 249)

IN the last year of the reign of the Emperor Philip, an uprising against the Christians broke out at Alexandria. Led by a so-called prophet, the pagans seized an old man, named Metras, and tried to force him to blaspheme. When he refused, they beat him until blood came, put out his eyes with pointed reeds, and finally stoned him to death.

Then they seized a Christian woman called Quinta, and led her to a temple to force her to adore the idol there. As she refused, she was dragged, hands and feet bound, over pointed cobbles, and she too was stoned to death.

It was during the same disorders that the virgin Apollonia ended her long and virtuous existence. These fanatics struck her so hard on the jaw that they broke all her teeth. They then led her outside the town, lit a great fire, and threatened to throw her on to it alive if she did not agree to repeat certain words, for her equivalent to apostasy. However, a short time was allowed to her for reflection. She made a show of accepting, then, taking advantage of the inattention of her torturers and impelled by a movement of the Holy Spirit, she flung herself into the flames and was quickly consumed.

St. RAYNALD (d. 1225)

A German nobleman, he was a monk at Fonte-Avellana, in Umbria, and died as bishop of Nocera near Assisi. He was at the Portiuncula in 1216, when St. Francis proclaimed the famous plenary indulgence he had just obtained from Honorius III.

St. NICEPHORUS

Martyred at Antioch in Syria about 260.

St. CYRIL OF ALEXANDRIA (d. 444)

Became bishop of that city in 412. This Father of the Church defended the divine motherhood of the Virgin Mary against Nestorius and other heretics. "Christ," he wrote, "is not a man into whom the Word has descended, but the very Word taking birth in flesh which is its own. It is in this sense that it is said in all truth that God is born, that he died, and that Mary is the mother of God."

St. SABINUS (d. 556)

Bishop of Canosa, in Apulia.

St. ROMANUS THE WONDER-WORKER (5th century)

Led a solitary life on a mountain near Antioch in Syria.

St. ANSBERT

Born at Chaussy-sur-Epte (French Vexin), became bishop of Rouen, after having succeeded St. Wandrille as abbot of Fontenelle (Normandy). He died in 695 at the abbey of Hautmont (Hainaut), where Pepin of Heristal had exiled him.

February 10th

ST. SCHOLASTICA (d. 543)

TWIN sister of St. Benedict, Scholastica was born, about 480, into a rich family at Norcia in Umbria. The mother of these children died in bringing them into the world. They loved one another tenderly and were brought up together until the age of fourteen, when Benedict left for Rome in order to pursue his studies there.

It is thought that Scholastica followed her brother when he became a monk and that, having become a nun, she settled in the valley of the Liris at the foot of Monte Cassino. Benedict directed her as he did other nuns placed under his guidance. He saw his sister once a year. On the appointed day Scholastica went to Monte Cassino; Benedict came to meet her; they passed some hours together in a guest-house of the abbey, and ate together, then each went his way.

Their last interview is reported by St. Gregory the Great. They were at table and the time was approaching for them to separate, when Scholastica said to her brother: "Don't let us part yet, but let us wait until morning."

"What are you thinking of, my sister? Not for the world would I pass a night outside the monastery."

Scholastica wept a moment in silence, then, inclining her head, hid her face in her hands. No sooner had she uncovered it than a crash of thunder shook the house to its foundations. The peaceful sky became black, flashes of lightning rent the night, the heaven opened its floodgates, the wind blew, and a tempest threatened to carry everything before it. "May God forgive you, but what have you done, my sister?" said Benedict.

"I asked you and you would not listen to me; so I have asked God, who has heard me, for I see indeed that you will not return to the monastery this evening."

They passed the night in pious conversation and parted at dawn, never to see one another again. Three days later, as he was at the window of his cell, St. Benedict saw the soul of his sister rising to heaven in the form of a dove. He gave thanks to God, sent for her body and had it placed in his own tomb, not wishing that death should separate them.

St. WILLIAM OF MALEVAL (d. 1157)

Led a hermit's life in the country of Siena in a wilderness called the "evil valley". His disciples, under the name of "Williamites," spread through Italy, France, and Germany.

St. AUSTREBERTHA (d. 704)

Daughter of a mayor of the palace, she fled from the Thérouanne country where she was born, became in succession abbess of a convent near Jumièges and of another at Pavilly (Normandy) where she died.

Blessed HUGH OF FOSSE (d. 1164)

Native of a place which is included in the present diocese of Namur, he was the first disciple of St. Norbert, and succeeded him as superior general of the Premonstratensians.

Blessed ARNOLD (d. 1255)

Abbot of the Benedictine monastery of St. Justina at Padua.

Blessed CLARE OF RIMINI (d. 1344)

Married twice, gave herself up to pleasure, and ended her life in penance.

February 11th
ST. ADOLPH (d. 1224)

WHEN he was canon of St. Peter's at Cologne, Adolph, count of Teklen-burg, paid a visit to the Cistercian monks of Camp, on the confines of the duchies of Cleves and Guelders. This Cistercian abbey was still in its first fervour, and the influence of St. Bernard, who had recently died, was still making itself felt. In full chapter, old men and youths confessed their smallest faults and in expiation whipped themselves till the blood ran. Seeing this, the young canon, whose life had till then been passed in pleasure, decided to leave the world and to think only of his salvation. He at once entered the community and quickly reached great perfection.

Having become bishop of Osnabrück in Westphalia, he kept the pious habits he had acquired in the cloister. His biographers show him administering his church with wisdom and having nothing closer to his heart than the splendour of the divine worship. They add that in aiding the poor it was to the lepers that his affection and his alms were given in preference.

One of these lepers, who lived in a hut at some distance off, was visited by him every time he went that way. The prelate would spend many hours consoling him, speaking with him of Our Saviour's passion. This vexed his companions, who had to wait outside in the cold. One day he had once more to pass that way, and they removed the leper; thus, they thought, when Adolph passed he would find the hut empty and go on his way, and they themselves would lose none of their precious time. But they were mistaken in their reckoning. By a kind of miracle the unfortunate man was back in his wonted place when the bishop arrived, and still had the strength to thank his great friend for his goodness and his charitable exhortations; then he gave up the ghost in Adolph's presence.

After having ruled the church of Osnabrück for twenty-one years, Adolph died in the odour of sanctity, and a number of miracles took place around the burial-place.

Commemoration of the APPARITIONS OF LOURDES (1858)

St. GREGORY II

Pope (d. 731).

St. PASCAL I

Pope (d. 824).

St. LAZARUS

Bishop of Marseilles (d. about 450).

St. SÉVERIN

Abbot of Agaunum. He was called to King Clovis, whom he cured of fever, himself fell ill on the return journey and died at Château-Landon (about 507).

St. JONAS

Lived eighty-five years in the monastery of Muchon, in Egypt (4th century).

St. EUPHROSYNE

Reputed to have lived thirty-five years in an Alexandrian monastery (d. about 470).

The Blessed PETER PASCHAL and CATALLAN

Franciscan inquisitors, put to death in 1321, in the diocese of Valencia, by the Vaudois.

February 12th
ST. EULALIA (d. 304)

EULALIA was born of Christian parents, and from her early youth burned with a desire to become a martyr. When the edicts of Diocletian and Maximianus were issued, she hastened to the tribunal and spontaneously confessed her faith. Although scarcely fourteen years old, the prefect made her undergo divers tortures, then finally burned her alive on a pyre.

That is all that the documentary sources tell of St. Eulalia, so highly honoured in Spain.

However, scholars have begun a discussion not yet concluded. Certain of them claim that there were two girls of the same name: Eulalia of Barcelona and Eulalia of Mérida; others, that there was only one. However it may be, no one denies that, either at Barcelona or at Mérida, or in both these towns, a child martyr named Eulalia died in the above-mentioned circumstances.

St. JULIAN THE HOSPITALLER or THE POOR (date uncertain)

His legend relates that he had killed his parents in error; that he left his wife, sold all his goods, and went to care for the poor in a hospital which he had founded.

St. BENEDICT OF ANIANE (d. 821)

A native of Languedoc, chief cup-bearer to Pepin the Short, he left the court by stealth in order to become a monk at Saint-Seine, in the diocese of Langres. Having taken flight in order not to be elected abbot of this monastery, he reached his native country and settled on the banks of the Aniane, where some disciples very soon came to join him. He spent the

rest of his life reforming the Benedictine order. After enjoying the confidence of Charlemagne, he obtained that of Louis le Débonnaire, who
placed all the Benedictine monasteries of Languedoc, France, and
Aquitaine under his authority. Benedict died when over seventy at the
abbey of Cornelimünster near Aix-la-Chapelle in 821.

The SEVEN FOUNDERS OF THE SERVITE ORDER or "Servants of the Virgin Mary"

These former Florentine merchants were called: BUONFIGLIO DEI
MONALDI (1198–1262), GIOVANNI MANETTI (1206–1257), GHERAR-
DINO DI SOSTEGNO (1204–1282), RICOVERO DEI LIPPI-UGGUCCIONI
(1206–1282), BENEDETTO DELL' ANTELLA (1203–1268), BARTO-
LOMEO DEGLI AMIDEI (1204–1266), ALESSIO or ALEXIS FALCONIERI,
who died at the age of a hundred and ten, in 1310.

February 13th
ST. MARTINIAN (d. about 398)

BORN at Caesarea in Palestine about the middle of the 4th century,
Martinian led a hermit's life from the age of eighteen until his death. Among
the temptations he suffered, two are recalled by his biographer; they are
perhaps a trifle legendary.

The first came from a woman named Zoe, who one evening knocked at
his door and begged hospitality. She appeared so aged, miserable, and
unkempt that, moved by pity, he unhesitatingly took her under his roof.
The next day, having changed her clothing, the poor wretch appeared as she
was, that is to say, a very beautiful woman; and, when she proposed to
Martinian to become his wife, he for a whole day came very near to assenting.
However, he recollected himself in time and went to expiate this weakness
on a rock surrounded by the sea on all sides.

It was there, after six years of terrible hardships, that he saw approaching
a young woman who had escaped from a shipwreck. This time he forestalled all communication. "Here," he said to the escaped girl, "is all the
bread and water that are left; I leave them for you. The sailor who brings me
provisions three times a year will come back in two months. Tell him your
plight, and he will take you safely to harbour." At these words Martinian
threw himself into the sea and miraculously reached the shore.

He died at Athens, attended by the bishop of that city, about 398.

St. POLYEUCTUS (d. 250)

Officer of the Roman legion stationed at Melitene (Armenia), he was beheaded for having, in his zeal as a neophyte, torn up the imperial edict of persecution and broken the idols which the pagans were carrying in procession.

St. STEPHEN

Abbot of a monastery at Rieti (6th century).

St. ERMENILDA

Daughter of Ercombert, king of Kent, married Wulfhere, king of Mercia, and, after being widowed, was successively abbess of Sheppey and of Ely (d. about 700).

St. GILBERT (d. about 1010)

Native of Ham, studied with the canons of St. Quentin and died bishop of Meaux.

Blessed JORDAN OF SAXONY (d. 1237)

Succeeded St. Dominic as general of the Order of Preachers.

Blessed JOHN DE TRIORA

Franciscan martyred in China, in 1816.

February 14th

ST. VALENTINE (d. about 270)

TODAY is celebrated the feast of two saints named Valentine whose rather similar stories have not been entirely clarified.

The first was a priest in Rome said to have been arrested under Claudius the Goth. Appearing before the emperor, he openly confessed his faith, and when questioned by him about Jupiter and Mercury, declared that they were shameless and contemptible characters. He was then committed to a magistrate named Asterius, who had an adopted daughter who was blind. Valentine cured her and converted at the same time Asterius and his family. Learning this, the emperor had him beaten and later decapitated on the Flaminian Way. In the 4th century, Pope Julius I built a church in honour of this martyr; in the 7th century, Pope Honorius I restored it and it became a very popular centre of pilgrimage.

The other St. Valentine is reputed to have occupied the see of Terni in Umbria in the year 223. Informed of his virtues and miracles, a Roman philosopher named Crato begged him to come and cure his son, stricken by an incurable malady. The bishop went to Rome and promised to do what was asked if the father and his family would be converted. The condition was accepted and fulfilled, and even three young Athenians, disciples of Crato, renounced the gods to embrace Christianity. On his side, Valentine worked the cure he promised.

As soon as the prefect Abundius learned what had happened, he had the bishop beheaded. His body was then taken back to Terni by the converted Athenians, and St. Valentine is still honoured as patron of that city.

In medieval days it was believed that birds began to pair on February 14th, whence the origin of the custom of sending "Valentines".

St. ANTONINUS
Abbot of St. Agrippinus at Sorrento (d. about 830).

St. MARO
Solitary and wonder-worker in Syria (d. about 423).

February 15th

ST. GEORGIA or GEORGETTE
(d. beginning of 6th century)

St. GEORGIA is known to us from what is told of her by Gregory of Tours, her compatriot of Auvergne and almost her contemporary.

A maiden, living at Clermont in the first years of the 6th century, she withdrew into the nearby countryside in order to meditate. She fasted every day and prayed almost without ceasing.

Her funeral was marked by an event which is supposed to have been miraculous. A flight of doves accompanied her body from the house where she had died to the church, and during the service they hid in the roof. They reappeared when the funeral procession left for the cemetery, flying above her mortal remains. Then they flew up to heaven whence they came, for they were said to have been angels who, to honour the purity of the dead girl, had taken the form of white doves.

ST. FAUSTINUS (d. beginning of the 2nd century)

IT is told how two brothers, Faustinus and Jovita, one a priest and the other a deacon, began to preach the Gospel at Brescia, their native town.

At about this time Hadrian, returning from the East, appeared in Lombardy to secure his succession to the Emperor Trajan. Count Italicus went to meet him and told him of the success of the Christian preaching. Arriving in Brescia, the new emperor wished to conduct the trial of the two apostles himself, and he began by inflicting divers torments on them. Then he took them with him to Rome, renewing the interrogation and the tortures at every stage of the journey. Nothing could shake the constancy of the two brothers. That is why, from Rome, Hadrian sent them back to Brescia, so that they might be beheaded there where they had shown their zeal.

St. EUSEBIUS

A hermit of Syria (5th century).

St. SEVERUS

Priest of the province of Valeri in the Abruzzi. In his *Dialogues*, Pope St. Gregory tells that he raised from the dead a man whom the demons were dragging down to hell, in order to convert him (d. about 550).

St. WALFRID (d. about 765)

Native of Pisa, he married, had five children, then built a monastery to which he retired, while his wife also entered the religious life.

St. SIGFRID (d. about 765)

English priest who evangelized Sweden.

February 16th

ST. ELIAS (d. 309)

WITH four Egyptian compatriots, Elias had accompanied some Christians condemned to the mines of Cilicia, in order to bring them comfort. He was returning to his country when, travelling through Palestine, he was arrested with his companions at the gates of Caesarea. On being questioned, they made no secret of their beliefs and were put in irons.

They appeared then before Firmilian, governor of Palestine, who first asked what their names were. They replied that they were named Elias, Jeremias, Isaias, Samuel, and Daniel. These were in fact the names which they had taken for their own at baptism.

Firmilian asked whence they came. Elias, their spokesman, said that they all came from Jerusalem. "Does not St. Paul say," he added, "that Jerusalem, Jerusalem on high, is our mother?"

"And where is this Jerusalem on high?" asked Firmilian.

"This Jerusalem," replied Elias, "is the true country of Christians; it is situated in the East, beside the true Sun and only Light."

It is to be supposed that Firmilian could understand nothing of this symbolic language borrowed from the Scriptures. He did not, however, succeed in making the Christians use any other. Perhaps, furthermore, he believed that they were speaking of an Eastern city where the Christians were organizing themselves against the Romans. In any case these strange words threw him into a fury and he passed sentence of death on the five travellers.

ST. JULIANA OF NICOMEDIA (d. about 305)

AFRICANUS, a pagan, the father of Juliana, promised his daughter to a young noble named Evilase. In order to gain time, Juliana said to her betrothed: "You must become prefect of Nicomedia before I consent to marry you." When Evilase had been named prefect he came to Juliana, who said to him: "Now you must become a Christian for me to agree to be your wife." In the suitor's eyes this was an impossible condition. It was in vain that Africanus inflicted every kind of ill treatment upon his daughter. Weary of her opposition, he handed her over to Evilase, who as prefect called her before his tribunal and, to have done with the matter, had her beheaded.

Such is the biography which has been published of this martyr, but it is legendary. The only fact that is certain is that Juliana was put to death for the faith under Maximianus.

St. ONESIMUS (1st century)

Slave of a Colossian Christian named Philemon, he committed a theft and fled from punishment. In Rome, where he went into hiding, he met St. Paul and was converted by him.

St. HONESTUS (3rd century)

Native of Nîmes, converted by St. Saturninus who sent him to convert Navarre and Biscay.

Blessed PHILIPPA MARERIA (d. 1236)

Poor Clare and a native of the Rieti valley.

February 17th

ST. SILVINUS (d. 717)

SILVINUS, considered by some as a native of the Toulouse country, by others of Belgium, spent his youth at the court of Kings Childeric II and Thierry III. He left the world on the eve of his marriage and departed for the Holy Land. Returning by Rome, he received consecration as bishop. However, he was never attached to any particular diocese; he was what is called a "regionary" bishop, one of those travelling missionaries to whom the episcopal dignity gave more prestige and greater facilities for showing their zeal.

Silvinus evangelized chiefly the district of Thérouanne and the Belgian coast where paganism still counted many followers. He converted a great number by his words and his example.

He was kindness itself toward his neighbour, and toward himself unbelievably austere, sleeping on a board or on the bare ground, wearing iron chains, living on herbs and fruit. His devotion to the Blessed Sacrament was great. In the churches he liked to see abundant lights, sumptuous ornaments, and perfect cleanliness. He desired to find someone always in prayer there, and the utmost beauty in the chanting. His love of the poor was such that he divided his garments among them when he had nothing else to give them.

Silvinus had always hoped to be able to shed his blood for the faith, or at least to end his days in the desert. When, at the end of his strength and quite infirm, he realized that these graces were to be refused him, he retired to the shadow of the abbey of some Benedictine nuns at Auchy in Artois. It was there that he died while, according to his wish, those present sang psalms at his bedside.

St. MARIAMNE (1st century)

It is said that after the ascension of the Saviour this pious widow accompanied St. Philip and St. Bartholomew to Hieropolis, and that afterwards she carried the Gospel to Lycaonia and died there.

St. THEODULUS

An old man who was crucified about 306, at Caesarea in Palestine, for having encouraged and embraced Christians condemned to death.

St. FULRAD

An Alsatian by birth, became abbot of St. Denis, served at the same time the interests of Pepin the Short with the popes, and the interests of the popes at the French court (d. 784).

Blessed EVERMODUS

Belgian Premonstratensian, friend of St. Norbert, became bishop of Ratzeburg in Denmark.

February 18th

ST. CONSTANTIA or CONSTANCE (d. about 354)

A DAUGHTER, according to some, according to others a niece, of the Emperor Constantine, Constantia is said to have been a leper when she heard of the miracles which were taking place at St. Agnes' tomb. Going there, she had a vision in which the saint herself promised her cure if she became a Christian. Restored to health, Constantia was baptized and decided to remain a virgin.

Sought in marriage by General Gallicanus, conqueror of the Persians, she declined the offer, which vexed Constantine greatly. Constantia then repented of her refusal and agreed to marry Gallicanus after he had conquered the Scythians, who were invading Thrace. Gallicanus left on this campaign, taking with him Paul and John, Constantia's servants. In exchange he confided Attica and Artemia, his own daughters, to her care. It was a way for the betrothed of ensuring that their promises should be kept.

However, as they were on their way, Paul and John persuaded the general that he would have better success in conquering the Scythians if he embraced Christianity. Constantia for her part never ceased begging God to take from Gallicanus all idea of marrying her. Her prayers were granted. After his victory, Gallicanus, now a Christian, gave up the thought of marriage to devote himself to good works. Later he was martyred with Paul and John, under Julian the Apostate. As for Constantia, she passed her life, together with Attica and Artemia who had been converted, near the Church of St. Agnes, and she was buried there.

ST. ANGILBERT (d. 814)

ANGILBERT or Engelbert was raised at the court of the Frankish kings and became Charlemagne's secretary. A friend and disciple of Alcuin, his poetic compositions aroused the admiration of his contemporaries and earned him the name of the Homer of his day. He had also the qualities of a statesman and warrior, for Charlemagne appointed him temporarily as prime minister to his son Pepin who had become king of Italy; and when the Norman incursions ravaged the French coast he named him governor of Ponthieu.

Angilbert, who lived at Centula, near the monastery founded by St. Richarius, resolved to leave all and to enter that abbey; he became its abbot a little later. Meanwhile Charlemagne, who had appointed him his chaplain-general, still frequently sought his counsel. Thus it came about that Angilbert was sent thrice to Rome as ambassador, and that he accompanied the ruler to his imperial consecration. In 811 he signed Charlemagne's will. The latter had charged him with the execution of his last wishes, but Angilbert only survived by a few weeks the death of his emperor.

St. SIMEON (d. about 107)

Son of Cleophas and first cousin of Our Saviour. He followed James the Less as bishop of Jerusalem and was crucified at the age of one hundred and twenty.

St. FLAVIAN

Bishop of Constantinople (d. 449).

St. COLMAN

Bishop of Lindisfarne (d. 676).

St. HELLADIUS

Archbishop of Toledo (d. about 631).

St. THEOTONIO (d. 1166)

One of the founders, at Holy Cross of Coimbra, of the congregation of canons regular to which St. Anthony of Padua at one time belonged.

Blessed JOHN PETER NÉEL

Priest of the Foreign Mission, born at Sainte-Catherine-sur-Riverie (Rhône), martyred in China in 1862.

February 19th

ST. CONRAD (d. 1351)

BORN at Piacenza of a noble family and married to a woman who was admirable in every respect, Conrad lived happily and at peace until a hunting party suddenly changed his destiny. He ordered his servants to set fire to a thicket in which the quarry had taken refuge. As ill luck would have it, the wind arose and, coming nearer and nearer, the flames destroyed the surrounding harvests.

Conrad and his people were able to save themselves in time. A culprit had to be found, and a man who was collecting wood in the place was arrested and condemned to death. As he was being led to the place of execution, Conrad confessed. Responsible for making good the vast damage, he had to sell all his goods, pledge his wife's dowry, and he, who till then had lived as a great noble, fell into poverty.

With his wife Euphrosina, he thought deeply about the precariousness of worldly happiness, and both decided to think henceforth only of their salvation. Euphrosina entered the Poor Clares of Piacenza, and Conrad joined the Franciscan tertiaries who led a life of solitude not far from that town. His fervour brought him rapid progress in virtue; people began to speak of his saintliness, and visitors began to come to his door.

In order to avoid their attentions, Conrad left for Sicily. He lived there thirty-six years, sometimes caring for the sick in the hospital at Noto, at others retiring into a nearby hermitage. The austere life he led did not always shelter him from carnal temptations. Like his father, St. Francis, he had to roll among the thorns to drive them away. God gave him the gift of miracles. Today he is still invoked for the cure of hernia.

St. GABINIUS

Roman martyr (d. 296).

St. BARBATUS (d. 682)

Born in the district of Benevento, he became a priest and pursued his ministry in that region. After having slandered his morals, the people chose him as bishop and venerated his saintliness.

St. BEATUS (d. 798)

Priest of the Asturias, wrote a commentary on the Apocalypse and died in the abbey of Valcarado.

Blessed BONIFACE

Born in Belgium, taught at Paris and Cologne, became bishop of Lausanne, and ended as spiritual director of the Cistercians of La Cambre at Brussels (d. 1265).

Blessed ALVAREZ OF CORDOVA

Dominican, who exercised his zeal in Andalusia (d. 1420).

Blessed ELIZABETH PICENARDI (d. 1468)

Servite tertiary, born and died at Mantua.

February 20th

ST. EUCHERIUS (d. 738 or 743)

A NATIVE of Orléans, Eucherius had a very pious mother, and his god-father was Ansbert, bishop of Autun. He began his studies at the age of seven. St. Paul's epistles were the great discovery of his life and constituted his favourite reading. "The fashion of this world is soon to pass away" (I Cor. vii, 31), said the apostle to the Corinthians, and again: "This world's wisdom, with God, is but folly" (I Cor. iii, 19). These maxims, the continual subject of the young man's meditations, determined his vocation. He entered the abbey of Jumièges, in Normandy, and remained there seven years.

When his uncle, Suaveric, bishop of Orléans, died, the clergy and faithful of that town asked Charles Martel to give them Eucherius as his successor. The mayor of the palace sent an officer to Jumièges with the order that if Eucherius resisted, he was to be taken to Orléans by force. He resisted stoutly but in vain. "My dearly beloved," he said weeping to his brethren, "will you allow me to return to the world and be thrown into the claws of the demon?" It was as if he foresaw the ills that would beset his path.

When Charles Martel had to fight the Saracens, he decided to draw upon the goods of the Church to pay his war costs and to reward his companions. Eucherius rose up in protest against these levies which were openly abused. Doubtless he was thought to be unfavourable to the change of dynasty then in preparation. However that may be, after his victory at Poitiers, Charles returned through Orléans and constrained Eucherius to follow him to Paris. From there he exiled him to Cologne.

The prelate was greeted there with so much enthusiasm and respect that he was hastily taken to a castle in the neighbourhood of Liége for fear of political complications. Finally he obtained permission to retire to the monastery of Saint-Trond, where he lived six more years.

St. ELEUTHERIUS (456–532)

Born at Tournai, became bishop of that town, defended the doctrine of the Incarnation against heretics who, as he was leaving church one day, inflicted on him wounds from which he died.

Blessed WULFRIC (d. 1154)

Native of the district of Bristol, first led the life of a worldly priest, repented, and afterwards lived as a penitent near Hazelbury (Somerset).

St. Amata

Niece of St. Clare. After a dissipated youth, she became a Poor Clare and died about 1250.

February 21st

BLESSED NOEL (d. 1794)

Youngest of a family of sixteen, Noel Pinot was born at Angers in 1747. He was ordained priest in 1771, was successively curate of Bousse and Corzé, became almoner of a hospital for the incurable at Angers in 1781, and was named pastor of Louroux-Béconnais in 1788. He gave in alms almost the entire income which he drew from this fervent parish.

Early in the year 1791, the municipality of Louroux-Béconnais notified Noel and his curate that they must subscribe to the oath of fidelity to the civil constitution of the clergy. The curate complied but the pastor refused. When a constitutional bishop was installed in Maine-et-Loire, Noel protested from the pulpit that he would never recognize him, which caused him to be accused of fomenting revolt, and he was placed under arrest. The tribunal of Beaupréau condemned him to withdraw eight leagues from his parish.

His existence then became that of a host of priests classified as "refractory". They were reduced to exercising their ministry in secret and to constantly changing their places of hiding. Noel hid in turn at hospitals for the incurable at Corzé, Beaupréau, and Saint-Macaire. The advance of the Vendeans allowed him to reappear in their wake at Louroux-Béconnais, but their withdrawal obliged him to leave his parish again. Even so, Noel did not abandon his flock. By day he went underground; at night he heard confessions and celebrated Mass in some isolated farm.

It was at the farm of La Milandrie, belonging to the widow Peltier, that he was discovered on the night of the 8th or 9th of February 1794, as he was preparing to go up to the altar. Arraigned on February 21st before the revolutionary tribunal sitting in the bishop's palace at Angers, he was condemned to death for refusing the oath and for fanaticism. He was executed on the same day, clad in the liturgical robes which he wore at the time of his arrest, although at the last moment they removed the chasuble which might have interfered with the action of the guillotine.

St. Severian

Bishop of Scythopolis, put to death in 452 by the partisans of Eutyches.

Blessed PEPIN OF LANDEN

Father of St. Gertrude and St. Begga, grandfather of Pepin of Héristal and forebear of Pepin the Short. Mayor of the palace, he was teacher of King Dagobert and tutor of King Sigebert (d. about 640).

St. DANIEL

Persian priest martyred under Sapor II in 344.

St. IRENE

Spaniard, sister of Pope St. Damasus (d. 379).

St. FELIX

Bishop of Metz, lived, it is believed, in the 2nd century.

February 22nd
BLESSED ISABEL (d. 1270)

DAUGHTER of Louis VIII and of Blanche of Castile, youngest sister of St. Louis, Isabel of France was born in March 1225. To her mother's pious care she responded with precocious gravity, self-control, and a love of prayer which impressed those around her. St. Louis liked to tell how one morning when the footman was rolling up Isabel's mattress and counterpane, a faint voice came from out of the roll; it was the voice of his little sister, so absorbed in prayer that she had not noticed she was being bundled up. She studied the Holy Scriptures, natural history, medicine, logic, and Eastern languages, and acquired a perfect knowledge of Latin.

The court of France was held in turn at Paris, Saint-Germain, Vincennes, Melun, Pontoise, and Compiègne. It was at Saint-Germain that the young princess fell so sick as a result of mortifications that her life was despaired of. A holy person brought to her bedside foretold that she would recover sufficiently to consecrate herself entirely to God.

At the age of ten she had been promised to the son of the count of Angoulême. This betrothal was broken and St. Louis had to pay a forfeit of 10,000 silver francs. Later Frederick II asked her in marriage for his son Conrad, heir to the Empire. To Innocent IV, who supported the request, Isabel replied that she preferred being last in the ranks of the Lord's virgins to being the greatest empress in the world.

Her plans were realized in 1228 when she founded the abbey of Long-champ, opposite Mount Valerian, on the right bank of the Seine. Sixty nuns, belonging for the most part to the court circle, there followed the rule of St. Clare. Although Urban IV softened it as much as possible, the princess herself was too ill to follow the rule strictly, so she confined herself to living within the convent enclosure without pronouncing any vows.

There she passed the last ten years of her life, repairing with her own hands the clothing of the poor, patiently suffering innumerable ills, watching maternally over her daughters. She died in her forty-sixth year, lying on a bed of straw.

St. PASCHASIUS
Bishop of Vienne in Dauphiny (d. 312?).

St. MAXIMIAN
Bishop of Ravenna (d. 556).

St. MARGARET OF CORTONA (1247-1297)
Born at Laviano, Margaret was a great beauty. Her father became a widower and remarried a woman who caused the girl great suffering. She was seduced by a lord of Montepulciano, with whom she lived for nine years, and by whom she had a son who later became a friar minor. The assassination of her lover caused Margaret to reflect upon her way of life and, after a three years' period of trial, she was admitted to the Franciscan third order at Cortona. She passed the last twenty-three years of her life in that town, practising the severest penances and favoured with extraordinary graces. The dog with which she is usually depicted represents the pet animal which helped her to find the body of her lover.

Blessed GIOVANNA MARIA (1606-1670)
Was born near Vicenza, and became a Benedictine at Bassano. She was treated as a madwoman before her sanctity was discovered.

Blessed JAMES CARVALHO
Portuguese Jesuit, martyred in Japan in 1616.

February 23rd
ST. PETER DAMIAN (d. about 1072)

A NATIVE of Ravenna, this future cardinal and doctor of the Church had the most lowly beginnings. The youngest child of a large family, his mother refused to nurse him. She died soon afterwards and so did her husband. An elder brother took charge of little Peter and sent him out to watch the swine. Another brother, named Damian, later rescued him and enabled him to go to school. It was in memory of this second brother that Peter added his first name to his own.

Peter Damian became a brilliant teacher at Faenza and Ravenna, but, fearing for his salvation, entered Fonte Avellana in Umbria when he was about eighteen. Here the eremitic life was followed and he endeared himself to the austere monks and soon became their prior. He founded hermitages similar to Fonte Avellana and kept a firm hand over them; he had disciples who themselves were saints, such as St. John of Lodi, who wrote his life, St. Rodolfo, bishop of Gubbio, and St. Dominic, called *Loricatus*. Despite the occasional sharpness of his zealous nature, no one has so loved the Blessed Virgin or spoken more beautifully of her than this ascetic.

There exist a hundred and fifty-eight of his letters, sixty minor works, several lives of the saints, and a number of admirable sermons. With sharp frankness he wrote to popes, to anti-popes, to the emperor, to prelates, abbots and abbesses. It is true that scandals abounded at that time in all ranks of the Church.

In 1057, in order to persuade Peter Damian to let himself be named cardinal-bishop of Ostia, it was necessary to threaten him with excommunication. From that time on, he was employed on the most difficult missions. However, after five years he succeeded in having his resignation accepted and returned to Fonte Avellana. He died on a journey to Faenza at the monastery of St. Mary of the Angels. He was buried there and the following epitaph, composed by himself, was placed on his tomb: "What you are, I was; what I am, you will be. Remember me, I pray you. Have pity on the dust of Peter who lies here. Pray, weep, and beg God to spare him."

St. Peter Damian, who had much insomnia and suffered terribly with headaches, is invoked against this malady.

St. FLORENTIUS

A virtuous character who died at Seville in 485.

St. SERENUS

A gardener martyred at Sirmium in Pannonia, in 307.

St. MEDRALD

Died abbot of Vendôme in the 9th century.

St. DOSITHEUS

Infirmarian monk, died at Gaza in Palestine about 530.

St. LAZARUS

A religious and a painter who was persecuted by the Iconoclasts. In 856, the Emperor Michael sent him as ambassador to Pope Benedict III. He died about 867 in his monastery at Constantinople.

February 24th
ST. MATTHIAS (d. 1st century)

WE only know of St. Matthias what we are told by the first chapter of the Acts of the Apostles.

There it is recounted that, after seeing Jesus ascend to heaven, the apostles came down from the Mount of Olives and returned to Jerusalem. They went to their habitual meeting-place to await the Holy Spirit promised by the Saviour. With them were the Virgin Mary, the holy women, and those who had followed Our Lord during His ministry; in all, about a hundred and twenty persons.

To this gathering Peter began to speak. "Brethren," he said, "there is a prophecy in scripture that must needs be fulfilled; that which the Holy Spirit made . . . about Judas, who showed the way to the men that arrested Jesus. Judas was counted among our number, and had been given a share in this ministry of ours. (With the price of his treachery, this man came into possession of a field; and, afterwards, when he fell from a height, and his belly burst open, so that he was disembowelled, all Jerusalem heard of it, and the field came to be called, in their language, Haceldama, that is, the Field of Blood.) Well, in the book of Psalms the words are written, Let their camping-place be deserted, and let no man be found to dwell in it. And again, let another take over his office. There are men who have walked in our company all through the time when the Lord Jesus came and went among us. . . . One of these ought to be added to our number as a witness of his resurrection. So they named two of these, Joseph called . . . Justus, and Matthias. And they offered this prayer, Lord, who knowest the hearts of all men, show us which of these two thou hast chosen to take his place in this work of apostleship, from which Judas has fallen away, and gone to the place which belonged to him. They gave them lots; and the lot fell upon Matthias, and he took rank with the eleven apostles" (Acts i, 15-26).

Such is the account given in the Acts. Some add that St. Matthias evangelized Palestine and there suffered martyrdom; others, that it was in Ethiopia that he preached the Gospel and shed his blood. But those are only opinions.

St. SERGIUS

A former magistrate who became a monk and was beheaded at Caesarea in Cappadocia in 304.

St. LIUTHARD (d. about 597)

Was bishop in the Canterbury district after having been bishop in the north of France.

Blessed ROBERT OF ARBRISSEL (d. 1116)

Born at Arbresec in Brittany, Robert, after having been vicar-general at Rennes and professor of theology at Angers, withdrew into the forest of Craon, where numerous anchorites placed themselves under his guidance. Entrusted by Urban II with preaching the crusade, he pledged those who could not leave for the Holy Land to embrace the religious life. Thus were founded at Fontevrault, in 1099, four great monasteries, one for men and three for women; the latter he placed under the rule of a single abbess. This new St. John the Baptist, as he was called, died at Orsan in Berry, a priory dependent on Fontevrault.

February 25th
ST. AVERTANUS AND BLESSED ROMEO
(d. about 1370)

ABOUT 1370, two pilgrims coming from France arrived at the hospital of St. Peter at Lucca; they were called Avertanus and Romeo, and they seemed to be in a dying condition.

A native of Limoges, Avertanus had always been very pious. When the moment came for him to choose a state in life, heaven prompted him to enter the Carmelite order at Limoges. His parents begged him not to leave them. "Have pity upon my white hair," said his father. "I shall die soon and whom will I have to close my eyes?" said his mother. To such words as these Avertanus replied that God never abandons those who do His will, that the happiness of parents consists in that of their children, and that life in religion seemed preferable to him to the finest throne in the world.

If his historian, more eloquent than exact, is to be believed, Avertanus practised all the virtues in the cloister. Like St. James the Less, bishop of Jerusalem, he remained kneeling for so long that the skin of his knees became like leather; like St. Francis of Assisi, he held that money was poison, refused to touch it, to look at it, and even to soil his lips by speaking of it; his love of sinners was so great that he would have sacrificed his own life a thousand times to convert them.

Avertanus had a strong desire to make a pilgrimage to Rome. His superiors gave their permission and they gave him Romeo, a lay brother of the Limoges convent, for his companion. Seldom, writes our historian, was a pilgrimage accomplished in a more edifying manner. One would have said they were two angels keeping company on the road. They prayed ceaselessly and visited all the churches which they passed.

They had a thousand difficulties in crossing the Italian frontier, so much did people fear that they were bringing the plague with them. They did in fact bring it, and they had to stop in the town of Lucca where they both died, a week apart.

St. CAESARIUS (d. 369)

Brother of St. Gregory of Nazianzus.

St. WALBURGA

A native of England, came at the request of St. Boniface to found schools and convents in Germany (d. 779).

St. TARASIUS (d. 806)

Patriarch of Constantinople.

Blessed CONSTANTIUS OF FABRIANO

Italian Dominican; died at Ancoli, in 1481.

Blessed SEBASTIAN D'APARICIO (1502–1600)

He began as a shepherd in the kingdom of Galicia, his native land; going to Mexico, he acquired an immense fortune. After having been twice married, he became a Franciscan at seventy-two and died almost a centenarian at Pueblo de los Angeles.

February 26th

ST. NESTOR (d. 250)

WHEN the persecution of Decius broke out, Nestor occupied the episcopal see of Magydos in Pamphylia. So noted were his courage and authority that the Roman magistrate or irenarch said: "Until we have got the better of the bishop, we shall be powerless against the Christians." Foreseeing the plight in which his flock would be placed, Nestor advised them to flee. He himself stayed at home, praying to God for his flock.

Those who came to arrest him were struck by his calm and majestic bearing. Moreover, they had orders to treat him with honour, and he was held in a building beside the forum. The magistrate appeared benevolent at first; then the interrogation became stormy; the bishop ended by telling the magistrate that he was possessed by a demon, and the magistrate by threatening the bishop with cruel tortures. "I only fear the torments of my God," replied Nestor. "Yours will never prevent my confessing Christ, the Son of the living God."

The same day the magistrate took Nestor to Perge, capital of the province, and the next day he sent the governor the following report: "Eupator, Socrates and all the council, to the most excellent lord president, greetings. When your highness received the divine letters of our master, the emperor, commanding all the Christians to sacrifice, your highness wished these orders executed with mercy. But this kindness served no purpose. These men were obstinate in disobeying the imperial edict. In spite of our insistence and that of the counsel, Nestor would not take our advice. Invited to come to the temple of Jupiter, he replied with blasphemy against the immortal gods, sparing neither the emperor nor yourself. For this reason the counsel has judged fit to bring him before your highness."

In virtue of the imperial edicts, the governor had then himself to interrogate the accused. Following the new interrogation Nestor was condemned, like his divine master, to die on the cross.

St. Victor

Born at Troyes, passed the greater part of his life at the site of the present ArcissurAube (6th or 7th century).

St. Porphyrius

Born at Thessalonica, was bishop of Gaza for twentyfive years (d. 420).

St. Alexander

Patriarch of Alexandria, great opponent of Arianism (d. 326).

Blessed Philippa of Guelders (1462-1547)

Wife of René II, duke of Lorraine; brought twelve children into the world; became a widow and entered a convent of the Poor Clares at PontàMousson where she lived twentyseven years more. On Friday, February 26th, 1547, she answered her sisters who told her she was about to die, "I shall not die today, I know, because the happiness which I have enjoyed in the world came to me on a Saturday. It was Saturday that I married the late good King René, a Saturday that I came to Lorraine, a

Saturday that I made my profession of religion; and it is again a Saturday that will take me to paradise." And, in fact, she died on Saturday, February 27th, 1547.

February 27th
ST. LEANDER (d. 596 or 601)

BORN at Cartagena in Andalusia about 535, brother of St. Florentina, St. Isidore, and St. Fulgentius, Leander early became a monk and was made bishop of Seville in 579. He founded a monastery there to which he brought the two sons of Leovigild, king of the Visigoths.

The latter, who was an Arian, unloosed against those who held to the Nicene Creed a persecution which turned into civil war. "We have reached the point," wrote St. Leander, "where there is not a single free man in Spain."

Of the two sons of Leovigild, one, Recared, had foresworn the Catholic faith; the other, Hermengild, had remained faithful to the lessons of his master. He even took it on himself to send Leander to Constantinople to ask the help of the Byzantine emperor. His father had him murdered and sent the bishop into exile.

After Leovigild's death, Recared succeeded him, and Leander resumed his see. The bishop regained his influence over the new king who became a Catholic again. Then he convoked a national council where the representatives of the clergy and of the people made a unanimous profession of orthodoxy. It was declared unanimously that, under God, the bishop of Seville was responsible for this happy outcome.

Almost nothing remains of the writings of St. Leander, but several letters which St. Gregory the Great addressed to him have been preserved. They breathe affection and show how highly the pope esteemed his friend.

"My letter is very short," he wrote to him. "Why am I so crushed beneath the weight of my duties that I write so little to the friend I love best in the world? I send you my books; read them carefully, and you will deplore the fact that I practise so ill what I seem to know so well."

"I send you the pallium," he wrote him on another occasion, "for your use at solemn masses. I ought at the same time to outline for you the rules of a holy life, but your virtues have forestalled my words and dispense me from saying anything more."

In other parts of their correspondence, the pope and the bishop, who both suffered from gout, mutually exhorted each other to consider this cruel ill as a heaven-sent favour and the best means of expiating their sins.

St. HONORINA

A virgin believed to have been martyred in Normandy in the 4th century.

St. GALMIER or BALDONOR (d. about 650)

Born in Forez, first followed the trade of locksmith, then became a monk at St. Justus.

St. MARVATUS (d. 855)

First a monk at Ferrières in Gâtinais; then ruled the abbey of Prüm in Ardenne.

February 28th
ST. ROMANUS (d. 463)

A NATIVE of Upper Bugey, Romanus began his religious life at about the age of thirty-five, entering a monastery in Lyons. He soon left it, taking with him *The Life of the Desert Fathers*, and *The Institutions* of Cassian, and made his way east. It was in a place named Condat (today Saint-Claude) that he found what he was seeking: some fields, some trees, and a spring. Thus, forgetting the world and forgotten by it, he was able to divide his time between prayer, manual work, and reading.

Afterwards his brother Lupicinus became a widower and joined him, and later his sister came to find them; so that three monasteries came into being: Condat, Leuconne, and Beaume, directed respectively by Romanus, Lupicinus, and their sister. The rule they followed was inspired by St. Basil, St. Pachomius, and Cassian, notably forbidding the use of meat and prescribing manual labour.

The contrast between St. Romanus and St. Lupicinus was striking. One showed himself easy-going; the other tended to proscribe all indulgence. "You must choose your candidates and not pick them up at hazard," Lupicinus said to his brother. "In your house mediocre folk take the place of others to the prejudice of the common edification."

Romanus replied that it was fitting to have trust in all while awaiting the clear manifestation of the will of God. For the rest, the qualities and defects of the two saints blended happily, and Romanus often converted monks of whom his brother despaired.

Romanus was ordained priest at Besançon about 444, by St. Hilary of Arles. Besides the monasteries mentioned above, he founded others in the Jura, the Vosges, and as far away as Germany. Among the miracles attributed to him we must mention one which took place near Geneva when he embraced two lepers. After the saint had gone, they were quite surprised, when they looked at one another, to see that their fearful illness had entirely disappeared.

Romanus died about the age of seventy, attended by his brother and sister. So that the contemplation of his own monastery should not be disturbed, he asked to be buried at the abbey of Beaume.

St. ERMINE

Honoured in Ireland (6th century).

St. PROTERIUS

Patriarch of Alexandria, massacred for his orthodoxy in 457.

St. OSWALD (d. 992)

Of Danish origin, was in turn monk at Fleury-sur-Loire, bishop of Worcester, and archbishop of York.

Blessed ANTONIA

Born at Florence; was married and had a child; entered the Poor Clares; died at the convent of Aquila in 1472.

Blessed AUGUSTUS CHAPDELAINE (1814–1856)

Priest of the Foreign Missions, native of Normandy, martyred in China, February 29th, 1856.

Blessed VILLANA DE' BOTTI

Dominican tertiary, native of Florence, who, after a very worldly youth, sanctified herself in the married state (d. 1360).

THE SAINTS OF MARCH
March 1st
ST. ALBINUS

T. ALBINUS, so popular in France in the middle ages, was born of a noble family in the region of Vannes in 469. He was over sixty when, having ruled the abbey of Tintillant for thirty-five years, he became bishop of Angers.

At that time there prevailed among the Franks the custom of consanguinary marriages of the first degree. Albinus fought against this with all his might. Certain people bore him such a grudge that for a long time he expected to die, like St. John the Baptist, a victim of his own intransigeance. In 538 and 541 he called together councils at Orléans, which set severe penalties upon such abuses, and contributed to raise the standard of public morality.

This fearless and generous man was also gifted with the power of miracles. We are told by his biographer of one he worked in the village of Douillé in favour of a certain Etheria, who had been cast into prison for debt. King Childebert had himself given his approval to this imprisonment, and the wardens took advantage of it to maltreat the unfortunate woman. The bishop having gone to visit her, she threw herself at his feet and implored his help. A soldier began to strike her. It sufficed for Albinus to breathe in the face of this brutal fellow for him to fall dead. After that it was quite easy to reach a settlement with the creditors of the prisoner and to obtain her deliverance.

Another time, passing by the tower of Angers, he heard the prisoners' cries of pain. It was in vain that he implored the clemency of the magistrate on whom their freedom depended. He then began to pray at the foot of the tower and, about midnight, a landslide occurred, opening a way out for the prisoners. They followed their liberator to the Church of St. Maurilius, giving thanks to God and promising to remain thenceforth on the straight path.

St. EUDOCIA (d. 152?)

A former courtesan of Heliopolis who redeemed her sinful life by penances and martyrdom.

St. SIMPLICIUS

Bishop of Bourges, died about 480.

St. ANTONINA (d. about 306)

Condemned to death as a Christian at Nicaea in Bithynia, was sewn into a sack and thrown into a pond.

St. DAVID

Most celebrated of the Welsh saints and founder of monasteries, died bishop of Menevia in 589.

Blessed ROGER LE FORT (d. 1367)

He was nephew of Cardinal de la Chapelle, bishop of Toulouse, and was himself successively bishop of Orléans, Limoges, and Bourges.

March 2nd

ST. CHAD or CEADDA (d. 672)

A NORTHUMBRIAN by birth, Chad was a monk of the abbey of Melfont in Ireland before becoming abbot of the monastery of Lastingham in York-shire. Soon afterward the bishop of that district died, and the monk Wilfrid was made his successor. He went to France to receive consecration, but stayed so long that the king of Northumbria, tired of waiting, designated Chad as his successor. Chad became bishop in 666 and began to tour his diocese on foot. When Wilfrid returned and found the see occupied, he retired to his old abbey without the least sign of discontent.

Thereafter, Archbishop Theodore of Canterbury, visiting the English church, observed to Chad that his election was by no means canonical. "I ask nothing more," replied Chad gently, "than to renounce a charge of which I am so unworthy," and he returned to the monastery of Lastingham, leaving to Wilfrid the care of the church of York.

However, the episcopal see of Lichfield became vacant, and Archbishop Theodore designated Chad to occupy it. He obeyed with his customary simplicity. For two and a half years he visited his diocese, counting it his greatest happiness to preach to the poor and resemble them as much as possible. When the great winds rose, he would stop everything and pray for the people and for their harvests. When the growl of thunder was heard, he would go to the church and recite psalms until the storm was over. Archbishop Theodore had desired him to travel on horseback, at least when the journey was a long one, but the holy bishop declared that he wished to imitate the apostles and continued to trudge about on foot.

He died, a victim of the plague, in his beloved abbey of Lastingham. A week before, an invisible concert of music had been heard above his cell. Chad opened the window and said to Brother Owen who was listening in the garden: "That is the angels who are singing; in seven days they will come back to fetch my soul."

The name of St. Chad has become associated with many legends in England, and before the Reformation devotion to him was very widespread there.

St. Luke Casali

Born in Sicily, died abbot of Argira about the year 800.

Blessed Charles the Good

Count of Flanders, put to death in the Church of St. Donatian at Bruges, by political enemies in 1127.

Blessed Henry Suso

Born at Uberlingen, he became a Dominican at Constance at the age of thirteen. His works place him with Eckhart and Tauler in the ranks of the great German mystics. Frightful slanders were heaped upon him and he spent long years in a dungeon. He died at Ulm in 1366.

March 3rd

ST. MARINUS (d. about 262)

THERE was no trace of persecution anywhere, wrote Eusebius, when a centurion's post fell vacant in the legion stationed at Caesarea in Palestine. A Christian officer named Marinus had every chance for the appointment, but a rival cited a certain ancient law by which no one could be a centurion unless he sacrificed to the emperor. Without circumlocution, Marinus confessed his faith, and he was given three hours to choose between apostasy and death.

Leaving the praetorium, he met the bishop Theotecnus who took him to a church and, showing him his sword and the Gospel, adjured him to make a choice worthy of a Christian. The officer at once put his hand on the holy book. The bishop dismissed him, saying: "Count on the divine grace to be faithful to your choice, and to deserve the rewards promised by the Gospel."

The three hours' delay having passed, Marinus presented himself again before his chiefs. He declared that he could not render to the emperor homage which belonged to God alone, and he was beheaded on the spot.

ST. WINWALLUS (d. about 530)

WINWALLUS, also called Guénolé or Guengalaenus, was born about 462, in a place named later Plou-Fragan. His parents, Welsh nobles recently emigrated to Brittany, confided him while still young to the holy Abbot Budoc, who directed a monastery in an islet near the island of Bréhat.

When he was twenty, Winwallus wished to go to Ireland to venerate the remains of St. Patrick; the latter inspired him rather to devote himself to founding a new monastery in Brittany. Budoc confided to him eleven monks with whom he went to settle on the island of Tibidi, opposite the mouth of the Faou. The soil was so poor there and the tempests so frequent, that the little colony remained only three years, after which they returned to the south-west coast and settled at the mouth of the Faou on a peninsula covered with water, rocks, and woods.

There Winwallus remained until his death, eating rye bread mingled with ashes, drinking only water, sleeping on the sand or on bark, and accomplishing miracles which have rendered him perennially popular in Brittany.

St. KUNIGUNDE (d. 1040)

Daughter of Siegfried, count of Luxemburg, married Henry, emperor of Germany, lived with him in continence and, after his death, became a nun at Kaffungen near Cassel.

St. CAMILLA

Was won to God by St. Germain of Auxerre when he was passing through Ravenna; she died at Écoulives, near Auxerre, about 437.

St. TITIANUS

Of Germanic origin, died bishop of Brescia. It is believed that he lived in the 6th century.

St. GERVINUS

Former canon of Rheims, was abbot of St. Riquier, and died a leper in 1075.

Blessed FREDERICK (d. 1175)

After having been vicar of Hallum (Frisia), his native town, he became a Premonstratensian and governed simultaneously the three abbeys of Mariengarten, Gröningen, and Dockum.

March 4th
ST. CASIMIR (d. 1484)

OF the thirteen children who issued from the marriage of Casimir III, king of Poland, with Elisabeth of Austria, Casimir was third to come into the world, and was born on October 5th, 1458. He had as teacher John Dugloss, bishop of Lemberg, and although well endowed for study and applying himself conscientiously, he chiefly profited from the spiritual teaching of his virtuous master.

Very early he gave the impression of wanting to become a saint; indifferent to honours and to pleasure, watching attentively over his senses, meditating and weeping over the passion of Our Saviour, seeking and finding happiness in prayer. Thanks to a discreet servant, he was able, without attracting too much attention, to practise the penances he preferred, such as sleeping on the floor at the foot of a comfortable bed, wearing a hair shirt, and passing the night kneeling at the church doors.

In 1471, discontented with their king Matthias, the Hungarian diet offered his crown to Prince Casimir, then aged thirteen. His father hastened

to send him at the head of an army to take possession of the throne of
Hungary. On arriving at the frontier, the young prince found himself face
to face with the army of King Matthias. He concluded from this that the
enterprise on which he had engaged was unjust, and, most happy to renounce
it, he retired for three months to the castle of Colzki, as much to avoid
reappearing before his father as to expiate, he said, his own sins.

From 1479 to 1483, he had to govern Poland in the absence of Casimir
III, then occupied in Lithuania. An attempt was made at this time to make
him marry the daughter of the emperor of Germany. He refused in order to
remain faithful to the vow of continence which he had taken. A few years
earlier, the most learned doctors had advised him to marry, assuring him that
only marriage would cure a lingering illness; but he had opposed them.

Casimir died at the age of twenty-three years and six months on March
4th, 1484. At his wish, he was interred holding in his hand the hymn
Omni die dic Mariae, which he had so many times recited during his life, in
honour of the Blessed Virgin.

St. Lucius I

Pope from June 25th, 233, to March 5th, 254.

St. Leonard (d. about 614)

Endowed with Herculean strength and with a hot-headed disposition,
he was at first the scourge of his district of Avranches; then he reformed
and occupied for some thirty years the episcopal see of the city.

St. Basinus

A native of Lorraine, was abbot of St. Maximinus and bishop of
Trier (7th century).

Blessed Humbert III (1136–1189)

After the death of his second wife, he entered the monastery of Hautecombe; but for political reasons, his barons obliged him to leave and to
reassume charge of the affairs of the county of Savoy.

March 5th

ST. JOHN JOSEPH OF THE CROSS (d. 1734)

BORN on the island of Ischia on August 15th, 1654, John Joseph Calosirto
had five brothers who vowed themselves to the service of God. He himself,

at the age of sixteen, entered the order of friars minor of the Alcantarine reform at Naples.

At twenty, he was entrusted with the founding of a convent of the same observance in Piedmont; at twenty-four he was named novice master; then he became guardian, definitor, and provincial of his order. In the meantime he had received the priesthood in obedience to his superiors. The first thirty years of his religious life were employed in promoting the Franciscan reform of St. Peter of Alcantara in Italy. Then, at his own request, the pope deprived him of all office, and he passed the rest of his existence as director of souls in a monastery at Naples.

By his mortifications, his miracles, and the mystic gifts which were granted him, John Joseph of the Cross is one of the most extraordinary saints possible, and one most difficult of imitation.

His body was covered with sores which he carefully kept open with harsh disciplines, with sandals bristling with nails, with a spiked cross a foot long, which he wore on his shoulders next to the skin. He avoided raising his eyes, listening to music; slept sitting on the ground; and he remained thirty years without taking the smallest drink.

His love of sick folk and sinners inspired him to many acts of heroism and caused him to accomplish his most touching miracles; sometimes he obtained from God to take upon himself their ulcers and spiritual pains. John Joseph foretold the future, read the secrets of hearts, was constantly ravished in ecstasy. His process of canonization mentions several phenomena of levitation and bilocation with which he was favoured in the presence of numerous witnesses. It also records the admirable reply he made to someone who was criticising Providence in his presence. "How do you expect," he said, tapping his forehead, "that with a bone three fingers high, we should understand the meaning of the designs of God."

He died with the calm and smiling face he had always had during his lifetime, casting a look of supreme love towards the image of the Blessed Virgin.

St. THEOPHILUS

Bishop of Caesarea in Palestine (d. about 195).

St. ADRIAN

Martyred at Caesarea in Palestine, with St. Eubulus, in 308.

St. PHOCAS

Syrian Christian, martyred at Antioch about 320.

St. EUSEBIUS OF CREMONA (d. about 423)

Disciple and friend of St. Jerome, he lived in a monastery built by St. Paul at Jerusalem.

St. VIRGILIUS (d. about 618)

A native of Aquitaine, he was a monk of Lérins, abbot of St. Symphorian at Autun, archbishop of Arles, and papal vicar in Gaul.

St. DRAUSINUS

Bishop of Soissons, died about 674.

Blessed ROMEO

Carmelite, died at Lucca in 1380. We have spoken of him on February 25th.

March 6th
ST. COLETTE (d. 1447)

THIS great Franciscan reformer was born at Corbie, near Amiens, January 13th, 1381. Her parents, almost sexagenarians, called her Nicolette in gratitude to St. Nicholas for her birth. Her father, Robert Boelet, was a wealthy and virtuous artisan; her mother went to confession every week. They died within a short space of one another, leaving their daughter of eighteen under the guardianship of Dom de Roye, Benedictine abbot of Corbie.

The latter wished to see her married; Colette refused and distributed her goods to the poor. He allowed her to enter the beguinage at Amiens, but she stayed only a year, finding the life too soft. She entered the hospital of the Benedictines at Corbie, and left that too. Then she became a Poor Clare in the convent of Moncel, near Pont-Saint-Maxence; but the rule of Urban IV followed there appeared not severe enough, and she left the convent.

Then she became a tertiary of St. Francis, and her guardian authorized her to take the vow of seclusion. On September 17th, 1402, on the feast of the Stigmata of St. Francis, she was immured in a cell between two buttresses of Notre Dame de Corbie, giving on to the church by a grill. There she lived for three years. Then, on the orders of St. Francis and St. Clare who had appeared to her, she undertook the reform of the Franciscan order.

The West was in full schism, and France, like Spain and Scotland, ranged themselves on the side of obedience to Avignon. Colette went to Nice to Pedro de Luna, called Benedict XIII. He imposed the veil and the seraphic cord upon her and named her superior general of all the convents of Poor Clares which she should found or reform. The Colettine reform, which still endures, quickly spread in France, Spain, Flanders, and Savoy. It even extended in part to the order of the friars minor.

Colette travelled enormously, worked many miracles, endured every kind of suffering, worked with St. Vincent Ferrer in extinguishing schism. She died at Ghent, March 6th, 1447.

St. CONON

Galilean gardener, martyred in Pamphylia about 251.

St. FRIDOLIN

Born in Ireland, became a monk at Poitiers, built churches in Alsace, Switzerland, and Burgundy; retired and died at the monastery of Säckingen, near Basle, about 540.

St. CYRIL OF CONSTANTINOPLE (1126–1224)

This great servant of the Blessed Virgin renounced the Jerusalem patriarchate to become a Carmelite, and died general of his order on Mount Carmel.

St. ROSE OF VITERBO (1235–1253)

Everything in the existence of this girl is remarkable; a tertiary of St. Francis who at the age of three restored a dead person to life, and at ten preached penitence to crowds of people. She was gifted with the spirit of prophecy and lived in friendship with the birds.

Blessed AGNES OF BOHEMIA (d. 1280 or 1282)

Daughter of Ottokar I, king of Bohemia, betrothed against her will to several rulers, notably to the Emperor Frederick II, she became a Poor Clare at the convent of Prague and died there after forty years of the religious life. Four letters which St. Clare wrote to her have been preserved.

March 7th
STS. PERPETUA AND FELICITAS (d. 203)

WHILE persecutions were ravaging Carthage, five catachumens were arrested there, among them a slave named Felicitas and a young woman of position named Perpetua. The first was eight months with child, the second had an infant at the breast. They received baptism between their arrest and their imprisonment.

Perpetua was allowed to take her son with her into prison. When the accused were interrogated, all frankly confessed their faith and were condemned to be thrown to the wild beasts on the anniversary of the Emperor Geta. The mother was then separated from her child. "God granted that he no longer asked my breast, and that I was not to be tormented with my milk," wrote Perpetua in the journal which she kept till the day of her death. She then tells of a vision in which her brother Dinocrates appeared to her as he was quitting purgatory thanks to her prayers, and another in which divine help was promised for her last struggle.

Felicitas feared that she would be prevented by her condition from dying with her companion, but she was delivered three days before the public games. As the pains of childbirth drew cries from her, a gaoler said: "Thou that makest complaint now, what wilt thou do when thou art thrown to the beasts?" "I myself now suffer that which I suffer," answered the young slave, "but there another shall be in me who shall suffer for me." She brought a little girl into the world who was adopted by a Christian woman.

With their three companions, Perpetua and Felicitas entered the amphitheatre joyfully. They were wrapped in a net and delivered to a savage cow. The people soon got tired of seeing the two young mothers tortured and demanded that they should be killed. They embraced one another for the last time; then Felicitas received the final blow without flinching. Perpetua fell into the hands of a clumsy fellow, who first missed her. Then "she had herself to set the trembling hand of the novice gladiator upon her own neck".

St. Thomas Aquinas

Doctor of the Church (d. 1274). Born of a father related to the emperors of Germany and of a mother stemming from the Norman princes, Thomas studied at Monte Cassino and at the University of Naples, then he entered the Dominican order in that city. Opposed to his vocation, his family seized him and shut him up in San Giovanni. The Emperor Frederic II having secured his release, Thomas went to Cologne, where Albert the Great was his master. He himself later taught in that city, as well as at Bologna and Paris, where he formed a friendship with St. Bonaventure. Among his writings may be noted the *Summa contra Gentiles*, the *Summa Theologica*, and the admirable *Office of the Blessed Sacrament*. He died at the abbey of Fossa-Nuova, when he was travelling from Naples to the Council of Lyons.

St. PAUL THE SIMPLE

Disciple and imitator of St. Anthony of the Desert (d. about 340).

The Blessed GERMAN GARDINER and JOHN LARKE

Executed in London in 1544, for having refused to recognize the spiritual supremacy of the king of England.

March 8th

ST. JOHN OF GOD (d. 1550)

BORN March 8th, 1495, at Montemor (Portugal), John Ciudad, later called John of God, fled when eight years old from his father's house and went to Madrid where, he believed, works of charity awaited his zeal. He fell faint at some sixty leagues from his village, and was employed as shepherd by a farmer of Orpeza (Spain). Later this farmer entrusted the management of his farm to him and offered him his daughter in marriage. At this proposal John took flight and enlisted in the troops which were fighting the French army at Fontarabia.

Camp life destroyed his piety. Condemned to be hanged but having the sentence commuted to dismissal from the army, he saw in this the Virgin's intervention, and recovered his former fervour. He returned to his first master, left him anew to avoid marriage, and went this time to Hungary to fight the Turks. His regiment was disbanded in 1536. Then he revisited his native village and learned that his mother had died twenty days after his flight, and that his father had ended his days as a Franciscan.

From that time on, John lived as a saint burning with the love of God, always seeking humiliations and suffering, displaying real heroism in serving the unfortunate. He devoted himself to the Christian prisoners of the Moors, returned to Spain, became a wanderer and a seller of images in order to make conversions. At Granada he feigned madness, let himself be imprisoned and flogged till the blood ran.

In that city he began, in 1437, the great institution which was to survive him. John sought out the infirm who had been abandoned and carried them on his back to an improvised shelter. His first resources came from faggots of dry sticks which he sold from door to door. Our Lord appeared to him to give him encouragement, and the angels sometimes came to help him care for the sick. Then, some persons aided him with money. His first helpers were two men who had been ready to kill one another but whom he reconciled. Thus was founded the order of charity which was approved in 1586 by Sixtus V, under the name of Brothers of St. John of God.

St. PONTIUS (d. about 262)

Deacon of Carthage and companion in exile of St. Cyprian, whose life he wrote.

St. SENAN

Irish bishop who travelled to England, France, and Italy, and died in 560 on the island of Inniscathy.

St. FELIX OF BURGUNDY (d. 646)

Burgundian priest who was bishop of Dunwich in England, and is reputed to have founded the University of Cambridge.

St. HUMPHREY

Born, it is believed, on the banks of the Meuse; was a monk of the abbey of Prüm (diocese of Trier) and died as bishop of Thérouanne in 871.

St. VINCENT KADLUBEK (d. 1223)

After having been bishop of Cracow for ten years, he resigned his charge and entered the Cistercian abbey of Jedrzejow where he lived for five years more.

March 9th

ST. FRANCES OF ROME

FRANCES was born at Rome in 1384. Her father was called Paul Bussa, her mother, Jacobella de' Roffredeschi; the husband given her at the age of twelve, Lorenzo de' Ponziani. The families to which she belonged by birth and marriage were very illustrious. She had three children, two sons and a daughter, born in 1400, 1404, and 1407 respectively.

Although her taste had always inclined to the religious life, Frances was a model mother and wife. Her husband first wished that, as was usual with women of her rank, she should cover herself with rich fabrics and jewelry. She complied, content to wear a rough hair shirt next her skin and to practise all sorts of secret austerities.

In Vanozza Ponziani, her sister-in-law, she found a rival in fervour. Together they met to pray in a grotto in the garden, cared for the sick in the hospital of the Sancto Spirito, gave alms to the needy. God accomplished several miracles in favour of the two friends; Frances herself was almost constantly favoured with the visible presence of her guardian angel. He called her attention to her faults, succoured her in a time of danger, and even chastised her when she deserved it.

Numerous and cruel were the trials which the saint had to undergo from men and from the devil. After forty years of marriage, she lost her husband who had become increasingly dear to her and whose piety was daily modelled on hers. Then she was able to enter the congregation of the Oblates of Mary which she had founded in 1433, inspired by the rule of St. Benedict and the statutes of the Olivetan monks.

However, she did not die among her sisters in religion at Tor di' Specchi, but at the Palazzo Ponziani where her sick son had called her to his bedside.

St. Frances of Rome left ninety-seven *Visions*, dictated to her confessor, in which there are many references to the pains of hell.

St. Gregory of Nyssa

Father of the Church (d. about 400). Professor of rhetoric, he left his wife, Theosebeia, who lived from that time in continence, and joined in their monastic solitude his brother Basil and his friend Gregory of Nazianzus. He was bishop of Nyssa and archbishop of Sebaste in Lesser Armenia. A prolific writer and a great opponent of Arius, he forms with the two Fathers of the Church mentioned above, the group called the "Cappadocians".

St. Vitalis

Hermit and founder of monasteries in Calabria (d. 990).

St. Pacianus

Bishop of Barcelona, died about 3.

St. Catherine of Bologna (1413–1463)

Born at Bologna and abbess of the Poor Clares of that town, this great wonder-worker enjoyed the gift of prophecy and was favoured with numerous visions. She has left a *Treatise on Spiritual Weapons*, and some *Revelations*.

March 10th

STS. LEONTIUS, CANDIDUS, CLAUDIUS AND OTHER MARTYRS OF SEBASTE (d. 320)

DURING the persecution under the Emperor Licinius, forty members of a legion which was quartered at Sebaste in Cappadocia were made martyrs. They were called Leontius, Candidus, Claudius, Melitho, Nicholas, Lysimachus, Theophilus, Quirio, Domnus, Domitian, Eunoicus, Sisinius, Heraclius, Alexander, John, Athanasius, Valens, Helianus, Ecditius, Acacius, Vivianus, Helias, Theodulus, Cyril, Flavius, Severian, Valerian, Chudio, Sacerdo, Priscus, Eutychius, Eutyches, Smaragdus, Philoctimo, Aetius, Xantheas, Augias, Hesychus, Caius, and Gorgo.

On an imperial order, Agrippa, governor of the province, had informed the army that it must sacrifice to the gods. The forty soldiers named above declared that they were Christians and could not obey this edict. Neither promises nor threats shook their firmness. "You have power over our bodies, which, by our profession, we hold in small regard," they replied, "but no man in the world has any power against our immortal soul."

As it was freezing cold, the governor had the idea of exposing them naked for a whole night on the ice of a lake. Warm baths, prepared on the bank, awaited those who wished to apostasize. "Lord," they said, taking their battle posts, "may none of the crowns prepared for us be lost, and of the forty of us in the arena, may forty come forth victorious."

Their prayer was not fulfilled in the manner they had expected. There was one who deserted his post and ran to plunge into the hot bath. He died almost at once; and it was one of the guards, touched by grace, who took his place on the frozen lake.

When morning came the legs of the tortured men were broken and they were carried off to be cremated. One alone, named Melitho, was still breathing. As the executioners left him there, still hoping that he would recant, his mother took him in her arms, and herself placed him on the cart which was taking the bodies to the pyre.

St. BLANCHARD (7th century?)

His relics are honoured at Nesle-la-Reposte (Marne).

St. DROCTOVEUS or DROTTÉ (d. about 576)

Native of the Auxerre country, was taught by St. Germain. When the latter became bishop of Paris, he put Drotté at the head of the abbey of St. Vincent, which was later called Saint-Germain-des-Prés.

St. Anastasia the Patrician (d. 567)

Lady-in-waiting of the Empress Theodora, she fled from the court of Constantinople to escape the attentions of the emperor, and for twenty-eight years in male attire led the life of a hermit in the desert of Scete.

St. Attalas (d. 622)

Of Burgundian origin, disciple and companion of St. Columbanus, whom he succeeded as abbot of the monastery of Bobbio (Italy).

March 11th

ST. EULOGIUS (d. 859)

Cordova, capital of the Saracens in Spain, had at that time a population of half a million, and the Caliph Abd-er-Rahman II held the most brilliant court in Europe there. The Arabs allowed the Christians who had remained in the country to worship freely on condition that heavy taxes were regularly paid.

However, in 850, there began a persecution of sorts which claimed several victims. The most illustrious was the priest Eulogius, whose family was among the most substantial in Cordova, and who himself had great influence.

He was a very pious and very learned man, burning with a desire to shed his blood for the faith. Imprisoned with some of the faithful, he passed the time of detention in exhorting them to martyrdom. Having left prison, he told of their glorious combat in a book entitled *The Memorial of Saints*. He also composed an *Apology of the Martyrs*, a justification of these heroes who were blamed by many for foolhardiness. The effect of these writings was profound, and many Christians were prevented by them from apostasizing.

When, towards the end of 858, the episcopal see of Toledo became vacant, the faithful and clergy were unanimous in appointing Eulogius to it; but he never took possession, for he was arrested in the meantime with the virgin Leocritia or Lucretia. This maiden was a recently converted Moslem upon whom her family had heaped ill treatment to make her recant. Fearing to succumb, she had turned to Eulogius who hid her at a friend's house. Finally she was found and implicated in a lawsuit with her protector.

The latter would not plead guilty in any way. He offered to prove to his judges that the Prophet was an impostor and to show them that Jesus Christ was the sole Saviour of mankind. But they refused to listen to him, and he was beheaded on Saturday, March 2nd, 859. Leocritia suffered the same fate the following Saturday.

St. BENEDICT

Bishop of Milan from 681 to 725.

St. VIGILIUS

Bishop of Auxerre, assassinated about 625, by order of Varadon, mayor of the palace.

St. CONSTANTINE

Scottish Christians honour two martyrs of this name: one (d. 598) son of Paternus, king of Cornwall, joined St. Columbanus and evangelized the Pict country; the other, son of Kenneth II, was murdered in a cavern near Crail, in 874, by the Danish invaders of his country.

St. SOPHRONIUS

Native of Damascus, travelled widely in the East and in the West; lived several years near John the Almsgiver at Alexandria, and ended his life as patriarch of Jerusalem in 639.

St. VINDICIANUS

Was born at Bullecourt in Artois and became bishop of Cambrai and Arras. As he was passing through Brussels, at that time part of his diocese, he felt the approach of death, and before he passed away asked to be interred at the abbey of St. Vaast (d. about 712).

March 12th
ST. MAXIMILIAN (d. 295)

THE prejudice created by Tertullian's writings against the profession of soldier were such that military service came to be considered by many as contrary to Gospel precept. It was thus in good faith that Maximilian chose to die rather than to be a soldier.

A son of Fabius Victor, recruiting officer, he was exactly twenty-one years, three months and eighteen days old when, on March 12th, 295, he appeared as a refractory recruit before Dion Cassius, procurator of Africa, at Thebeste in Numidia. "I am a Christian," he said. "A soldier of God,

I will not fight for secular things; imprinted with the seal of Christ, I will not wear the insignia of the emperor about my neck; and if it is imposed on me by force, I shall break it."

Having in vain tried to reason with him, Dion Cassius had his name erased from the roll of recruits and declared: "Since you refuse military service, you will be put to death; and the punishment of your disobedience will serve as an example to others." "For this I give thanks to God," replied Maximilian.

When he was led to the place of execution, he said to the Christians who surrounded him: "Take every measure to merit a like crown, beloved brethren, and thus obtain that you yourselves may soon see God." Then with a joyful face, turning towards his father, he added: "Give the new uniform you intended for me to the soldier who strikes me."

When his head had been cut off, a matron named Pompejana took away his remains in her litter and went to inter them at Carthage beneath the eminence where reposed the remains of the martyr St. Cyprian. She herself died thirteen days later and was buried in the same place.

As for Fabius Victor, the *Acta Maximiliani* show him returning proudly home and a little later dying in the same faith as his son.

St. Gregory the Great

Father of the Church (d. about 604). Of an illustrious family, Gregory was prefect of Rome, left the world, consecrated his vast wealth to the endowment of monasteries, and himself retired to the abbey of St. Andrew which he founded on the Coelian Hill. After a mission to Byzantium, he became secretary to Pope Pelagius II and succeeded him in 590. His activity was immense. He developed the liturgy, reformed ecclesiastical discipline, fought heresies, converted the Lombards, opposed the autono-mous views of the Orientals, encouraged the growth of the Benedictine order, sent missionaries to England, increased the patrimony of St. Peter, acquired possessions in Gaul, Africa, Dalmatia, Sicily, and Sardinia; intervened masterfully in contemporary politics. He wrote and preached a great deal, led an austere life, and ended his days in suffering.

St. Paul of Léon (d. 572)

Native of Britain, where he led an anchorite's life, he fled to Amorica to avoid becoming bishop. There he founded a monastery on the island of Batz but was soon constrained by King Childebert to accept the dignity of bishop. He established his see in an ancient Roman fortress, which was called Castel Paul and afterwards became Saint-Paul-de-Léon.

St. Theophanes the Chronographer (d. 817)

Born at Constantinople, married, entered religion as did his wife, lived
in the monastery of "the great acre" at Sigriano until the day when, for his
refusal to associate with the iconoclasts, Leo the Isaurian sent him to die
on the island of Samothrace. He wrote a *Chronography*, a sort of historical
abstract which runs from 284 to 813.

St. Fina or Josephine or Seraphina (d. 1253)

Tuscan virgin who passed her life, cared for by her nurse, in fearful
sufferings.

St. Muran or Mura

Abbot of Fahan in Ireland (7th century).

March 13th

ST. EUPHRASIA (d. about 412)

Euphrasia was only one year old when she lost her father, the senator
Antigonus, a relative of Emperor Theodosius the Great. The latter became
the protector of the little girl, and when she was five he promised her to the
son of a wealthy senator; but Antigonus' widow obtained deferment of the
nuptials till Euphrasia was of marriageable age.

Meanwhile the widow herself was surprised to be sought in marriage by an
important personage of the Empire. Having made up her mind to flee from
the world and the court, she left Constantinople and retired into Egypt.
After having traversed the Lower Thebaid, she settled with her daughter
near a convent where a hundred and thirty nuns lived in piety and fervour.
One day when the noble lady, desirous of being remembered in their
prayers, offered these nuns a great deal of money, they refused it, accepting
only a little oil for the lamp of their church and some incense to burn on the
altar.

In this convent Euphrasia was received as a nun at the age of seven.
Shortly afterwards her mother died. When this news reached Constantinople, the youth to whom Euphrasia was betrothed begged the emperor to
bring back from Egypt the girl he expected to marry. But the young nun
addressed a message to Theodosius in the following terms: "Knowing,
invincible emperor, that I have promised Jesus Christ to live in continual
continence, would you have me violate my promise by marrying a mortal
man, destined to become the prey of worms? By the generosity with which

you treated my parents, I beg you to dispose of the possessions they have left me, in favour of the orphans, the poor, and the churches. Grant freedom to my slaves, and to my farmers remission of their debts, so that it may be possible for me to serve God in future without any cares. May your prayers and those which I venture to beg of the empress, your wife, obtain for me the grace of being always faithful to the Lord."

This message was communicated by the emperor to the senate, where it was felt that the young nun's profession was sufficient to break off the matrimonial arrangements previously concluded.

Euphrasia died in holiness in her convent at the age of thirty. Devotion to her is much in favour with the Greeks.

St. GERALD

Abbot of Mayo in Ireland (d. about 722).

St. ELDRAD

Superior of the abbey of Novalese and of the hospice of Mount Cenis (d. 875).

Blessed AGNELLUS OF PISA (d. 1232 or 1236)

Established the Franciscan order in England.

Blessed ERIC or HENRY

Son of Aquinas, king of Denmark, Sweden, and Norway, renounced the throne, donned the habit of the Franciscan third order, led the life of a hermit and a pilgrim. He died at Perugia in 1415 or 1418.

St. PATRICIA

Martyred at Nicomedia with her husband Macedonius and her daughter Modesta (period uncertain).

St. RODRIGUEZ

Spanish priest, beheaded at Cordova in 837, having been denounced by his brother who had become a Mussulman.

March 14th

ST. MATILDA or MAUD (d. 968)

BORN in the last quarter of the 9th century, Matilda was a descendant of the famous Widukind, king of the Saxons. About 913, she married Henry the Fowler, with whom she lived for more than twenty years in perfect amity. From this union were born: Otto the Great, emperor of Germany; Henry, duke of Bavaria; Bruno, archbishop of Cologne; Gerberga, wife of Louis d'Outremer; and Hedwig, who was the mother of Hugh Capet.

During her pious life Matilda nevertheless committed one fault which she painfully expiated: it was to favour her second son at the expense of the first. However, she did not succeed in assuring the paternal succession for him, and the crown of Henry the Fowler fell to Prince Otto. He then made an arrangement with his brother Henry to rob their mother of her dowry and to oblige her to take the veil.

Matilda took refuge in the convent of Engern, in Westphalia, where she redoubled her fervour and austerity. To those who expressed indignation concerning her sons' conduct toward her, she only replied: "They carry out the divine will in my regard; may God be praised in all things!"

However, Queen Edith, wife of Otto, helped by the princes and bishops of Germany, succeeded in reconciling the sons with their mother. Matilda left the convent of Engern and regained her possessions. She used them to build hospitals and churches, and for the succour of the poor. She founded, notably, the famous monastery of Pöhlde where three thousand of the clergy were constantly occupied in the divine praises, and the abbey of Nord-hausen in Thuringia, to which she retired in 962 or 963.

In the last months of 967, feeling her end was approaching, she left for Quedlinburg, wishing to be placed at her husband's side in the tomb. Her grandson, archbishop of Mainz, came to minister to her. She passed away in peace, lying on a haircloth on the earth.

St. LUBIN

Bishop of Chartres (d. about 557).

Blessed JEAN DE BARASTRE (d. 1275)

Abbot for twenty-five years of Mont-Saint-Eloi near Arras.

Blessed PETER OF MONTICELLO or OF TREJA (d. end of the 13th century)

Franciscan of the Ancona Marches, friend and companion of Blessed Conrad of Offida and, like him, as the *Fioretti* tells, favoured with visions and ecstasies.

March 15th

ST. LOUISE DE MARILLAC (d. 1660)

BORN in Paris on August 15th, 1591, of Louis de Marillac, counsellor to the Parliament, and of his second wife, Marguerite le Camus, Louise lost her mother when very young. Carrying out her father's wishes she read extensively, learned drawing and the management of a house at an early age. In 1613, she married Antoine le Gras who, nine years later, was stricken with an incurable illness. Louise saw in this a divine punishment for having broken an earlier vow that she had made to enter the Capuchin order. This obsession and other interior griefs caused her to suffer for a long time. During the thirteen years she was married, she always reconciled the practices of piety with her duties as a wife and mother. After she became a nun she still took such good care of her only son that St. Vincent de Paul found it almost a fault. "You have more tenderness than any mother in the world," he wrote to her. "In the name of God, leave your son to the care of his Heavenly Father who loves him more than you; or at least, don't fuss so."

It was, in fact, under the guidance of "Monsieur Vincent" that she placed herself in 1624. He immediately associated her with his projects. The first Sisters of Charity were five "good country girls" whom Madame Le Gras assembled in 1633 and to whom she gave a rule: "It was such a good one," said Monsieur Vincent, "that I desired to add nothing to it."

The sisters at first employed themselves in teaching the catechism to little girls. Becoming more numerous, they devoted themselves to small schools, to retreats, to galley slaves, and to abandoned children. Later they founded hospitals for the poor and cared for the insane. The Congregation of Sisters of Charity received the king's approval in 1657, and that of the supreme pontiff in 1668. Louise, its superior-general, wished for continued simplicity, cordiality, and gaiety.

She died of gangrene on March 15th, 1660. Monsieur Vincent was gravely ill and unable to come to her succour. He sent her a message by one of his priests, "that she should go on ahead and he would hope to see her soon in heaven".

St. LONGINUS (1st century)

As early as the time of Gregory of Nyssa, it was believed that Longinus had pierced the Saviour's side with his lance, and that he had become one of the first bishops of Cappadocia.

St. Zachary

Pope from 741 to 752. The last edition of the Roman martyrology gives his feast as March 22nd.

St. Clement Mary Hofbauer (1751-1820)

Born of a poor family in Moravia, he was successively a baker's apprentice at Zwain, refectorian with the Premonstratensians of Bruck, a hermit near Mülfrauen, a baker again, then again a hermit. After studies at the University of Vienna, he left for Rome in 1784, became a Redemptorist, and was ordained priest in 1786. From that time until his death, Clement Mary gave himself to preaching and converted innumerable sinners, at Vienna, Warsaw, and in a host of other places. When he died, Pius VII declared that Catholicism had lost its mainstay in Austria.

St. Leocritia

Spanish virgin, already referred to on March 11th, in the life of St. Eulogius.

March 16th

ST. ABRAHAM (4th century?)

If the *Acts* of Abraham are to be believed, a subject still open to debate, the existence of this saintly hermit was not uneventful.

Born near Edessa of a wealthy family, his parents betrothed him at an early age to a very rich girl and then compelled him to marry her. The wedding festivities lasted a week, but at the last moment Abraham fled and hid in a large building which he walled up except for a dormer-window, through which food could be passed to him. Soon, realizing that he was lost to them, his relatives allowed him to live in peace the life of austerity and prayer which was his vocation.

After ten years, the bishop of Edessa drew him from his retreat against his will and, having ordained him priest, sent him to evangelize a pagan village called Beth-Kiduna, where no missionary had hitherto succeeded in making converts. Abraham built a church there and destroyed all the idols he found. His zeal brought him every kind of ill treatment which he bore patiently, and by force of perseverance and good example, he ended by converting and baptizing the inhabitants of Beth-Kiduna to the last man. He prolonged his stay among them for a year, to strengthen them in the faith; then, praying God to send them another and better pastor, he left them without farewell and returned to his hermitage.

He then immured himself in his cell which he hoped never to leave again. But he was once more compelled to leave to go to the aid of a niece named Mary, who was living a life of sin in a town at two days' journey. Disguised as a soldier, he succeeded in supping with her, making her ashamed of her conduct, and he had the happiness of persuading her to abandon her ways. In the desert Mary expiated her sins, and herself arrived at sanctity.

Abraham survived his niece's conversion and it is believed that he died a septuagenarian towards the middle of the 4th century. All the town of Edessa thronged to his funeral, and those considered themselves the most fortunate who could carry off a shred of his hair shirt.

St. GREGORY OF NICOPOLIS

Born in Armenia, was bishop of Nicopolis and ended his life as a recluse near Pithiviers in Beauce (d. about 1000).

St. DENTLIN OF SOIGNIES (7th century)

Son of St. Wandru and St. Vincent, he died at the age of seven; and miracles took place at his tomb.

Blessed TORELLO OF POPPI (1202–1292)

After a dissolute youth, he lived for sixty years in a cave near Poppi, his native town. It is debated whether he was a Franciscan tertiary or a Benedictine hermit.

Sts. JOHN DE BRÉBŒUF and GABRIEL LALLEMAND

French Jesuits martyred by the Iroquois in Canada, in 1649.

Blessed BENEDICTA (d. 1260)

Succeeded St. Clare as abbess of St. Damian at Assisi.

March 17th

ST. PATRICK (d. about 461)

IRELAND, Scotland, and Wales compete for the honour of having given birth to St. Patrick. His father, the deacon Calpurnius, had a farm beside the sea. About 404 it was pillaged by pirates who carried off Patrick, aged sixteen. They sold him to an islander who employed him for six years in tending his flocks, after which Patrick fled and returned to his parents.

In a dream he had a vision that caused him to devote himself to the evangelization of Ireland, still in idolatry. He crossed the sea, stayed with the monks of Lérins, then went to Auxerre where, from 415 to 432, he was at the school of the bishops St. Amator and St. Germain. It is thought that the first conferred the diaconate on him, and the second consecrated him bishop.

Recently freed from Roman domination, the Irish were then ruled by a host of minor kings. It was principally towards these personages that Patrick directed his zeal on arriving in the country. Wielding absolute power, their religion was their subjects'; monopolizing the land, they alone controlled the right to authorize the building of churches. The story of the evangelization of Ireland is almost entirely written in terms of the conversions made by St. Patrick among the heads of the clans and their families.

Many legends have been added to these accounts, such as the "Purgatory" of St. Patrick; and also the "Promises" which God made to him before his death. The Purgatory of St. Patrick is a great subterranean cave, situated on an island of Lough Dergh in Ulster, where the saint used to go to meditate on the judgment of God and to give himself up to penances. Since his death it has always been a place of pilgrimage, and certain souls have thought it sufficient to pass some time there to avoid the sufferings of purgatory in the world to come. As for the famous Promises, there is one which assures the Irish that they will be judged by St. Patrick on the last day.

At any rate, these legends express the extreme veneration of the Irish people for the apostle who made them Christian.

St. Gertrude of Nivelles (626–659)

After the death of her father, Blessed Pepin of Landen, Gertrude retired with St. Ita, her mother, into a convent of which she became abbess at Nivelles in Brabant. She called monks from Ireland to teach the Holy Scripture to her nuns and to evangelize the surrounding country. Devotion to her was most popular in the middle ages and spread not only throughout Belgium but to Germany and Poland. St. Gertrude is invoked against rats, mice, fever and madness, as well as for finding good lodgings when travelling.

St. Agricola (d. 580)

Was for almost fifty years bishop of Châlon-sur-Saone.

Blessed Thomasello

Dominican, born in Etruria, died at Perugia in 1270.

March 18th

ST. ALEXANDER (d. 220)

A NATIVE, it would seem, of Asia Minor, Alexander was brought up at the theological school of Alexandria; he had Pantaenus and Clement as masters and the famous Origen as a fellow student.

In the first years of the 3rd century, he became bishop of a town in Cappadocia of which the identity is not known. During the persecution of Septimius Severus, he was arrested and spent many days in prison. Released after the accession of Caracalla, he made a pilgrimage to the holy places. The episcopal see of Jerusalem was at that time occupied by St. Narcissus, who, in view of his advanced age, had need of assistance. Alexander was given him as coadjutor and became his successor.

Among the prelates of this time, writes Origen, none was more distinguished for his goodness and gentleness. He was, moreover, a faithful friend. He received in Cappadocia his master Clement when he was driven out of Alexandria; at Jerusalem he received the persecuted Origen, ordained him priest, allowed him to preach and teach, and upheld him against his enemies. Unable to do more for the great man in desperate straits, he procured for him at least a peaceful refuge at Caesarea.

Alexander had founded a library at Jerusalem where were gathered the writings and letters of the learned men of his time. Under Decius, he was imprisoned anew. "Crowned with his white hair," writes Eusebius, "he bore witness to his faith in the Praetoria and died in chains at Caesarea in Palestine."

St. CYRIL OF JERUSALEM

Was born in Palestine about 313, was ordained priest about 343, and became bishop of Jerusalem about 350. Although peaceful and tolerant, he passed sixteen years of his episcopal life in exile, driven from his see three times, sometimes by Arian bishops, at others by emperors favourable to heresy. His famous *Catecheses* are sermons which he preached to the catechumens and to the newly baptized in Jerusalem (d. 386 or 387).

St. NARCISSUS

Two saints of this name are honoured, one at Gerona in Spain, the other at Augsburg in Germany, but few authentic details are known about them.

St. EDWARD (d. 878)

King of England, was stabbed at the command of his mother-in-law, who wished to see her own son supplant him.

St. ANSELM

Bishop of Lucca, spiritual director of the countess Matilda (d. 1086).

St. SALVATOR OF HORTA (d. 1567)

A Franciscan of Catalonia, one of the most remarkable wonder-workers known. He had first been a shepherd, then a shoemaker. In the course of his religious life he was cook, mendicant, and porter. From all over Spain the sick came to him, and he is said to have cured about two thousand on a single day.

Blessed FRA GIOVANNI ANGELICO (1387-1455)

Son of Tuscan farmers, Guido di Pietro learned painting in Florence; at twenty entered the Dominican order at Fiesole, taking the name of Giovanni Angelico under which he has become famous. After living in Umbria for some years, he passed almost all the rest of his life either in Florence or in Rome where he died.

March 19th

ST. JOSEPH (1st century)

THE Gospel, sole source of information concerning the life of St. Joseph, tells us that the foster father of Jesus was an upstanding man, a scion of the house of David who practised the trade of carpenter at Nazareth.

Betrothed to the Virgin Mary, "he was for sending her away in secret . . . when an angel of the Lord appeared to him in a dream, and said, Joseph, son of David, do not be afraid to take thy wife Mary to thyself, for it is by the power of the Holy Ghost that she has conceived this child; and she will bear a son, whom thou shalt call Jesus, for he is to save his people from their sins. . . . And Joseph awoke from sleep, and did as the angel of the Lord had bidden him, taking his wife to himself; and he had not known her when she bore a son, her first-born, to whom he gave the name Jesus" (Matt. i, 19-25).

"Because there was no room for them in the inn," Mary and Joseph had taken refuge in a cave which served as shelter for men and beasts. It was there that the Virgin "brought forth a son . . . whom she wrapped in his swaddling-clothes, and laid in a manger. . . . And so (the shepherds) found Mary and Joseph there, with the child lying in the manger" (Luke ii, 7–17).

The wise men came in their turn to adore Jesus. "As soon as they had gone, an angel of the Lord appeared to Joseph in a dream, and said, Rise up, take with thee the child and his mother, and flee to Egypt; there remain, until I give thee word. For Herod will soon be making search for the child, to destroy him." After Herod's death, the angel reappeared to Joseph to enjoin him to leave Egypt. "So he arose, and took the child and his mother with him, and came into the land of Israel . . . and settled down in a city called Nazareth" (Matt. ii, 13–23).

When Jesus was presented in the temple, St. Luke notes: "The father and mother of the child were still wondering over all that was said of him"; and he adds that "every year, his parents used to go up to Jerusalem at the paschal feast". In the course of one of these journeys, Jesus, aged twelve, parted company with his parents. "It was only after three days that they found him. He was sitting in the temple, in the midst of those who taught there. . . . His mother said to him, My Son, why hast thou treated us so? Think, what anguish of mind thy father and I have endured, searching for thee." Jesus replied: "Could you not tell that I must needs be in the place which belongs to my Father? . . . but he went down with them on their journey to Nazareth, and lived there in subjection to them" (Luke ii, 33–51).

After which, the Gospels make no further mention of him who was worthy to be the foster father of Our Lord and the spouse of the Immaculate Virgin. Without doubt, he died before the Saviour's Passion, for, says St. Francis de Sales, it would have been unthinkable that Jesus on the Cross could have commended his mother to St. John, if Joseph had still been there to care for her.

St. LEONTIUS

Bishop of Saintes (d. 640).

Blessed ANDREA GALLERANI

Sienese soldier, banished for having killed a blasphemer with his sword, consecrated the rest of his life to works of mercy (d. 1221).

Blessed SIBYLLINA BISCOSSI (1287–1367)

Dominican tertiary who was born, lived, and died at Pavia. A young serving girl, she became blind at twelve years of age and passed sixty-seven years immured in a cell.

Blessed MARK OF MONTEGALLO (1426–1496)

Born of a noble family of the Marches of Ancona, he was a doctor, was married, was separated from his wife who became a Poor Clare, and himself became a Franciscan.

Blessed JOHN OF PARMA (1209–1289)

A Franciscan "spiritual"; taught at Paris; was general of his order from 1247 to 1257; had to resign; was persecuted; retired to the hermitage of Greccio, where he led a contemplative life for thirty-two years. He died at Camerino, on his way to the East to reconcile the Greeks, who held him in high veneration, with the Roman Church from which they had again separated.

March 20th

ST. JOACHIM (1st century)

NOTHING definite is known about the father of the Virgin Mary.

In her celebrated revelations the Venerable Maria de Agreda speaks of him in the following terms:

"St. Joachim had his family and his house at Nazareth. Illumined by heavenly light, he constantly implored God to fulfil his promises. He was humble, pure, and deeply sincere.

"For her part, Anne asked that a spouse be given her who would help her to keep the divine law. Joachim addressed the same prayer to the Lord. Their union in marriage was destined by God, and that from them should be born the mother of the Incarnate Word.

"The holy couple lived at Nazareth and kept the ways of the Lord. Each year they divided their income into three parts, offering the first to the Temple for the worship of God, distributing the second to the poor, and setting aside the third for their modest maintenance. Peace was inviolate between them; they lived in perfect conformity to custom, quietly and without quarrel. Anne submitted to the will of Joachim, who anticipated the wishes of St. Anne.

"They made a vow to the Lord that if a child were born to them, they would consecrate it to His service as a fruit of His blessing. Three years after the birth of Mary, Joachim and Anne left Nazareth and went with her to the Temple at Jerusalem. Our Queen knelt and asked their blessing, kissed their hands, and took leave of them. They returned poorer than they had come, and grieving at the loss of the rich treasure of their house, but the Lord made up for her absence, consoling them in every way.

"Six months after her entry into the Temple, our Queen learned from the Lord the day and hour of her father's death. She sent him angels from her guard to help him. They revealed to him that Mary would be the mother of the Saviour. At the same moment the holy patriarch lost his speech and, entering the way common to all men, he began his agony, struggling between the joyous news and the pains of death. He was sixty-nine and a half, and in his forty-sixth year of marriage with St. Anne; the Virgin Mary had been born to them after twenty years of marriage."

St. PHOTINA

According to some, the woman of Samaria taught by Jesus near Jacob's well. They add that she was martyred at Carthage, together with her sons, Victor and Joseph.

St. CUTHBERT (d. 687)

After having been a shepherd, Cuthbert entered the monastery of Melrose; he was then for twelve years prior of the abbey of Lindisfarne; then for eight years he lived as a hermit on a small island near by. Elected bishop of Hexham against his will, he persuaded the abbot-bishop of Lindisfarne to take his place and to give up his to him. A year before his death, he resigned the episcopate and again retired into his island solitude. Until the Reformation, St. Cuthbert was one of the most popular saints in England. Sailors have taken him as their patron.

St. HERBERT or HEREBERHT (d. 687)

A close friend of St. Cuthbert, he lived as an anchorite on an island of Lake Derwentwater and obtained the grace of dying on the same day as his friend.

Blessed MAURICE CSAKY (1281–1336)

Related to the royal family of Hungary, Maurice married Alberta de Luna with whom he lived for three years. They separated by common consent; he to become a Dominican friar, she a Dominican nun.

Blessed BAPTISTA SPAGNUOLO (1448–1516)

Born and died at Mantua, he was general of the Carmelites, and was dubbed the "Christian Virgil" for the sacred hymns he composed.

St. WULFRAM

Archbishop of Sens (5th century).

March 21st

ST. BENEDICT (d. 543)

BORN at Norcia in Umbria about 480, Benedict was pious and virtuous from childhood. He studied in Rome and the sight of the disorderliness of his fellow students made him fear to fall, in his turn, into sin; without taking leave of anyone, he fled to the mountains of Subiaco.

There a monk named Romanus gave him the religious habit and showed him as a place of retreat a cave known to none. Benedict had lived there for three years when the fame of his virtues reached some monks whose abbot had just died. They insisted that Benedict become his successor, but certain of them, finding him too severe, put poison in his wine. The glass broke when Benedict, according to his custom, traced the sign of the cross over his drink. "I have often warned you," he said, getting up, "that we would never suit each other." And he returned to his cave. However, more and more disciples placed themselves under his guidance. He built twelve monasteries for them, each of twelve monks, at the head of which was an abbot.

About 529, Benedict left Subiaco with Maurus, Placidus, and some others and turned towards Monte Cassino. There stood altars dedicated to Venus, Jupiter, and Apollo. The holy man broke the idols, upset the altars, set fire to the sacred grove, and in spite of all the persecutions of the demon built an abbey which has since been many times destroyed but which has always risen from its ashes.

The rule which was observed there, founded on silence, work, prayer, contrition of heart, and respect for the human person, is a monument of wisdom that has survived the centuries. There was a time when forty thousand monasteries followed it in the West.

A few weeks after the death of his sister Scholastica, Benedict had her tomb opened as he wished to be laid to rest beside her. He was then without warning taken with a violent fever. The sixth day he was carried at his wish into the oratory of St. John the Baptist and there received the viaticum; then, standing with his hands lifted to heaven, he drew his last breath.

St. LUPICINUS

Brother of St. Romanus. We have spoken of him on February 28th.

Blessed JOHN OF VALENCE (d. 1146)

After having been a canon of Lyons where he was born, he became abbot of the Cistercian monastery of Bonnevaux in Dauphiny, then bishop of Valence.

Blessed SANTUCCIA TERREBOTTI

Born at Gubbio, foundress of twenty-four convents in Italy. She had been married and her husband had become a Benedictine at Gubbio (d. 1305).

March 22nd

ST. LEA (d. about 383)

THE only information we possess on this pious matron comes from a letter of St. Jerome to St. Marcella. We learn from it that having lost her husband, Lea retired into a Roman monastery and later became its superior.

Not having to furnish his correspondent with the biographical details she already knew, St. Jerome confines himself to a fervent panegyric where he compares the actual fate of the departed with the presumed fate of a consul recently dead. This is how he expresses himself:

"Who will praise the blessed Lea as she deserves? She gave up painting her face and covering her head with shining pearls. Exchanging her rich attire for sackcloth, she ceased commanding others to obey all; she lived in a corner with a few sticks of furniture; passed nights in prayer; instructed her companions by example rather than by protests and speeches; awaited her arrival in heaven to be rewarded for the virtues which she practised on earth.

"Thus it was that henceforth she enjoyed perfect felicity. In Abraham's bosom where she is with Lazarus, she sees our consul, once clad in purple, and now arrayed in a shameful robe, asking in vain for a drop of water to quench his thirst. Although he went up to the capitol amid the applause of the populace, and his death put all the town into mourning, it is in vain that his wife impudently declares that he has gone to heaven and there occupies a great palace. The fact is that he is plunged into outer darkness, while Lea, who was willing to be thought a dolt here below, has been received in the house of the Father, at the feast of the Lamb.

"So too I beg you with tears in my eyes not to seek the favours of the world but to renounce all that is of the flesh. In vain may one attempt to follow both the world and Jesus. Let us live in renunciation, for our bodies will very soon be dust nor will anything else last longer."

St. BASIL OF ANCYRA (d. 362)

Priest who defended the orthodox doctrine against the Arians and was martyred at Ancyra in 362, on the orders of Julian the Apostate.

St. DEOGRATIAS

Bishop of Carthage (d. 457).

Sts. HERLINDIS and REINILDIS

These two sisters were brought up in a convent at Valenciennes and lived together in the abbey of Maeseyck in Belgium (8th century).

St. BENVENUTO

Franciscan born at Ancona, died bishop of Osimo in 1282.

St. NICHOLAS OF FLÜE (1417–1487)

Born near Sachseln (Switzerland), he was married, had ten children, took arms against the dukes of Austria who attacked his country, and passed the last nineteen years of his life in a hermitage in the canton of Unterwalden.

St. AVITUS

Soldier in the army of the Visigoths, was taken prisoner at the battle of Vouillé, died a hermit at Ruffes (Périgord) about 518.

March 23rd
ST. VICTORIAN AND OTHER AFRICAN MARTYRS (d. 484)

ALTHOUGH favourable to Arianism, Huneric, king of the Vandals of Africa, began by treating his orthodox subjects with moderation. Then he became hostile to them, and after having limited himself to the pursuit of priests and consecrated virgins, he ended, in 484, by persecuting all the Christians faithful to the Nicene Creed.

One of them, Victorian, lord of Adramiti in Byzacena, exercised, under the title of proconsul, the functions of governor of Carthage. Huneric told him to insist upon the administration of the edicts of persecution, promising that if he showed zeal and embraced Arianism he would be rewarded. Victorian replied that he would not deny his baptism and in consequence would never obey the king, even if he were given to the beasts or the flames. "If there were no other life but that here below," he added, "I would not for anything in the world pay back with ingratitude Him to whom I owe so many graces. But I believe in the words of Jesus Christ, my Lord and my God, and in Him I place all my trust." Enraged, Huneric condemned Victorian to perish in torment.

The Roman martyrology also honours today several other victims of the same persecution. It mentions, without giving their names, two brothers, natives of Aquae Reginae in Byzacena, who were taken to Tambala and hanged there with enormous weights tied to their feet. Overcome with pain, one of them begged a moment's respite; but encouraged by his brother, he recovered himself at once and died like him, roasted over a slow fire and torn with iron hooks. It then cites two Carthaginian merchants, both called Frumentius, about whom we have no other information. It also commemorates a Carthaginian doctor named Liberatus, and his wife and children; it is not known whether they died in exile or at the hands of the executioner.

St. TURIBIUS (1538–1606)

Born at Mayorga (Spain), he was president of the tribunal of the Inquisition at Granada, then archbishop of Lima. As such he became defender of the Indians, ill-treated by his compatriots, and reformer of the Peruvian Church. Having fallen ill, he promised to reward magnificently the first who would tell him his case was hopeless. Learning that he was about to die, he asked the psalm *Laetatus sum quae dicta sunt mihi* to be sung. "I was glad when they said unto me, let us go up into the house of the Lord."

St. JOSEPH ORIOL (1650–1702)

He was born of a poor family of Barcelona, and it was in this town that he passed his extraordinary existence as stipendiary priest of Our Lady of the Pines. He gave to the poor all that he had and practised fearful mortifications. Some good folk lent him a bed to die on as he had always slept on a bench. He asked them to sing him the *Stabat Mater*. Four children then came to sing the hymn at his bedside accompanied by a musician who played on the harp.

March 24th

ST. GABRIEL, ARCHANGEL

ST. GABRIEL, with St. Michael and St. Raphael, is one of the three archangels designated by name in Holy Scripture. The four episodes in which he is mentioned are connected with the mystery of the Incarnation.

Twice he came to explain to the prophet Daniel the meaning of certain visions relative to the coming of the Messias (Daniel viii, 16–26; ix, 21).

Later, at the dawn of a new epoch, he appeared to the priest Zachary in the temple at Jerusalem "at the hour of sacrifice . . . standing at the right of the altar where incense was burnt." It was to announce to him that his wife, advanced in age, would give birth to a son who would be the Precursor of the Saviour. As Zachary remained incredulous, he said to him: "My name is Gabriel, and my place is in God's presence; I have been sent to speak with thee, and to bring thee this good news. Behold, thou shalt be dumb, and have no power of speech, until the day when this is accomplished; and that, because thou hast not believed my promise" (Luke i, 11–20).

The third mission of this ambassador from heaven is that which he fulfilled to the Virgin Mary:

"Hail, thou who art full of grace," he said as he entered the house at Nazareth; "the Lord is with thee; blessed art thou among women. . . . Thou shalt bear a son and shalt call him Jesus. He shall be great and men will know him for the Son of the Most High . . . his kingdom shall never have an end."

"How can that be," replied Mary, "since I have no knowledge of man?"

"The Holy Spirit will come upon thee, and the power of the most High will overshadow thee."

"Behold the handmaid of the Lord; let it be unto me according to thy word," replied Mary.

"And with that the angel left her" (Luke i, 25–38).

Devotion to St. Gabriel seems to have begun in the 10th century. The Eastern churches celebrated his feast in December, March, November, June, and July. Since 1921 the West celebrates it on March 24th.

St. Catherine of Sweden

Daughter of Ulf, prince of Nericia, and of St. Bridget, Catherine was married to Count Eggard with whom she lived in continence and piety. Widowed, she never again left her mother, sometimes retiring to Rome with her, sometimes accompanying her on long pilgrimages. After the death of St. Bridget, she returned to Sweden with her body, which she placed in the monastery of Vadstena. Apart from a stay in Rome to secure the canonization of St. Bridget, Catherine did not leave Vadstena again. She became its abbess and died there in 1381, aged about fifty.

March 25th

ST. HUMBERT (d. about 680)

HUMBERT belongs to a group of holy persons who flourished in Neustria and in Austrasia towards the middle of the Merovingian epoch.

He was born of a noble family of Mézières-sur-Oise, near St. Quentin, in the first years of the 7th century. His mother was called Popita; his father, Evrard by name, was worthy to be declared blessed after his death.

From his early years Humbert showed himself so pious that he was given the tonsure before the usual time. He then became a monk at the abbey of Laon, where he received ordination as priest. Later the death of his parents led him to return to the world in order to administer his estate.

He was at his domain of Mézières when he received at his home St. Amandus, who had just resigned the bishopric of Maestricht, and who, with a monk of Elnon, named Nicasius, was going to the apostles' tombs. Humbert decided to accompany them to Rome. Afterwards he made the same pilgrimage again, and on his return he stayed with St. Amandus, at that time living in retirement at the abbey of Elnon. His conversations with the former bishop induced him to enter the recently founded monastery of Maroilles on the Hespres, to which he gave almost all his fortune.

It was there that St. Humbert spent the rest of his life. At rare intervals he went to Maubeuge to see St. Aldegundis, sister of St. Wandru and spiritual daughter of St. Amandus, to whom he was united by a great and edifying friendship.

The ANNUNCIATION OF THE BLESSED VIRGIN

The Church celebrates today the announcement to Mary of the mystery of the Incarnation and of the conception of Our Lord. Mention is found of this feast in the East as early as the year 692 and in the West ten years later.

The GOOD THIEF

According to apocryphal gospels, he was called DISMAS.

St. PELAGIUS

Bishop of Laodicea (d. 381).

St. LUCIA FILIPPINI (1672–1732)

Foundress of the Institute of "Pious Matrons" devoted to the education of young girls. Born at Corneto, she endured every kind of physical illness and persecution and died at Montefiascone.

St. CYRINUS or QUIRINUS
Martyred at Rome in 269.

March 26th

ST. LUDGER (d. 809)

BORN in Frisia about 743, Ludger evinced from childhood a great aptitude for study. After having had his first schooling in the monastery near Utrecht, ruled by St. Gregory, he left in 767 for York, where for four years he was a disciple of the celebrated Alcuin.

Returning to the Continent, he taught for a time at Utrecht, received the priesthood at Cologne, devoted several years to the conversion of Frisia, then went to spend three years at Monte Cassino in order to familiarize himself with Benedictine institutions. Charlemagne met him there in 787 and sent him into his country to Christianize the peoples dwelling around the delta of the Ems. Ludger worked for the conversion of Saxony and Westphalia. He founded a monastery at Werden, in the county of Mark, another at Helmstedt, and a third at Mimigardeford, which later gave rise to Münster.

Becoming bishop of that city in 802, Ludger devoted himself entirely to the training of a virtuous and learned clergy. He himself gave a lesson each day from the Scripture, led the most austere of lives, and almost all his revenue went to charity. He was represented to Charlemagne as having wasted the possessions of his see and as having neglected the upkeep of the churches. The emperor hailed him to court. Ludger obeyed, and was saying his breviary when a chamberlain informed him that his turn for audience had come. He replied that he would go when he had finished. When he presented himself, Charlemagne was vexed and said: "Bishop, it is not at all respectful to make me wait like that." "Sire," replied Ludger, "is not God infinitely above your Majesty, and do I not obey you in putting his service before all, since you bade me to do so when you appointed me bishop?" "That is true," said Charlemagne. Then he added: "I am happy to find you as I had believed you to be; and I will not give any credence to those who misconstrue your conduct."

St. EMMANUEL
Martyred, it is believed, in Asia Minor under Diocletian.

St. CASSIAN
Martyred at Rome at an unknown period.

St. THEODORE

Bishop, martyred in Pentapolis in Libya.

Blessed RINIERI (d. 1236)

Franciscan, provincial of his order, born and died at Muccia in the district of Camerino. He said that the shortest way to interior peace is to renounce self-love, to attach oneself to no creature, and to leave the disposition of one's time to the divine will. He had been, as we shall see, the companion in study of Blessed Pellegrino.

March 27th

BLESSED PELLEGRINO (d. 1232)

BORN in the diocese of Fermo, of the family of Falerone, Pellegrino was received into the Franciscan order in 1220, when Francis of Assisi, returning from the East, was passing through Romagna.

What is known of him is reported in the *Fioretti* as follows:

"Once on a time St. Francis came to the city of Bologna, and so wondrously he preached that he seemed to speak with the voice of an angel rather than of a man; his celestial words seemed to pierce the hearts of those that heard him, even as sharp arrows, so that during his sermon a great multitude of men and women were converted to repentance.

"Among whom were two students of noble birth from the Marches of Ancona, the one named Pellegrino, the other Rinieri. They came to St. Francis saying they desired to be numbered among his friars. Then St. Francis, knowing by divine revelation that they were sent of God and were to lead a holy life in the order, and considering their fervour, received them joyfully, saying, 'Thou, Pellegrino, keep the way of humility in the order, and do thou, Friar Rinieri, serve the friars.'

"And thus it was: for Friar Pellegrino would never go forth as a priest but as a lay brother, albeit he was a great clerk and learned in the canon law. And by reason of this humility he attained to great perfection of virtue. Consumed with the thirst for martyrdom, he left for Jerusalem in order to visit the holy places. The book of the Gospels in his hand, he followed in the steps of God made man. When he could see them with his eyes and tread them with his feet, he threw himself down on his knees, watering the ground with his tears, touching with his hands and covering with kisses the places sanctified by the passage of the Saviour.

"God willed that he should then return to Italy. He seldom visited his noble family; and then only briefly to exhort his relatives to scorn of the world and the love of God. He also said that nobility of soul is alone to be desired and that Jesus Christ bestows it."

In 1821 Pius VII confirmed the cult that had been accorded for six centuries to Blessed Pellegrino. He is invoked against toothache.

St. JOHN DAMASCENE

Doctor of the Church (8th century). He was grand vizier of the caliph of Damascus when Leo the Isaurian began his campaign against images. John took up the pen in their defence which cost him his post and his right hand. Then he became a monk at St. Sabbas and passed the rest of his life in study and in prayer. Among other writings, he composed the *Fountain of Wisdom* which is a summa of the Christian doctrine, some commentaries on St. Paul, and numerous and beautiful poems.

St. RUPERT or ROBERT OF SALZBURG (d. about 718)

Missionary bishop who evangelized Bavaria and Austria.

St. LYDIA

Martyred, it is said, in Illyria in the 2nd century, with her husband, the senator Philetus, and their two children.

St. JOHN OF EGYPT

Was almost as famous as St. Anthony of the Desert. He had at first been a shoemaker. At the age of twenty-five he placed himself under the direction of a hermit who made him accomplish many hard and apparently senseless tasks. When his master died, John travelled for five years, then settled on top of a rock, near Lycopolis, in a walled-up cell where he spent forty-eight years. He enjoyed the gift of prophecy and the power of miracles (d. 394).

March 28th

ST. JOHN CAPISTRAN (1386-1456)

A NATIVE of Capistrano, in the kingdom of Naples, renowned lawyer, former governor of Perugia, John asked to be admitted to the Franciscan monastery of Monte. Blessed Marco of Bergamo, the superior, replied that he would receive him when he had solemnly renounced the vanities of the world. John rode through Perugia mounted backwards on a donkey, wearing a paper mitre on which his greatest sins were listed. Among the friars minor he had as masters St. James of the Marches and St. Bernardine of Siena.

His career was prodigious. Friend and mainstay of four popes, he reformed his order, led a crusade, evangelized Italy, France, Germany, Austria, Hungary, and Poland. To him rather than to Hunyady is to be attributed the victory of Belgrade over the Turks. He died at the monastery of Vilak, near Sirmium. Having seen him at work, Enea Sylvio, the future Pius II, wrote: "Short of stature, already old, desiccated, thin, shrunken, having nothing but skin on his bones, he is always gay and indefatigable. Every day he preaches before twenty and even thirty thousand persons, clarifying the thorniest problems, pleasing the simple as much as the learned. He pronounces his discourses in Latin and an interpreter translates."

Blessed JEANNE MARIE DE MAILLÉ (1332–1414)

She was born, lived and died in Touraine. Married to the Baron de Silly, she lost her husband and her fortune and was reduced to being a servant. She was a Franciscan tertiary.

Blessed VENTURINO OF BERGAMO

Great Dominican missionary, made numerous conversions in Italy and the Near East. Born at Bergamo, he died at Smyrna in 1346.

St. GUNTRAM

Fourth son of Clovis and king of Burgundy, who although he sometimes gave way to debauchery, did penance and displayed his zeal for religion. When his estates were ravaged by a contagious disease known as "St. Anthony's fire," he wished the most unfortunate of his subjects to be cared for, imposed rigorous fasts on himself, and offered himself as a victim to divine justice for the good of his people (d. 593).

March 29th
ST. EUSTACE (d. 625)

BORN in Burgundy in the reign of St. Guntram, Eustace became a monk at Luxeuil and replaced St. Columbanus there when the latter was exiled by King Thierry II. After the death of that ruler he was sent by Clotaire II to Bobbio (Italy) to invite Columbanus to come and resume direction of the monastery which he had founded; but the exile, having good reasons for not reappearing in Gaul, declined the invitation. He only begged the king to give Luxeuil the benefactions which he wished to heap upon him, to which Clotaire II gladly consented.

Under the government of Eustace, the abbey knew a period of extra-ordinary prosperity. It counted six hundred monks, supported celebrated schools, and was extended to various places. At Luxeuil were trained, in the spirit of St. Columbanus, the abbots St. Waldebert, St. Romaric, and St. Amatus; and many bishops and saints began their religious life there.

Nevertheless, opposition to St. Columbanus continued, led by the monk Agrestius, former notary of Thierry II. A council was convoked at Mâcon in which Eustace defended the rule and work of his master. "If you persist in combatting our institutions," he said to the rebellious monk, "I will not give you a year in which to answer for your conduct before God's tribunal." And it happened indeed that Agrestius was killed shortly afterwards by a slave who felled him with a hatchet. St. Amatus and St. Romaric, who had at one time supported him, renounced their views and the incipient schism ended.

Among the miracles attributed to St. Eustace we may cite two: the restoration of her sight to St. Salaberga, abbess of Laon, and to St. Fara, spiritual daughter of St. Columbanus. We may also note that he converted the Volsci of Doubs and that he went to Bavaria with St. Agilus, in order to complete the evangelization of the Boii, begun by St. Severinus.

Sts. JONAS and BARACHISIUS

Two brothers martyred at Hubaham (Persia) about 327.

St. CYRIL

Deacon martyred at Heliopolis in 362.

St. GERY

Bishop of Sens (d. 711).

St. BERTHOLD

Born at Limoges, studied at Paris, left for the crusade and became a monk of Mount Carmel (d. 1188).

St. LUDOLFUS (d. 1250)

Premonstratensian, bishop of Ratzeburg (Saxony), died a victim of the ill treatment of Albert of Saxony.

March 30th
BLESSED AMADEUS OF SAVOY (d. 1472)

BORN at Thonon February 1st, 1435, Amadeus IX, duke of Savoy, was the grandson of Amadeus VIII who was elected anti-pope in 1438, but virtuously abdicated a few years later. Betrothed from his birth to Yolande, sister of Louis XI, king of France, he married her in 1451 and had seven children by her.

In 1465, Amadeus succeeded his father, Louis I, on the throne of Piedmont and Savoy; but, during the seven years of his reign, attacked by epilepsy, he actually shared his power with his wife, the duchess. Neverthe-less, the union of the two remained unbroken and they thought of nothing but the temporal and spiritual good of their subjects.

Although his way of life was that of his rank, and he himself was ready to face death at any moment, Amadeus never wished to force his people or to shed their blood in vain. Only libertines, extortioners, and blasphemers were objects of his severity.

At his example Francesco Sforza, duke of Milan, imposed fines on those of his courtiers who were heard to swear, and with the sums so received, built a chapel which he was able to decorate magnificently. Seeing the extreme goodness and indulgence which Amadeus showed towards the poor, this same prince said to him: "On your estates one might have thought oneself to be at the antipodes! Everywhere, in general, it is better to be rich than poor, but with you it is the poor who are honoured and the rich who are despised." The duke always practised prayer and penitence. To those who tried to dissuade him from fasting so much, he answered that nothing was more necessary to his health.

His last years were marked with a recrudescence of epilepsy. His wife and friends were very sad to see him so afflicted. "Why concern yourselves," he said, coming out of his crisis. "Humiliations give access to the kingdom of God." He died at Vercelli (Piedmont) on Easter Monday, 1472, in his thirty-eighth year.

St. QUIRINUS

The tribune, martyred at Rome with his daughter, Balbina, about 120.

St. JOHN CLIMACUS (d. after 649)

Celebrated anchorite, who, apart from a few months when he ruled the monks of Sinai, passed his existence in solitude. He has been given three names: John the Scholastic, in homage to his learning; John the Sinaite, in memory of the place where he lived; John Climacus, by allusion to his work, *The Ladder of Paradise* ("climax" in Greek means "ladder").

St. PETER DE REGALADO

Wonder-worker and Franciscan reformer, born at Valladolid in 1390, died at the convent of Aquilar in 1456.

Blessed JOACHIM OF FLORA (d. 1202)

Calabrian in origin, he left the court of Roger of Sicily, where he was a page, and made a pilgrimage to the Holy Land. After having preached to the crowd, he became a priest and entered the Cistercian order, which he tried to reform. Lucius III authorized him in 1183 to leave the monastery of Corazzo of which he was abbot, and to live as a hermit at Pietro Alto. He finally left the Cistercians and founded, in the wildest of the Calabrian mountains, the congregation of Flora. Great contemplative and pitiless critic of the clerical morals of his time, he wrote notably an exposition of the Apocalypse, and a concordance of the Old and New Testaments, which had an immense and prolonged influence. He believed that the era of the Holy Spirit would succeed the era of Christ, from 1260 onwards. The council of Lateran condemned the Trinitarian errors of the Joachimites in 1215.

March 31st

ST. BENJAMIN (d. about 422)

SAPOR, king of Persia, had attempted to throw off the Roman yoke and with the same blow to annihilate the Christian religion in his country. After his death, the Church was left in peace, but soon a violent persecution broke out again, which lasted about three years. It was at the outset of that period that the deacon, Benjamin, was imprisoned, his activity and influence having displeased Isdeberge, the new king.

Meantime, peace proposals were being exchanged between the ruler and the Roman ambassador. The latter demanded that Benjamin be set at liberty. The king consented on condition that the deacon promise not to display in future his zeal among the magi or priests of the Persian religion. But this promise could not be secured from the prisoner. He declared that he would never close the sources of divine grace to men, nor cease to make the true light shine before their eyes. "Otherwise," he added, "it would be to incur myself the punishment which the Master reserves for servants who bury their talent." Nevertheless the Roman ambassador, going bail for him, obtained his release.

However, Benjamin was scarcely out of prison when he again set to work to make converts among the magi and the fire worshippers. The king called him to appear before him, and this time ordered him to worship the fire and sun. "Do what you will with me," replied Benjamin, "but I will not deny the Creator of heaven and earth, and worship perishable creatures. What do you think of a subject who gives to others the allegiance due to you?"

Mad with rage, Isdeberge ordered them to put him to torture. A score of times they forced sharp reeds under his nails and into his joints. As he still persisted in refusing to apostasize, they inflicted on him the torture of the stake, and he expired, giving thanks to God.

St. Balbina

Daughter of St. Quirinus, who was mentioned under March 30th.

St. Daniel

Of German nationality, Daniel was a trader in Venice. His profits were spent in alms and he himself was given lodging with the Camaldolites of Murano. He was assassinated there in 1411 by robbers.

St. Guido of Pomposa (d. 1046)

Born at Casemar in Romagna, he ruled the monastery of St. Severus at Ravenna, then, from 998 till his death, the abbey of Pomposa.

Blessed Bonaventure Tornielli

Vicar-general of the Servites, born at Forli in 1411, died at Udine in 1492.

Blessed Camilla Pia

Poor Clare, foundress of the convent of Carpi, near Modena (d. 1504).

THE SAINTS OF APRIL

April 1st

ST. HUGH (1053–1131)

HUGH BECAME a bishop against his will and despite his own wishes, and remained one for more than half a century.

He was born at Châteauneuf-d'Isère in Dauphiny; his mother was a woman of outstanding piety; his father was an officer who ended his days at the Grande Chartreuse. After studying at the college at Valence, Hugh became a canon in that town. At a council held at Avignon in 1080, delegates of the Grenoble clergy came to ask for him as their bishop. The legate of Gregory VII who presided at this council had considerable difficulty in persuading him to accept the post.

After two years' tenure Hugh withdrew to Chaise-Dieu. He had been living there happily for some fifteen months under St. Benedict's rule, when the pope obliged him to leave his retreat and return to his bishopric.

Three years later, St. Bruno was passing through Grenoble with six companions, like him desirous of leading the life of a hermit. Hugh led him to the wildest place in his diocese; there was founded the Grande Chartreuse, and the bishop came often thereafter to share in the life of the monks. St. Bruno became his spiritual director and always had difficulty in persuading him to moderate his austerities.

Hugh disposed of his horses and went about on foot; he fasted to the point of contracting headaches and ailments of the stomach from which he suffered until his death; he sold his ring and his gold chalice to succour the poor; he refused to listen to gossip; watched over his eyes so carefully that he could not recognize any woman by sight. He was an appealing and touching preacher; he was also a judge so wise and just that none dreamed of appealing against his decisions. God permitted him to be tempted to blasphemy for many years.

Hugh sought permission to abandon his post; he even made a journey to Rome to convince Honorius II of his unworthiness; but as we have said, these efforts were unavailing with the five pontiffs who succeeded to the see of Rome during his lifetime.

St. GILBERT

Bishop of Caithness (Dornoch) in Scotland (d. 1245).

St. MELITO

Bishop of Sardis in Libya, orator and writer, composed an apologia addressed to Marcus Aurelius in favour of the Christians (2nd century).

St. VENANTIUS

Bishop of Salone in Dalmatia (d. 257?).

St. VALERY

Born in Auvergne, founded the abbey of Leucone under the rule of St. Columbanus (d. 619).

St. CELSUS (1079–1129)

Bishop of Armagh in Ireland; he was, said St. Bernard, "a good and timorous soul."

April 2nd

ST. THEODOSIA OR THEODORA (d. 307)

ON Easter Day, 307, Theodosia, a girl of eighteen, was present at the trial of several Christians at Caesarea in Palestine. Hearing them condemned to death, she threw herself before them to felicitate them and to recommend herself to their prayers. No more was needed to secure her arrest and to have her taken before the governor Urbanus. He had her breasts and her sides torn with iron hooks, and, since she was still breathing, he ordered her body to be thrown into the sea.

Certain martyrologists give Theodosia the name of Theodora.

ST. MARY OF EGYPT (d. 430)

ACCORDING to a legend which was already known to Gregory the Great and to the Fathers of the second Council of Nicaea, the following was, in short, the life of this penitent, as she related it to St. Zosimus in the desert at twenty days' journey from the Jordan:

"I was born in Egypt. At twelve, leaving my parents' house, I went to Alexandria where, for seventeen years, I gave myself up to a dissolute life. My perversity became such that meeting some young Libyans, who were going to Jerusalem to be present at the Exaltation of the Cross, I embarked with them to seduce them. I seduced them all to the last one. Arrived at the Holy City I wished to take part in the feast and joined the crowd going into the temple, but I found it impossible to cross the threshold and I remained rooted to the spot. Light came to me that it was my crimes that prevented me from entering. Seeing an image of the Virgin Mary, I made this prayer: 'O Mother of Him who died for sinners, let me too venerate the Holy Cross; then I will follow the way you show me.' My prayer was granted. After the ceremony, I went to implore the Holy Virgin anew. 'Cross Jordan,' a voice told me, 'and you will find peace.' After receiving the sacraments of confession and Communion, I crossed the Jordan, and pushed on to this place. Here I have been for forty-seven years, without meeting any human being, eating roots and herbs, and only speaking with God. The first seventeen years of my solitude were filled with temptations and trials, but the Virgin succoured me, and it is she who obtained for me the profound peace which I have since enjoyed."

Having said this, Mary prayed Zosimus to come back on Holy Thursday of the following year to bring her the Eucharist. The monk kept the tryst. He came back a year later; but this time Mary was dead, her body lying on the sand. The aged hermit wished to bury her. He had just set to work when a lion appeared to help him; and it was the lion which, with his paws, dug and filled in the grave of Mary of Egypt.

St. URBAN
   Bishop of Langres (d. about 450).

St. NICETIUS

Bishop of Lyons for twenty years (d. 573).

St. FRANCIS OF PAULA (d. 1508)

A great contemplative and miracle-worker, born at Paula in the kingdom of Naples. He was first a Franciscan, then founded an order of hermits named Minims; came to France in 1482 to cure King Louis XI. He did not cure him, but prepared him for death. Francis himself died, ninety years of age, at Plessis-lez-Tours.

April 3rd
ST. RICHARD (d. 1253)

BORN at the manor of Wyche near Worcester, Richard saw his noble parents fall into indigence. He restored their fortunes; for the sake of peace gave his share of the inheritance to his brother; and went to study at the universities of Oxford and Paris.

He then spent seven years taking the course of jurisprudence at Bologna and finally took the place of his professor who was ill. The latter offered him his daughter in marriage and wished to leave him his whole fortune, but Richard refused and went back to England. There he became successively chancellor of the University of Oxford and legal adviser to St. Edmund, archbishop of Canterbury. He followed this prelate to his exile at Pontigny and never left him until his death.

After having studied theology and received ordination as priest at the Dominican monastery of Orléans, Richard was elected bishop of Chichester against the will of Henry III, who for two years deprived him of all revenues. This was no privation for this Christian who chose the company of the sick and poor, and who preferred, he said, to sell his horses and silver plate rather than leave the members of Jesus Christ in misery. He was endlessly kind and indulgent, except towards those of the clergy whose incorrigible conduct was harmful to the welfare of souls.

Richard partook in the efforts which the Christians were then making to recover the Holy Sepulchre, by preaching the crusade throughout England. He fell ill on his way to Dover. Having arranged the details of his funeral and recommended his soul to God, he made this prayer to the Virgin which all those around him repeated until his death: "Mary, mother of God and mother of mercy, defend us from the enemy and receive us in heaven."

St. PANCRATIUS (1st century)

It is said that he was a native of Antioch, that he was a disciple of St. Peter, and that he became bishop in Sicily.

St. SIXTUS I

Pope and martyr (d. 126).

Sts. AGAPE, CHIONIA, and IRENE (d. 304)

These three sisters who lived at Thessalonica were burned alive for having been found in possession of the Holy Scriptures, which, by an edict of Diocletian, was punishable with death.

St. BURGUNDOFARA or FARA

Born in the neighbourhood of Meaux, she refused to marry, and founded at Evoriac, later called Faremoutiers, a monastery of which she was abbess for forty years. She was the sister of St. Chagnoaldus, monk of Luxeuil, and of St. Faro, bishop of Meaux (d. 667).

Blessed GANDULPHUS

Franciscan hermit, died at Polizzi (Sicily) in 1260.

April 4th

ST. ISIDORE OF SEVILLE (d. 636)

St. ISIDORE, bishop of Seville and Doctor of the Church, was the younger brother of Sts. Leander, Fulgentius, and Florentina. We do not know the date of his birth or whether he came into the world at Cartagena or Seville. He was orphaned early and was a poor student, receiving frequent correction from his brother and tutor, Leander, who had undertaken his education. One day when he was playing truant to avoid being beaten, he noticed on the edge of the well some grooves worn in the stone. It was explained to him that this was the result of the rubbing of the rope. Isidore concluded that repeated efforts would also finally overcome the dullness of his mind, and he went back to his studies.

His episcopate of nearly forty years was fruitful and glorious. With his brothers he contributed to the conversion of the Arian Goths and, thanks to his zeal, the "acephalous" heretics, who denied the dual nature of Jesus Christ, were unable to propagate their errors.

He founded a magnificent college near Seville, where he himself expounded the Holy Scriptures and the profane authors. The fourth Council of Toledo over which he presided in 633, recommended the establishment of similar ones throughout Spain.

In addition to the *Origines*, the *Historia de Regibus Gothorum*, exegetical treatises, and many other works of piety and erudition, St. Isidore compiled a missal and a breviary for the use of the Church of Spain. He thus deserves to be considered the creator of the Mozarabic liturgy, one of the most beautiful of Christian liturgies.

He died at an advanced age. Shortly before his death, he had himself carried into the Basilica of St. Vincent where, clad in haircloth and stretched upon ashes, he recapitulated his life and implored the divine mercy before his clergy and the assembled faithful.

Sts. AGATHOPUS and THEODULUS

Respectively deacon and lector of the church of Thessalonica, and both put to death at the commencement of the persecution of Diocletian.

St. ZOSIMUS (5th century)

He has been mentioned on April 2nd, in connection with Mary of Egypt. After fifty-three years passed in a monastery in Palestine, he chose a retreat in the vicinity of the Jordan. It was about 430, it is said, that he met Mary in the desert, and a few years later that he died.

St. PLATO (d. 814)

A very celebrated Greek monk, born of a family related to the emperors. He governed the monastery of the Symboleon on Mount Olympus, and that of Sakkudion, near Constantinople, practising great austerities and suffering fearful persecutions.

St. BENEDICT THE MOOR (1526–1589)

Born of negro slaves, this Franciscan wonder-worker, who could neither read nor write, spent his life in Sicily, sometimes as cook, sometimes as superior or novice master in his monastery.

April 5th
ST. GERARD (d. 1095)

A MONK at Corbie, his native town, and cellarer of the abbey, Gerard was attacked by fearful headaches which rendered him almost incapable of any work. In 1050 he left for Rome, and was ordained priest by Leo IX. In the pilgrimages which he made on that occasion to Monte Gargano, Monte Cassino, and the apostles' tombs, he sought his cure in vain. He obtained it some years later at the intercession of St. Adelard of Corbie, whose life he wrote out of gratitude.

About 1073, Gerard made a journey to the Holy Land. On his return, the monks of St. Vincent of Laon asked for him as their abbot. He accepted, in order to try to reform them, but he did not succeed and at the end of five years left them, taking with him the two best monks. A recluse named Ebroin joined them, as well as five knights, inspired by the same desire for a life of fervour.

The little flock visited successively the sanctuary of St. Denis near Paris, the Church of the Holy Cross at Orléans, and the tomb of St. Martin at Tours. They reached Poitiers on the day that William III, duke of Aquitaine, entered the city. Having questioned our pilgrims as to their intentions, the prince offered to help them and pointed out the forest of Grande-Sauve (*sylva major*) between the Garonne and the Dordogne, six leagues from Bordeaux.

Gerard took possession of it on October 28th, 1079. On May 11th, 1081, he laid the foundation stone of the monastery he established there, under the rule of St. Benedict, reinforced by special statutes. Dedicated to the Holy Virgin and to the apostles St. Simon and St. Jude, this abbey later took the name of Notre Dame de la Grande-Sauve.

St. Gerard is the author of a *Hagiology* or *Martyrology*, in which he mentions several holy personages whose names, but for him, would not have come down to us.

When he was ready to die, he received the last sacraments, blessed and embraced all his monks, then asked them to retire in order to give place to the angels and saints who, he said, were coming to fetch his soul and take it to heaven.

St. ALBERT

Bishop of Montecorvino (Italy), died in 1127.

St. JULIANA OF CORNILLON (1192-1258)

A nun of Liége born at Rhétines, died at Fosses. It was at her instance that the feast of Corpus Christi was established.

Blessed EVE

Recluse of Liége, friend and confidant of St. Juliana, died about 1265.

St. Vincent Ferrer

Celebrated preacher and Dominican miracle-worker, born at Valencia (Spain), January 23rd, 1350; died at Vannes (France), April 5th, 1419. He traversed Spain, Italy, Switzerland, and France "like an angel flying in the midst of the sky," says Pius II in the bull of canonization, "spreading the words of salvation and showing that the day of judgment is near".

St. Catherine Tomas

Canoness regular of St. Augustine, born in 1533 at Valdemuzza (Majorca), died at Palma in 1574.

Blessed Crescentia Höss (1682–1744)

Franciscan nun, celebrated for her ecstasies, born and died at Kauf-beuren (Germany).

April 6th
ST. PRUDENTIUS (d. 861)

A THEOLOGIAN much neglected today, but still consulted as a historian, Prudentius was the best writer of his era. He was first called Galindo and was born in Spain. He came to France very young and learned everything that was then known. About 830, he was at the court of the Frankish kings, occupying, it is said, the post of chaplain palatine. It was there that he composed for the consolation of a great lady in her affliction an anthology of the most beautiful passages of the psalms. It was intended, possibly, for the Empress Judith, wife of Louis the Débonnaire. Soon this collection was widely used by the itinerant clergy whose travels prevented them from being present at divine office.

When about 844, Prudentius was named bishop of Troyes, his knowledge and virtue placed him at once in the front rank of the episcopate. He visited the monasteries within his jurisdiction and tried to establish discipline; in 849, with twenty-one other bishops meeting at Paris, he wrote a letter to the duke of Brittany reproaching him with abusing the churches in his duchy; he guided to sanctity chosen souls like Maure of Troyes, who had great influence over their fellow citizens. Early in his episcopate he had published a dogmatic and moral code, under the title of *Precepts*, drawn from Scripture, which all his priests had to know by heart.

It is not possible here to enlarge upon the part which he played in the dispute then raging on the subject of predestination. The fact that the

Jansenists have claimed Prudentius shows clearly enough that, under the pretext of anti-Pelagianism, his theology tended to diminish the part played by human liberty in the work of salvation.

It is better to emphasize his merit in continuing the so-called *Annals of St. Bertin*, making himself a precise and usually faithful chronicler of contemporary events. He reports the details of ecclesiastical and secular matters, the deeds and acts of kings, their voyages, wars, peace treaties, and, in general, all that happened between 836 and his death. Besides this, his talent as a writer appears on every page as does also his great love for God and souls.

St. MARCELLINUS

Notary at Carthage, disciple of St. Augustine, officially took the part of the latter against the Donatists, who revenged themselves by having him legally but unjustly put to death (d. 413).

St. EUTYCHIUS

Patriarch of Constantinople, died in 582.

St. VINEBAUD

Abbot of the monastery of St. Lupus at Troyes (d. about 620).

St. WILLIAM OF ESKILSÖE

A French monk much involved in the political and religious affairs of his time; died superior of a Danish monastery in 1203.

Blessed NOTKER BALBULUS or THE STAMMERER

Born about 840 at Elk (Switzerland), was monk of the abbey of St. Gall. He is the author of numerous sequences, a *Life of Charlemagne*, and a *Martyrology* (d. 912).

April 7th
BLESSED HERMANN JOSEPH (d. 1241)

THIS holy person is supposed to have been one of the most devoted servants of Mary and one of the greatest contemplatives of the middle ages. From his childhood, it is said the Virgin treated him with a maternal familiarity, talking to him in German, caressing him, putting the Infant Jesus into his arms, bidding the angels keep visible watch over him. His whole life was, indeed, filled with visions and ecstasies; and a hundred instances are cited of the gift he had for reading hearts.

Born of poor parents at Cologne, he entered the Premonstratensians at Steinfeld at the age of twelve; they first sent him to finish his studies in a Frisian monastery, then received his profession and made him their sacristan. This duty was particularly agreeable to Hermann Joseph, allowing him to be continually in church during the day without affecting the long visits which he made during the night.

Having become a priest, he was entrusted with the direction of convents of Norbertine and Cistercian nuns. He composed various pious treatises for them and, like many another mystic desirous of expressing his sublime experiences, wrote a commentary on the Song of Songs.

Besides the many ailments from which he suffered throughout his life, he was continually troubled with headaches which only ceased when he went up to the altar to celebrate Mass; they redoubled their violence at the approach of the liturgical solemnities, which made him say, playing on words: "*Festa sunt mihi infesta*; On feast days I am not feasting." All of this did not, however, prevent him from dying a nonagenarian.

"Hermann Joseph thought so much about God," wrote his biographer, "that he was completely indifferent to the world. However," he adds, "his heart was like a general hospital where, beginning with the afflicted and his fellow monks, all men found a tender welcome and a sure refuge."

Sts. Epiphanius, Donatus, and Rufinus

African martyrs about whom there is no information.

St. Hegesippus

Ecclesiastical writer whose works have been almost completely lost. "Very near to the time of the apostles," wrote St. Jerome of him, "he was the imitator of their virtues and of their life as well as of their manner of speech." It is believed that he was born in Judaea and that he died at Rome about 180.

St. Calliopius

Christian of a patrician family martyred in Cilicia in 304.

Blessed Evrard or Eberhard (d. 1075)

German prince, relative of the Emperor Henry II and of Pope St. Leo IX. By mutual accord, Evrard and his wife Itta separated, he to enter the abbey of All Saints and she the convent of St. Agnes at Schaffhausen.

April 8th

ST. WALTER or GALTERIUS (d. 1095 or 1099)

ST. WALTER is invoked for the deliverance of prisoners, because, when a novice at the abbey of Rebais in the diocese of Meaux, he not only brought bread every day to a peasant held in the monastery prison, but at night he entered his dungeon, broke his bonds, and gave him the key to the grounds.

An abbey having been established at Pontoise, Walter was given its direction against his will. There he introduced the rule of St. Benedict, built a chapel to St. Martin and then, to escape his increasing fame, fled about 1072 to the abbey of Cluny, then governed by St. Hugh. Keeping his identity concealed, Walter was living there peacefully and happily when, armed with an order from John of Bayeux, archbishop of Rouen, his monks traced him and obliged him to return to St. Martin of Pontoise.

In vain Walter arranged a retreat in a secluded grotto; his reputation for sanctity attracted so many visitors and so much admiration that he believed it necessary to escape again, this time to an island in the Loire, near Tours. There he served a chapel dedicated to Sts. Cosmas and Damian, devoting almost all his time to prayer. Many inhabitants of Tours got into the way of coming to consult him and asking for his prayers; in return they loaded him with presents, which went to the poor and to the pilgrims who also had not been slow in finding the way to his hermitage.

It was one of them, named Garin, who recognized Walter and told the monks of Pontoise of his discovery. They came to beg their father to resume the rule of their abbey which, they said, was falling into ruin. Walter yielded to their insistence. Soon an opportunity was offered him to leave for Rome. He thought he could convince Gregory VII of his unworthiness and obtain discharge from the burden of authority for ever. But the pope reproached him with his excessive modesty, and under threat of anathema, ordered him to fulfil all his duties as abbot from that time on.

Walter, who was a native of Andainville (Picardy), died at Pontoise in 1095 or in 1099.

St. DIONYSIUS

Bishop of Corinth (d. 180).

St. PERPETUUS

Was bishop of Tours for thirty years (d. 491).

St. ALBERT OF JERUSALEM (1149-1215)

Born of a noble family at Gualtieri (Italy), he was in succession bishop of Bobbio and of Vercelli, became patriarch of Jerusalem in 1205, codified the customs of the hermits of Mount Carmel, and died stabbed in a Church of St. John of Acre.

Blessed JULIE BILLIART (1715-1816)

Born at Cuvilly (diocese of Beauvais), was paralysed from her twenty-second to her forty-fourth year, obtained her cure, founded the Institute of the Sisters of Notre Dame, endured many persecutions and died in Belgium.

Blessed JULIAN OF ST. AUGUSTINE

Franciscan lay brother, born at Medina Coeli (Castile), and died at Alcala in 1606.

April 9th

ST. WANDRU (d. 688)

BORN at Coulsore in Hainaut, St. Wandru or Waldetrude belonged to a family almost all of whose members were canonized. Married by her parents, St. Walbert and St. Bertilia, to Madelgaire, the future St. Vincent, she had four children by him: Landric, Dentlin, Aldetrude, and Madelberte. The first became a monk, perhaps even a bishop, and is honoured on April 17th; the second died in infancy after baptism; the last two became nuns at the convent of Maubeuge of which their aunt Aldegundis was abbess, and are honoured respectively on February 25th and September 7th.

When all their children were vowed to the service of God, the couple separated. Leaving the court of the Merovingian kings, Madelgaire entered the abbey of Hautmont; on her part, Wandru built on a hill, where afterwards rose the town of Mons, a convent which she ruled until her death. There she sometimes received visits from St. Aldegundis, her sister, and benefited by the spiritual direction of St. Ghislain, abbot of Celles.

She endured many temptations of the devil, not to mention the memory of the delights of her secular life which came back to her, and the discouraging thoughts with which she was obsessed. Finally she found peace; heaven even sent her great consolations. Already during her marriage she had devoted her disposable income to the ransom of captives and the support of the unfortunate; her charity to the poor increased yet more as a nun; and

God sometimes miraculously procured her the money she lacked to help them. He also accorded her the gift of healing sick children.

Formerly, the town of Mons celebrated not less than four annual feasts in honour of St. Wandru, its patroness.

ST. CASILDA (d. about 1007)

ALDEMON, Moorish king of Toledo, hated the Christians and always kept a great many of them in chains. Out of compassion his daughter Casilda frequently visited them in secret. One day as she was going towards the prison, a basket on her arm, she met her father who asked to see what she was carrying. The loaves in her basket changed, it is said, into red roses, which changed back into bread again as soon as the king had gone away.

Attacked by an incurable illness, Casilda went to Burgos, where she obtained a cure by bathing in Lake St. Vincent. Till that time she had only been a catechumen. Then she received baptism and constructed beside the lake an oratory and a little house. After being widowed, she passed her last years in this retreat.

St. MARY OF CLEOPHAS

Close relative, it appears, of the Blessed Virgin; followed Jesus to Calvary, was present at His burial, and had the happiness of seeing Him after He had risen.

St. MARCELLUS

Bishop of Dié, died, according to some, in 474, to others, in 510.

St. GAUCHERIUS

Born at Meulan-sur-Seine, founded two monasteries in Limousin, and died in 1140 of a fall from a horse.

St. ACACIUS

Bishop of Amida (Diarkebir) in Mesopotamia, sold the golden vessels of his church to succour seven thousand Persian prisoners held captive by the Romans (5th century).

St. BADEMUS

Persian solitary, put to death by a Christian apostate on the orders of King Sapor in 375.

Blessed ANTONIO PAVONI

Dominican inquisitor, killed by heretics at Bricherasio (Piedmont) in 1374.

April 10th

ST. FULBERT (d. 1029)

OF Roman origin according to some, from Aquitaine according to others, Fulbert studied at Rheims where he had Gerbert as professor of mathematics and philosophy. When the latter donned the tiara under the name of Sylvester II, Fulbert followed him to Rome and for some time was his assistant; then he returned to France, became chancellor of the church of Chartres, and founded in that town a school of theology which became the most celebrated in the kingdom.

Elevated, in 1007, to the episcopal see of Chartres, he disputed with Berengarius of Tours, his former pupil, who was at that time propagating false interpretations of the Eucharistic dogma. He became the mouthpiece of religious France of his time. Taking part in 1008 in the Council of Paris, he signed immediately after the two metropolitans, before the other bishops who were mostly his elders in the episcopate.

There remain a hundred and twenty-five of Fulbert's letters, treatises, verses, liturgical prose, and some sermons. These letters are addressed to King Robert whose friend he was, to princes, prelates, and the simple faithful. They reveal a noble and courageous man as well as one gentle and humble of heart.

In 1020, in the course of a fire which consumed almost the whole town, the cathedral of Chartres was entirely destroyed. The bishop undertook its reconstruction on a magnificent scale, generously aided by Canute, king of Denmark, and William, count of Poitiers.

Fulbert died on April 10th, 1029; he was buried at the monastery of Saint-Père-en-Vallée, where he often withdrew to pray.

Blessed PATERNUS

Irish monk who lived as a recluse near Paderborn and perished in the fire which destroyed the town in 1058.

Sts. TERENTIUS, POMPEIUS, and ZENO and other martyrs

Victims of the persecution of Decius at Carthage, about 250.

St. EZECHIEL

His prophecies form a book of the Old Testament. He was married and lived in Tell-Abib, south-west of Babylon. His ministry lasted from 592 to 570.

St. MACARIUS OF ANTIOCH

Armenian by birth, he was archbishop of Constantinople; travelled through Palestine, Epirus, Dalmatia, and Bavaria; stayed at Mainz, Cologne, Maubeuge, Cambrai, Tournai, Malines; and died at the monastery of St. Bavo at Ghent in 1012.

Blessed MADDALENA OF CANOSSA

Born at Verona in 1774, as a young girl she attracted the notice of Napoleon, to whom she had the appearance of an angel; she entered Carmel; left it to found the congregation of the Daughters of Charity for the instruction of peasants and the care of the sick; and died in 1833.

April 11th

ST. LEO THE GREAT (d. 461)

HIS father was called Quintianus. He himself is supposed to have been born in Rome in the last years of the 4th century. He became pope in 440 and died in 461, fifteen years before the downfall of the Roman Empire in the West.

The emperor at that time lived at Ravenna. Already Africa belonged to Genseric, king of the Vandals, who from Carthage was threatening Rome. The Huns, after having pillaged Thrace, were now devastating Gaul. In 452, Attila reached the outskirts of Mantua; an embassy, led by St. Leo, went to meet him and made him agree to withdrawal. But three years later, Genseric came to sack the city of Rome. On the other hand, the Visigoths and the Burgundians were everywhere crossing the frontiers. It was in the midst of this general upheaval that St. Leo ruled the Church.

Among the barbarians, the Vandals, the Alani, and the Goths were Arians. The Pelagians and the Manichaeans multiplied; Nestorianism and Eutychianism had countless followers. The names of Nestorius and Eutyches are today almost forgotten, but in the 5th century these people troubled the world as much as Genseric and Attila. The latter piled up material ruin; the former caused evils which might be irreparable in the spiritual order. In denying the mystery of the Incarnation, they shook Christianity to its very foundations. The glory of St. Leo the Great is to have shown himself equal to the occasion and to have triumphed over all the difficulties which assailed the Church at that time.

His authority was such that, the day following the Council of Ephesus at which Nestorius had been condemned, the Fathers of the Council of

Chalcedon in their condemnation of Eutyches merely cited as the rule of faith the pope's letter to the archbishop of Constantinople, crying: "Peter has spoken by Leo."

This pontiff has left ninety-six sermons and a hundred and seventy-three letters, but his writings give no information concerning either his personal or his inner life.

St. PHILIP

Bishop of Gortyna (Crete), died about 180.

Blessed ULRICH

Monk of Lutzel (Bavaria), died in 1155.

Blessed RAYNERIUS

Lived twenty-two years as a recluse near the door of the cathedral of Osnabrück (d. 1237).

St. GUTHLAC

Issue of the younger branch of the royal family of Murcia (England), became a brigand chief, was converted, became a monk at the abbey of Repton, then lived as a hermit on the island of Croyland (d. 714).

St. GEMMA GALGANI (1878-1903)

Born at Camigliano (Tuscany) of a modest family which had just settled in Lucca and fallen into poverty, Gemma passed many years in fearful sufferings, favoured with extraordinary graces and with heavenly revelations.

April 12th

ST. JULIUS I (d. 352)

OF Roman origin, son of a citizen named Rusticus, Julius I succeeded Pope St. Mark on February 6th, 337. His pontificate was filled with difficulties caused by the Eusebians or partisans of Eusebius, patriarch of Constantinople. These held a middle road between the true faith and Arianism recently condemned at Nicaea.

They bore a mortal grudge against St. Athanasius, bishop of Alexandria, whom they had deposed at the Council of Tyre. When this great adversary of Arianism wished to take possession of his see, they opposed it and had recourse to the arbitration of Julius I, hoping that he would rally to their side. The pope convoked a council at Sardica in Illyria in order to resolve the conflict.

Meanwhile he greeted Athanasius in Rome and received him at Communion, thus showing that he approved his doctrines. Learning of this, the Eusebians foresaw that the Council of Sardica would rule against them, and they abstained from taking part in it.

Nevertheless, Julius I addressed them in the most fraternal terms: "Why have you replied to me in so haughty a way," he said, "when I write to you in all the charity and sincerity of my heart? You have done wrong to let the sun set on your wrath. Are you irritated by the fact of having been invited to a council? Those whose conduct is right do not object to being examined. The great Council of Nicaea has moreover agreed that the decrees of one council can be examined by another, because the judges will take even more care in examining matters if there is a possibility of their judgment being revised."

The assembly of Sardica confirmed the innocence and faith of Athanasius, and from that time it was recognized that any bishop, deposed in a synod of his province, had the right to appeal to the see of Rome.

Julius I died on April 12th, 352, and was interred in the cemetery of Callistus on the Via Aureliana.

St. VICTOR

Martyred, it is said, in the 4th century at Braga (Portugal).

St. DAMIAN

Bishop of Pavia, died 710.

St. ZENO

Bishop of Verona from 362 to 380 (?). The language of his treatises and sermons gives rise to the belief that he was of African origin.

St. SABBAS

Martyred in Gothland in 372.

Blessed MECHTILDE (d. about 1200)

She is believed to have been Scottish, and lived and died in a hut at Lappion (diocese of Laon).

Blessed ANGELO CARLETTI

He was born at Chivasso (Piedmont) in 1411, and died at Cuneo in 1495. Having been a senator of the duchy of Montferrat, he entered the Franciscan order of the strict observance in 1444; composed a *Summa*

Angelica of cases of conscience for the use of confessors; was the spiritual director of several saints; as apostolic nuncio preached the crusade against the Turks; and filled the highest duties of his order till the age of eighty-two.

April 13th
ST. IDA (1040–1113)

A DAUGHTER of the duke of Lorraine, Ida was married at the age of seventeen to Eustace II, count of Boulogne, like herself a descendant of Charlemagne. Among her numerous children a daughter became the wife of Henry IV, emperor of Germany, who, as is known, had to make honourable amends to the pope at Canossa.

Of her three sons the most celebrated is Godfrey, duke of Bouillon, who fought Gregory VII at his brother-in-law's side, then sold his duchy to go on the crusades and, after a series of exploits, was proclaimed king of Jerusalem in 1099. When he died the next year, his brother Baldwin succeeded him.

The Countess Ida had as her spiritual director St. Anselm, then abbot of Bec in Normandy. He sometimes visited her in Boulogne, and also wrote her edifying letters in which he sometimes calls her his "well-beloved sister," and sometimes his "very dear daughter in Jesus Christ."

Ida was humble and practised mortification and charity in proportion to her considerable wealth. Her favourite occupation was making fine ornaments for altars. After the death of her husband, with whom she was always on good terms, she consecrated all her disposable goods to found and endow religious establishments.

Her body was buried at the abbey of Vasconvilliers, near Boulogne.

St. ROMANUS (d. 489)
Was bishop of Metz when Clovis took this city.

St. URSUS
Bishop of Ravenna, died in 398.

St. MARTIUS
Hermit, later founder of a monastery in Auvergne (d. about 530).

St. HERMENGILD
Patron of Seville (d. 586). He was a son of Leovigild, king of the Visigoths and protector of the Arians, who had him imprisoned and put

to death; he is mentioned on February 27th in connection with St. Leander, his master and friend.

St. CARADOC

Welsh hermit, died in 1124 on the island of Barry. He played the harp and had been a troubadour at the court of King Rhys.

Blessed IDA

Cistercian nun, born at Louvain and died at the abbey of Ramiège in 1260.

April 14th

ST. JUSTIN (d. about 166)

BORN at Nablus in Syria at the beginning of the 2nd century and brought up in paganism, Justin, son of Priscus and grandson of Bacchius, was, it seems, of Latin origin.

In his *Dialogue with the Jew Tryphon,* he himself has told how, seeking an explanation of the world and uneasy about his own destiny, he made a survey of all philosophies which claimed to determine the truth. He passed over the Epicureans whom he despised and took as master a Stoic who affirmed that the philosophy he professed did not concern itself with any God. He then addressed himself to an eminent Peripatetic but left him almost at once, disgusted by his avarice. He then saw a celebrated Pythagorean who before teaching him philosophy demanded that he study astronomy, geometry, and music. Impatient to reach his goal, Justin entered the school of a Platonist who had just settled in Nablus. "This master," he said, "gave wings to my spirit and I believed that very soon I should know God. To hasten that longed-for hour, I retired to a solitary place on the seashore."

It was there that he met an old man who said to him: "To cross the limits of reason, divine help is necessary; this help, God has procured for us through the prophets, Christ, and the apostles. Pray, if you wish the gates of light to be opened to you." Justin read the Holy Scripture and prayed; then faith was granted him, as well as peace of mind and heart.

About 135 he met at Ephesus the Jew Tryphon, with whom he had the long and vain discussions reported in the *Dialogue.* He then went to Rome, where he opened a sort of school of apologetics and theology. The two *Apologies* which he then wrote and his *Treatise against Heretics,* which has never been found, complete the list of his works. It is these writings which have placed him in the ranks of the apostolic Fathers.

Justin entered into a discussion with the cynic Crescentius and has abused him somewhat in his second *Apology*. Without other means of having the last word, this philosopher denounced his adversary to the prefect of Rome, Junius Rusticus. The latter cited Justin to appear for trial with Evelpistos, Paeon, Hierax, and Chariton, and he had them all decapitated.

Sts. TIBURTIUS, VALERIAN, and MAXIMUS

Martyred with St. Cecilia.

St. LAMBERT

Bishop of Lyons from 678 to 688.

St. BERNARD OF ABBEVILLE

Reformer of a Benedictine congregation known as that of Tiron (1046–1117).

St. BÉNÉZET (1165–1184)

A young shepherd credited with building the famous bridge of Avignon.

St. LIDWINA OF SCHIEDAM (1380–1433)

Dutch mystic who endured innumerable ills and whose life was written by Thomas à Kempis and by J. K. Huysmans.

April 15th

ST. PATERNUS (5th or 6th century)

IT is known for certain that there was at Vannes, at the end of the 5th or the beginning of the 6th century, a holy bishop named Paternus. The rest of his biography is not very certain.

According to the ancient authors, he was born in Armorican Brittany of parents who separated the day following his birth: Gueana, his mother, continued to bring up her child; Petranus, the father, left to lead the religious life in Ireland. Having grown up, Paternus wished to follow in his father's footsteps and with some companions embarked for England. Having settled in Cardigan, he built a monastery there of which he became the superior, and a church which, since that time, was called Llan-Padern-Vaur—sanctuary of Paternus the Great. Then he went to visit his father in Ireland and reconciled two minor kings who were at war. Later he made the journey to the Holy Land and received episcopal consecration from the hands of the patriarch of Jerusalem, and then returned to Llan-Padern-Vaur, which thenceforth became the seat of a bishopric. Twenty years later, Paternus was persuaded by King Caradoc to exchange this diocese for that of Vannes. Thus he found himself once more in his native country. But his fellow citizens persecuted him and, judging it good to get away, he betook himself to die among the Franks.

St. LEONIDAS

Bishop of Athens (6th century).

Sts. ANASTASIA and BASILISSA (1st century)

Said to have been two great Roman ladies who were beheaded for having given burial to the bodies of St. Peter and St. Paul.

St. CRESCENS

Martyr at Myra in Lycia (epoch unknown).

St. PETER GONZÁLEZ or ELMO

Born at Astorga (Spain), about 1190, he was at first a worldly and vain canon. One day, in full view of the city, he fell from his horse into the mud; the people assembled to mock him. "Since the world mocks me," he said as he picked himself up, "henceforth I will mock the world"; and he became a Dominican. He travelled over the kingdoms of Leon and Castile, converting many souls; for a long time he accompanied the king of Castile on his expeditions against the Moors; he exercised a fruitful apostolate in the seaports and died at Tuy in 1246. The Spanish and Portuguese sailors who have taken him as patron invoke him under the name of St. Elmo. It is thought that "Elmo" comes from "Erasmus," a martyr of the 4th century in whom, before the time of González, the Mediterranean navigators placed their confidence (*see June 2nd*).

April 16th

ST. BERNADETTE (1844-1879)

THE celebrated confidante of Mary Immaculate was born at Lourdes on January 7th, 1844. François Soubirous and Louise Casterot, her parents, were very poor, and the child was put into service from the age of twelve to fourteen. She came back to her family at the beginning of 1858 to prepare for her first Communion. Some days afterwards, as she was collecting fire-wood with her sister and a friend, the Blessed Virgin appeared in the crevasse of a rock on the bank of the Gave. This apparition took place on February 11th.

Clad in a white robe, girdled with a blue sash, a white veil covering her head, her bare feet ornamented with a golden rose, a rosary hanging from her right hand, Our Lady seemed to be sixteen or seventeen. She returned eighteen times before the following July 16th. She entered into conversations with the little girl and, among other things, said to her: "I promise to make you happy, if not in this world, at least in the next (February 18th). Pray for poor sinners (February 21st). Penance! Penance! (February 24th). Go and tell the priests that a chapel should be built here (February 27th). I am the Immaculate Conception (March 25th)."

The sisters of Nevers had a house at Lourdes where they cared for the sick and instructed children. They received Bernadette, taught her to read and write, completed her religious instruction, kept her busy with light work until the day when, aged twenty-two, she was admitted as a sick and indigent person into their congregation.

Bernadette left for Nevers in July 1866 to commence her novitiate at the motherhouse. There she passed the rest of her life, employed at one time as infirmarian, at another as sacristan; usually ailing, often in bed, constantly humiliated and even a little persecuted by her superiors. She always suffered with courage and sought to be despised. In her agony she was heard to murmur: "Holy Mary, mother of God, pray for me, poor sinner, poor sinner." A few instants later she softly drew her last breath.

St. PATERNUS
Bishop of Avranches, died in 565.

St. FRUCTUOSUS
Bishop of Braga (Portugal), died in 665.

St. TURIBIUS
Bishop of Astorga (Spain), died about 460.

Sts. MARTIAL, URBAN, EVENTIUS, CAECILIAN, JULIA, and their companions
Martyred at Saragossa about 304.

St. DROGO
Former shepherd, lived for many years as a pilgrim, ended his life as a recluse at Sebourg, near Valenciennes, in 1189.

Blessed HERVÉ

Touraine landowner who reconstructed the basilica of St. Martin, then lived as a hermit and died at Tours about 1021.

St. BENEDICT LABRE

Famous pilgrim, born at Saint-Sulpice d'Amettes in 1748, died at Rome in 1783. Strange and silent, he lived in ceaseless prayer, seeking only suffering and scorn; a mysterious figure which recalls that of Christ, spat upon, beaten, and crowned with thorns.

April 17th
ST. ANICETUS (d. 166)

ST. ANICETUS succeeded Pope Pius I and reigned, it is thought, from 155 to 166. It was at that time that St. Polycarp, a disciple of St. John, came to Rome to discuss with the pope the date of the feast of Easter. At that time East and West celebrated it on different days; agreement on this subject was delayed until the Council of Nicaea in 325. Some say Anicetus died a martyr, and it is commonly thought that he was interred in the Vatican, near the tomb of St. Peter.

St. ROBERT OF CHAISE-DIEU

Founder of the monastery of that name in Auvergne (d. 1067).

Blessed MARIANA OF JESUS (1565–1624)

Foundress in Spain of the discalced nuns of Our Lady of Mercy.

St. LANDRIC

Son of St. Wandru (*see April 9th*).

Sts. ELIAS, PAUL, and ISIDORE

Monks put to death by the Arabs at Cordova in 856.

St. STEPHEN HARDING (d. 1134)

An English monk, co-worker of Robert of Molesme (*see April 29th*).

April 18th

ST. PERFECTO (d. 850)

CORDOVA, where this holy person was born, lived, and died, was at that time still in the power of the Arabs. Perfecto, who was exercising his priestly ministry there, was stopped in the street one day by some Moors who asked him what he thought of Jesus and of Mohammed. He declared that Jesus was the Son of God and God Himself, that He had suffered to redeem us, and that His merits would obtain salvation for us. As for Mohammed, he would prefer to be silent in order not to irritate his questioners. As they urged him to speak frankly, promising not to get angry, Perfecto said finally that Mohammed was a false prophet and that they must renounce him to be saved. They would not listen further, but having given their word, they left him on this occasion to return in peace to his house.

Nevertheless, when they judged that enough time had gone by to render their promise void, the Moors charged some fellow believers to execute their vengeance. Thus it was that Perfecto was unexpectedly arrested, brought before the Arab judge and condemned to death as a blasphemer. His execution took place on the Moslem Easter; his last words were to bless Christ and to curse Mohammed and his Koran.

ST. GALDINO (d. 1176)

BORN of the noble Milanese family of Della Scala, Galdino was a great supporter of the Roman papacy during the schism which followed the death of Adrian IV in 1159.

Alexander III having been elected pope, a group of cardinals supported in opposition to him Victor IV, who was recognized by Frederick Barbarossa and his subjects. The church of Milan, of which Galdino was archdeacon, took a position of obedience to Alexander III. The German emperor, suzerain of the Lombard towns, then came to besiege Milan which was reduced in six months. On this occasion the three holy bodies from the Church of St. Eustrogius, said to be those of the Magi kings, were transported to Cologne.

Galdino did not await the end of the siege to rejoin Alexander III who was then at Genoa; he followed him to Maguelonne, Montpellier, and Clermont when the pope had to take refuge in France; he again followed him into Sicily, and finally to Rome when Alexander III returned in 1165.

That year he was named cardinal of St. Sabina, the following year, archbishop of Milan, the year after, apostolic legate for all Lombardy.

Galdino took possession of his see as soon as the lieutenants of Barbarossa
had been expelled from Italy by the league of the Lombard towns. He was
thenceforth occupied in restoring discipline in his church, in deposing the
Lombard prelates who remained faithful to the anti-pope, in consecrating
new bishops at Lodi, Alba, Cremona, Vercelli, Asti, Turin, Navarre,
Brescia, and Alexandria. He died in the pulpit, on Low Sunday, 1176, as
he was preaching in the Church of St. Thecla.

St. Eusebius

Bishop of Fano, died in prison at Ravenna in 526.

St. Agia (d. 707)

Wife of Hidulf, of the counts of Ardennes. The couple separated to
enter religion. Hidulf retired to Lobbes (Belgium) and Agia to the abbey
of Mons, ruled by her saintly aunt Wandru.

Blessed Marie de L'Incarnation

Born at Paris in 1566, died at the Carmel at Pontoise in 1618. When
she was sixteen and a half she married Pierre Acarie with whom she lived
thirty-one years. When he died, she entered the convent and there passed
the last four years of her life.

April 19th

ST. EMMA (d. about 1050)

THE name of her father is not known. As for her mother, she was called
Adela; temperamental and violent in character, she was descended, it was
said, from the terrible Widukind whose defeat and baptism were celebrated,
at the order of Pope Hadrian I, by three days of processions throughout
Christendom. Emma had a brother named Meinwerk, bishop of Paderborn. Imad, the son born of her marriage with Count Ludger, also occupied
the episcopal see of that town.

After being widowed, Emma consecrated to good works the forty years
she survived her husband. Her immense fortune was employed in support
of the unfortunate, the construction of churches, and for other important
foundations in the diocese of Bremen. She died about 1050. When later

her tomb was opened, her body was found reduced to dust, with the exception of the right hand which was intact; it was deposited in the church of the abbey of St. Ludger at Werden.

St. GEORGE

Bishop of Antioch in Pisidia, exiled by the Iconoclasts, died in exile in 818.

St. URSMAR (644–713)

Abbot of Lobbes (Belgium).

St. EXPEDITUS

It is believed that he was martyred at Melitene in Armenia in the 4th century. He is sometimes invoked for the settlement of long-delayed negotiations.

April 20th

ST. MARCELLINUS (d. 374)

AFRICAN by birth and Christian by education, he was inspired to go forth and evangelize Gaul. He landed at Nice and began to journey through the neighbouring mountains. Eusebius of Vercelli, then in exile in that country, consecrated and established him as bishop of Embrun.

One day some muleteers, one of whose beasts had just collapsed, obliged him to take its load and carry it as far as the town. Marcellinus complied, simply saying: "Since our Saviour has taken our faults upon Himself, why should not I carry this burden as He Himself carried His cross?" And lifting his eyes to heaven he added with the psalmist: "Lord, I am like a beast of burden before Thee, but I am with Thee."

Arianism, supported by the Emperor Constantius, was then widespread. Marcellinus sent word to the Christians of Arles, Vienne, and Béziers, begging them to repudiate this heresy, and thereby brought upon himself all kinds of persecution. The imperial authorities tried to arrest him; the heretics tried to throw him into a gorge; he was forced to hide for a long time in the mountains.

The accession of Julian the Apostate, successor to Constantius, permitted the orthodox prelates to show themselves again in the light of day and Marcellinus to come out of hiding. He had succeeded in Christianizing the greater part of the Maritime Alps when, on April 13th, 374, he died in the midst of his people.

ST. THEOTIMUS (5th century)

THEOTIMUS the Philosopher was bishop of Tomi in Scythia under the emperors Theodosius and Arcadius. He had received a Greek education and had acquired great philosophical knowledge. After he had foresworn paganism, his life was entirely devoted to piety, zeal, and penance. Several times he went down the Danube in an attempt to spread the Gospel among the Huns. The latter admired him so greatly that they called him "the god of the Romans." Although he did not succeed in converting them, at least he helped to soften them and rendered less frequent their incursions among the Scythians who had submitted to the Roman Empire.

Theotimus was a beloved and faithful friend of St. John Chrysostom and always took his part against Theophilus of Alexandria and his other persecutors. At the Synod of Constantinople, assembled by St. Epiphanius with the object of condemning Origen, he refused to proscribe in a general way the writings of this great doctor. In this matter he shared the opinion of St. Athanasius and St. Gregory of Nyssa, and also of St. Jerome, who said very justly: "As the good works of Origen cannot accredit those which are less so, it would be an injustice if the latter were to prejudice the former."

Sts. SULPICIUS and SERVILIAN
Roman martyrs (period unknown).

Blessed HARDUIN
Monk of St. Wandrille (d. 811).

St. MARCIAN
Sanctified himself in a lifetime of watching the herds of the abbey of Auxerre (d. about 488).

St. AGNES OF MONTEPULCIANO
Dominican, died in this town in 1317.

St. HILDEGUND (d. 1188)
A nun who lived under the name of "Brother Joseph" in the Cistercian monastery of Schönau near Heidelberg.

Blessed ODA (d. 1158)
Prioress of a convent of Premonstratensians in Hainaut.

April 21st

ST. ANSELM (d. 1109)

ANSELM was born at Aosta in Piedmont about 1033. Gundulf, his father, was related to Countess Mathilda; Ermenberga, his mother, was thought to be descended from the founder of the dynasty of Savoy.

After a childhood devoted to study and piety, Anselm wished to embrace the religious life but Gundulf prevented this and brought him out into the world. The young man acquired a taste for pleasure and devoted several years to it. Meanwhile, Ermenberga died; the father and son quarrelled, and Anselm fled from his father's castle.

With a donkey carrying his baggage, he crossed Mount Cenis where he thought he would die of hunger. He stayed some time in Burgundy, passed three years in France, then became a monk at the abbey of Bec in Normandy, where flourished one of the most celebrated schools in the West and where the famed Lanfranc was a teacher. Anselm was his pupil and afterwards his successor.

He became abbot of the monastery in 1078, and his reputation for learning and goodness quickly spread throughout Europe. "The good odour of your virtues has reached us here," Gregory VII wrote to him. "Come as soon as possible to see us," Urban II bade him for his part, "so that we may together enjoy the affection which unites us." As he felt the approach of death, William the Conqueror had recourse to the ministry of Anselm.

The interests of his abbey sometimes took Anselm to England. In 1092 he was constrained by King William Rufus to remain, and the next year to accept the episcopal see of Canterbury. From then on he had to undertake frequent journeys to Rome to settle the conflicts which incessantly arose between the English court and the Holy See. It is surprising that in the midst of such diplomatic and administrative labours he was able to compose writings so numerous and so profound.

St. Anselm is considered, in fact, to be one of the great philosophers and theologians of the middle ages. He is also the author of some admirable prayers. Alexander VI canonized him in 1492 and in 1720 Clement XI placed him among the ranks of Doctors of the Church.

St. SIMEON

Bishop of Seleucia, died a martyr in 341.

St. ANASTASIUS SINAITA (630–700)

Celebrated theologian and apologist of the Eastern Church.

St. WOLBOD

Bishop of Liége (d. 1021).

Blessed BARTHOLOMEW OF SAVIGLIANO

Dominican inquisitor, put to death by heretics at Cervere in 1466.

April 22nd
ST. OPPORTUNA (d. 770)

THIS holy abbess, to whom so many French churches were dedicated, was born at the castle of Exmes, not far from Argentan. Her brother, Chrode-gang, became bishop of Séez; her aunt, St. Lanthilda, was abbess of Almenèches. It was in the neighbourhood of this abbey, in a little monastery whose name is lost, that the youthful Opportuna became a nun. Her gentle-ness and patience caused her to be chosen unanimously as superior of the community.

Two charming miracles are told of her. One was accomplished to teach a lesson to a peasant who had stolen the convent donkey, and who persisted in keeping it despite all claims to its possession. The abbess had recourse to God, and the next morning the peasant's meadow was covered with a layer of salt, which made him decide to think better of the matter and take the donkey back to the nuns. He also gave them his meadow, which from that time was known as the salt-meadow (*pré-salé*).

The same year, a flock of birds came and ate all the seeds in the garden. Opportuna told these pillagers that they were to regard themselves as prisoners. When they appeared, the abbess reproached them with their con-duct, then dismissed them. But instead of going, they fluttered round her for a long time chirping their repentance and good resolutions.

Opportuna died of sorrow caused her by the death of Chrodegang, killed by an opponent in the village of Nonant. She interred his body at the abbey, then asked God to reunite her to this beloved brother. She gave up the ghost after twelve days of illness, in a state of ecstasy, greeting the Virgin who, she said, was coming to meet her.

ST. LEONIDAS (d. 204)

To the glory of dying for the faith, Leonidas, a local rhetorician, joined that of being the father of Origen and of having guided his first steps in study.

The child revealed such precocious genius, piety, and innocence, that the happy father often went, while he slept, to uncover his chest and kiss it respectfully. When under Septimius Severus, Laetus, governor of Egypt, had Leonidas arrested with other inhabitants of Alexandria, Origen, anxious also to die for the faith, wished to follow the accused to the tribunal. His mother had to hide his clothing to prevent him from going out of the house. Then, he wrote to his father a sublime letter: "May the thought of her and the others you leave behind you," he said, "not weaken your courage. Face the tortures valiantly, God will take care of us." Leonidas was beheaded, his possessions were confiscated, and God did, in fact, inspire a rich matron to watch over the needs of his wife and seven orphans.

Sts. SOTER (d. 175), CAIUS (d. 296), and AGAPETUS (d. 536)

Popes.

St. LEO

Bishop of Sens (d. 547).

St. THEODORE OF SIKION (Galatia)

Celebrated anchorite and wonder-worker of the Eastern Church (d. 613).

April 23rd

ST. GEORGE (d. about 303)

ST. GEORGE suffered martyrdom at Lydda in Palestine shortly before the accession of the Emperor Constantine. These words contain all we know certainly of him whom the Greeks call "the great martyr" and whose devotion also spread far to the West.

Beginning with the 5th century the Christians of Syria and Egypt consecrated monasteries and churches to him. The same thing occurred a hundred years later in France and Germany. However, it was in England that St. George became and remained the most popular. In 1222, the National Council at Oxford established a holy day of obligation in his honour; in the first years at the 15th century the archbishop of Canterbury ordered that this feast be given the same solemnities as Christmas. Earlier, King Edward III had founded, in 1330, the celebrated order of the Knights of St. George also called Knights of the Garter.

Among legends relating to this martyr, the best known is that in which he worsted the dragon. This fearful animal, says the *Golden Legend*, lived in a lake near Silena in Libya. Whole armies sent against it had not been able to do away with it. Sometimes it came out of the lake, breathing fire and annihilating all that obstructed it. In the end it was appeased by being given two sheep to eat every day. When sheep were scarce, it had to be given a maiden, for whom lots were drawn. Actually the lot had fallen on the daughter of the king, when George, a military tribune, came through that country. Moved to pity, he made the sign of the cross, went off on horse-back to meet the dragon which was already advancing with open mouth, and killed it at once with a blow of his lance. He then made a fine speech to this idolatrous people, after which the king and his subjects embraced the true faith and asked for baptism. The prince offered a great sum of money to the saviour of his town and of his daughter as well; but George gave it to the poor, and he went on his way, keeping nothing for himself.

St. GERARD

Born at Cologne in 935, died bishop of Toul, in 994

St. ADALBERT

Bishop of Prague, first apostle of the Prussians, put to death by them at Tenkitten in 997.

St. PUSINA (5th or 6th century)

Born at Perthes (Champagne), died at Baisieux near Corbie. Alpin, bishop of Châlons-sur-Marne, placed the virgin's veil on her as on her five sisters who were: Sts. EMMA, HOUE, FRANCULA, LINDRUA, and MENEHOLDA.

Blessed GILES OF TYRE

Born at Nantilly, near Saumur, became chaplain of St. Louis and accompanied him on the crusade (1245); was named archbishop of Tyre and died at Dinant (Belgium) in 1266.

Blessed EGIDIUS or GILES OF ASSISI (d. 1252)

Was one of the first and most colourful companions of St. Francis, a great contemplative, caustic observer, and often *enfant terrible*. The collection of his sayings, known by the title of *Propositions of Brother Egidius*, is a charming and useful little book.

April 24th
ST. FIDELIS (1577–1622)

MARK ROY or Rey took the name of Fidelis when he entered the Capuchins at the age of thirty-five. Born at Sigmaringen, he was a brilliant student of philosophy and law at Freiburg in Breisgau; he then became the tutor of three young princes and travelled throughout Europe in their company for six years; then, after having practised as a lawyer at Colmar, he decided to leave the world. In the testament he drew up at that time he wrote: "I want from this time on to live in extreme poverty, chastity, and obedience, in sufferings and persecutions, in austere penance, and deep humility. Having come naked out of my mother's womb, I strip myself of all and abandon myself naked into my Saviour's arms."

Father Fidelis possessed great gifts of oratory. Appointed guardian of the convent at Feldkirch, he preached at Biberach, Altdorf, Kienzheim, Rheinfelden, Fribourg in Switzerland, and in a number of country churches. The town of Feldkirch, especially, was entirely transformed by him.

As Protestantism was spreading in Switzerland, notably in the Grisons, the Roman Congregation of the Propaganda entrusted the Capuchins with combating it, and Father Fidelis was placed at the head of the missionaries. "You soon will see me no more," he said to his friends at Feldkirch. "I have been called to give my blood for the faith." And from that time he signed his letters: "*P. Fidelis, prope diem esca vermium*"—who will soon be food for worms.

He entered the district occupied by Austria in January 1622, and began to preach with success. The enraged Protestants prepared a revolt, and the missionary warned the Austrians. Soon there was an uprising throughout the Grisons. On April 24th, Father Fidelis was preaching at Sévis when the cry "to arms" went up. The people of the Grisons went out to face the imperial troops which had just broken through their outposts. They thought it was Father Fidelis who had called them in. At first they let him go, but as he was returning from Grusch soon afterwards, twenty soldiers felled him with their sabres, having first tried in vain to make him apostasize.

St. HONORIUS
Bishop of Brescia (d. 586).

St. DEODATUS
Abbot, born at Bourges, died in the Blois country after 531.

St. Bova and St. Doda, her niece

Both abbesses of St. Peter at Rheims (7th century).

St. Wilfrid

Archbishop of York (d. 709).

St. Egbert

English monk, died in the island of Iona (Scotland) in 729.

St. William Firmat

Abbot of Tours in 1026, died at Mortain in 1103.

St. Mary Euphrasia Pelletier (1796–1868)

Reformed and developed the Congregation of the Good Shepherd at Angers.

April 25th

ST. MARK THE EVANGELIST (1st century)

St. Mark the Evangelist is generally identified with the person called in Acts and Epistles sometimes John, by his Jewish name, sometimes Mark, by his Greco-Roman name.

He was a cousin of St. Barnabas and a native of Jerusalem, where his mother Mary lived in a big house which served as meeting-place for the first Christian community. St. Peter went there directly on leaving the dungeon where Herod Agrippa had imprisoned him. Rhoda, a young servant, came to let him in, and the apostle found numerous persons at prayer (Acts xii, 12). It was doubtless he who baptized Mark, since he calls him his "son" (I Pet. v, 13).

In the same year 44, St. Paul and St. Barnabas arrived at Jerusalem, bringing help for the Christians who were in distress because of famine. When they left again for Antioch, Mark joined them, and accompanied them to Cyprus and to the coast of Asia Minor. At Perge in Pamphylia he left them, and while they entered the defiles of the Taurus to reach the high plateau of Pisidia and Lycaonia, he returned to Jerusalem. His conduct displeased Paul and caused the difference he later had with Barnabas.

When, in the year 50, the two apostles were deliberating over a visit to the churches founded by them on their first voyage, Barnabas wished to take Mark with them; Paul opposed it, so that each went his way, Paul taking Silas and the road to Cilicia, while Barnabas sailed for Cyprus with his cousin Mark. St. Paul nevertheless bore no grudge against St. Mark, for some ten years later we find them together in Rome, and shortly before his martyrdom the apostle sent word to Mark to leave the East and return to him.

Mark was also the collaborator of St. Peter and had from him, it is believed, the facts and incidents from which he composed his Gospel. An ancient tradition makes Mark the founder of the church of Alexandria, another, more recent, affirms that he suffered martyrdom under Trajan.

St. ERMIN (d. 737)
Monk of Lobbes (Belgium).

St. HERIBALDUS (d. about 837)
Bishop of Auxerre.

St. PHOEBADIUS (d. about 393).
Bishop of Agen.

The GREAT LITANIES

On April 25th, the Romans of pagan Rome went in procession to the sanctuary of the god Robigus, who was invoked against rust (*robigo*) of wheat. The Christians of the new Rome continued to hold the procession, but in honour of the true God, and they gave their prayers to a more general object. These litanies, sometimes called the litanies of St. Mark, existed long before the feast of the evangelist was formally instituted.

April 26th

ST. RICHARIUS OR RIQUIER (d. 643)

RICHARIUS, born near Centula, in Ponthieu, learned of Christianity through two apostles named Fricor and Cadoc, who came from Ireland. After his conversion he began to travel about the country, preaching the Gospel and curing the sick. Having been almost killed by his horse, he disposed of this fiery animal and took as mount a donkey on which he read his psalter more at ease.

One day Dagobert came to visit him at the monastery which he founded at Centula. The apostle took advantage of the occasion to give him all kinds of good advice, especially to take no notice of flatterers. Pleased at this frankness, the king invited him to his table and gave him a sum of money. Other substantial alms which he received enabled him to help a great number of the poor and lepers, and even to ransom captives in England.

When he felt himself failing, Richarius had a shelter made in the forest of Crécy, not far from Argoules, some fifteen miles from his monastery. And there, alone with his disciple Sigobart, he made ready to appear before God. Shortly before he died, he said to his companion: "Farewell, my son; go and prepare my coffin. May Jesus, Saviour of the world, have mercy on me." Sigobart, in tears, went to cut a great oak in the forest, and it was first in the trunk of this tree that the body of St. Richarius was placed. It was afterwards transported to the abbey of Centula, and, a century and a half later, Charlemagne gave a golden shrine to enclose it.

ST. PASCHASIUS (d. 865)

FIRST he was called Radbertus; Paschasius is a pseudonym which he took, according to the custom of that time, in the course of his career as a writer. Some nuns had found him, a new-born child, deserted on the steps of Notre Dame of Soissons; they confided his upbringing to the monks of St. Peter. Although he had received the tonsure, Paschasius did not behave very well until his twenty-second year, when he entered the abbey of Corbie. Later he became a teacher there and contributed to making the school of the monastery one of the most famous of its time. From 822 to 849, Paschasius Radbertus travelled through France, Germany, and Italy, was present at various councils, and was often entrusted with important political and religious negotiations.

Although he was only a deacon and wished so to remain always, the monks of Corbie put him at their head in 844. Troubles broke out in the community seven years later, whether of doctrinal or disciplinary origin is not known. With humility Radbertus made sacrifice of his post to re-establish peace, and retired to St. Riquier at Centula. There he resumed his interrupted literary work, "flinging himself", as he said, "into the arms of philosophy and wisdom, so as to be fed in the autumn of life with the same the milk of Scriptures which he had imbibed in its springtime." He returned to Corbie later but lived there as a simple monk, wholly devoted to piety, and to writing the historical and theological works which have rendered him famous.

Sts. CLETUS (1st century) and MARCELLINUS (d. 304)

Popes and martyrs.

St. LUCIDIUS

Bishop of Verona (4th century).

St. TRUDPERT

Irish monk put to death near Breisgau (Germany) in 607.

Blessed ALDA

Sienese widow, member of the third order of the Sisters of the Holy Humility of Mary (1249–1309).

April 27th

ST. ZITA (1218–1272 or 1278)

THE LITTLE maid of Lucca formulated in her youth this maxim: "Do what pleases God and avoid what displeases him," and sanctified herself in her humble state.

Her parents cultivated a little piece of land near Lucca. When she was twelve, they sent her with a basket on her arm to sell the garden produce in the town. She had so much charm that she always came home with her basket empty. Among her customers the Fatinelli family was one of the richest. Zita went into their service at the age of eighteen and stayed there until her death.

She is shown to us sacrificing an hour of sleep every morning to attend Mass; continually fasting to save the greater part of her food for the poor; giving her bed to homeless women and sleeping on the floor at their feet. Her habits of piety never prevented her from being amiable and exact in her duties. If from jealousy some fellow worker misquoted her words or accused her unjustly, she believed that he only wished her well and went to thank and embrace her denouncer.

One might have thought that after so many years of service with the Fatinelli family they would have wished to treat her as a friend rather than as a servant, and would have spared her certain duties, but Zita never consented to leave to others the unpleasant tasks which she still could do. She died after five days of sufferings endured with the same joy and serenity which she had always shown.

St. THEOPHILUS

Bishop of Brescia (d. about 445).

St. ANTHIMUS

Bishop of Nicomedia, died a martyr in 303.

St. PETER CANISIUS

Jesuit, Doctor of the Church, born at Nijmwegen in 1521, died at Fribourg (Switzerland) in 1597. He passed more than thirty years in Germany, combating Protestantism and there expanding his order considerably. He is the author of numerous minor works of piety and three catechisms.

April 28th

STS. THEODORA and DIDYMUS (d. 304)

UNDER the emperors Diocletian and Maximianus, Proculus, prefect of Alexandria, had Theodora brought before him, and the following dialogue took place between them:

"Why, being free and of noble race, do you not wish to marry?"

"Because I have resolved to remain a virgin for the love of Christ."

"You know that the will of the emperor is that virgins who refuse to sacrifice to the gods shall be condemned to dishonour."

"If I am outraged, it will be against my will; I will never voluntarily commit the least fault."

"I have pity on your beauty; do not cover yourself with disgrace; do not make your family ashamed; do not oblige me to treat you as a slave to carry out the will of the emperors."

After having in vain given her three days to reflect, the prefect had Theodora taken to a house of ill fame. As she was entering it, a Christian soldier named Didymus ran up, saying to her: "I have come the first, to save you. Exchange clothes with me and leave here under God's protection." Theodora fled.

To the libertine who presented himself shortly afterwards, Didymus, lifting the virgin's veil which covered his head, declared: "You see that the

Lord has wished to favour both the virgin and the soldier: the virgin in saving her from your impure hands, the soldier in delivering him to you to be led to martyrdom."

Led before Proculus, Didymus openly rejoiced at having spared an innocent girl from dishonour and having himself been worthy to confess his faith. This double crime cost him his head and the burning of his body.

The *Acts* which we have just summarized say nothing of what happened to Theodora, who had been set free; but St. Ambrose affirms that in order not to leave her liberator to die alone, she rejoined him before the tribunal and was beheaded with him.

St. ARTHEMIUS

Bishop of Sens (d. 609).

St. VITALIS and St. VALERIA, his wife

It is said that the first suffered martyrdom at Ravenna and the second at Milan (1st or 2nd century).

St. PATRITIUS

Bishop of Brusa (Bithynia), died a martyr about 360.

Blessed LUCHESIUS

First Franciscan tertiary, died at Poggibonsi in 1250.

St. LOUIS MARIE GRIGNON OF MONTFORT

Born at Montfort in 1673, died at Saint-Laurent-sur-Sèvres in 1716. He preached chiefly in Brittany, wrote a treatise on *True Devotion to the Blessed Virgin*, founded the Daughters of Wisdom and the Society of Mary.

April 29th

ST. ROBERT OF MOLESME (d. 1110)

BORN about 1024, of a noble family of Champagne, Robert entered the Benedictine monastery of Moutier-la-Celle, near Troyes, at the age of fifteen. He was named its prior while still young. Some years later the monks of St. Michael at Tonnerre chose him as abbot; they were so lax that after trying in vain to reform them, Robert left them and returned to Moutier-la-Celle. Under obedience he then took over direction of the priory of St. Ayoul.

After this had taken place, nine hermits who lived in the wilderness of Collan, not far from Tonnerre, obtained permission from the pope to have Robert as their head. He wished for nothing better than to join these fervent hermits. Judging the forest of Collan too unhealthy, however, he moved the community to the forest of Molesme.

There in huts made of branches, around a chapel dedicated to the Holy Trinity, the life of the ancient monks of the Thebaid flourished for a time. But the admiration which it aroused was fatal to Molesme. Gifts flooded in, luxurious buildings replaced the huts made of branches; manual work was abolished; laxness became such that Robert fled to live alone in retreat. An order of the pope obliged him to rejoin his abbey. This time his stay lasted for a year, but as the abuses mounted, he abandoned these incorrigible monks, taking with him Stephen Harding, Alberic, and two other monks, like himself desirous to observe St. Benedict's rule in its strict form. They attempted to settle in the wilderness of Vinic, but the bishop of Langres expelled them.

After so many trials, the time had come for the saint to realize his dream. In the diocese of Châlon-sur-Saône, Renaud, viscount of Beaune, owned a stark valley in an impenetrable forest. He gave it to Robert and his companions, who established there the monastery of Cîteaux, from which began the reform of the Benedictine order called "Cistercian."

However, Robert only passed thirteen or fourteen months at Cîteaux. He went back to Molesme where the monks were still clamouring for him; but this time he was so successful in reforming them that Molesme thenceforward rivalled Cîteaux in the strict observance of the Benedictine rule.

He lived nine years more and died March 21st, 1110.

St. WILFRID THE YOUNGER

Bishop of York (d. about 744).

St. PETER OF VERONA

Dominican inquisitor, killed by the Cathari between Como and Milan, in 1252.

St. HUGH OF CLUNY (1024-1109)

Disciple and collaborator of St. Odilo, friend of St. Anselm and St. Peter Damian, confidant of all the popes and sovereigns of his time, Hugh, during the sixty years of his rule at Cluny, played a leading part in the political and religious affairs of Christendom. It was he who arranged the meeting at Canossa, at which he was also present.

April 30th

ST. MAXIMUS (d. 250)

WITH few omissions, we here translate the *Acts* of the passion of St. Maximus. These are considered a model of what are called "the proconsular acts," which were made from a text furnished by the clerk of the tribunal examining the martyrs.

"In order to suppress the Christian religion, the Emperor Decius had published throughout the Empire a decree ordering the adoration of the idols under pain of torture. Maximus, a native of Asia, a man of the people, and a merchant by calling, was taken before the consul Optimus. After making him undergo a preliminary interrogation to which the accused answered by declaring his name, profession, and status as a Christian, Optimus said to him:

" 'Do you not know the decrees of our invincible emperors?'

" 'Which decrees?'

" 'By which the Christians must deny their superstitions, recognize the true ruler, and worship the gods.

" 'I have knowledge of this unjust edict; that is why I have declared myself a Christian.'

" 'Sacrifice to the gods.

" 'I sacrifice to one God alone, to whom I have had the honour of sacrificing since childhood.'

" 'Sacrifice to save your life; if not I shall make you die in torment.

" 'I have always wished it; it is in order to pass out of this short and miserable life to the life eternal that I have declared my faith.'

"Neither tortures with rods or on the rack, could change the fidelity of God's servant. Finally, the proconsul pronounced his sentence: 'For having infringed our holy laws and refused to sacrifice to Diana the Great, this man is condemned to be stoned.' Then the athlete of Christ was led by the servants of the devil outside the walls and there expired under a hail of stones. This happened on May 14th in the province of Asia."

Sts. LOUIS, AMATOR, and PETER

Killed by the Moors at Cordova in 855.

Sts. MARIANUS and JAMES

Died as martyrs at Lambesa (Numidia) in 259.

St. Suitbert the Younger (d. 807)

English by birth, he worked for the conversion of the Saxons conquered by Charlemagne, and died bishop of Werden (Westphalia).

St. Catherine of Siena (1347–1380)

Celebrated Dominican tertiary, favoured with extraordinary graces and revelations, one of the greatest mystics of the West. She had numerous disciples, reconciled enemy factions, made distant journeys, wrote to all the rulers in Europe, tried to bring back the popes from Avignon to Rome, worked for the extinction of schism, and exercised a great influence on the political affairs of the Church. It is above all in her *Letters* and her *Dialogue* that her spiritual doctrine is set forth.

St. Joseph Benedict Cottolengo

Born at Bra (Piedmont) in 1786, died at Chieri (Turin) in 1842. He has been called the "Italian Vincent de Paul." He founded several institutions for men and women, devoted to penance, the care of the poor, and the rescue of the derelict.

THE SAINTS OF MAY

May 1st

ST. PHILIP (1st century)

LL THAT is known of this apostle is what the Gospel of St. John relates.

Philip, who was, it is believed, a disciple of St. John the Baptist, was one of the first to follow Our Lord. "And now he found Philip; to him Jesus said: Follow me. This Philip came from Bethsaida. . . . And Philip found Nathanael, and told him, We have discovered who it was Moses wrote of in his law, and the prophets too; it is Jesus the son of Joseph, from Nazareth. When Nathanael asked him, Can anything that is good come from Nazareth? Philip said, Come and see" (John i, 43-46).

Philip is mentioned again at the time of the miracle of the feeding of the five thousand: "So Jesus went up on to the hill side. . . . And seeing that a great multitude had gathered round him, Jesus said to Philip, Whence are we to buy bread for these folk to eat? In saying this, he was putting him to the test; he himself knew well enough what he meant to do. Philip answered him: There is a boy here, who has five barley loaves and two fishes; but what is that among so many?" (John v, 3-9).

It was through Philip, on the day following the entry into Jerusalem, that the pagans came to meet Our Lord ". . . and made a request to him; Sir, they said, we desire to see Jesus. Philip came and told Andrew, and together Andrew and Philip went and told Jesus" (John xii, 21-22).

Finally, the evangelist shows Philip interrupting Jesus during his last discourse to the apostles: "Jesus said to him, I am the way; I am truth and life; nobody can come to the Father, except through me. . . . Philip said to him, Lord, let us see the Father; that is all we ask. . . . Jesus said to him . . . Whoever has seen me, has seen the Father" (John xiv, 6-9). It is believed that St. Philip went to preach the Gospel to the Scythians, and that he died at Hierapolis, well on in years.

ST. JAMES THE LESS (1st century)

THERE were two apostles named James: James the Greater, son of Zebedee and brother of St. John; and James the Less, the son of Alphaeus and brother of St. Jude. James the Greater, whose feast is on July 25th, received his call during the early days of the ministry of Jesus Christ; James the Less was called later. It is for this reason, or because of his age that, to distinguish him from his namesake, he was called James the Less.

It is known that the first bishop of the church of Jerusalem was also called James. He enjoyed an unequalled prestige, and the part which he played in the infancy of the Church was a major one. St. Paul took great pains to remain on good terms with him; the Jewish people themselves held him in great veneration. It is said that he had passed so much time on his knees that their skin hardened like a camel's. He was arrested in A.D. 62 by the doctors of the Law who flung him from the Temple roof. As he was not dead he was then stoned, and a fuller finished him off with a blow from a crowbar. Many believe that this martyr and the son of Alphaeus are one and the same.

Sts. BERTHA and GUMBERT (d. end of 6th century)

They were related to the kings of the Franks. Married, they parted; Gumbert went to convert Ireland, where he was martyred; Bertha founded a convent near Avenay in Champagne, of which she became abbess; it was there that she was killed by her nephews who objected to her generous gifts to the churches.

St. JEREMIAS

Prophet of the Old Testament, born about 650 B.C.

St. ANDEOL

Born at Smyrna, ordained subdeacon at Lyons by St. Irenaeus, martyred in 208 at Bergoiate on the Rhône.

St. BRIEUC (d. about 502)

Born in Wales, converted at Verulam by St. Germain of Auxerre, came to preach the Gospel in Brittany and there died as a nonagenarian.

St. SIGISMUND (d. 524)

King of Burgundy, was conquered by the Frankish princes. He was thrown into a well at Coulmiers, with his wife and children.

St. THEODULF or THIOU

Abbot of St. Valery at Rheims (d. about 590).

Blessed AUGUSTIN SCHOEFFER

A priest of the Foreign Missions from Lorraine, was beheaded at Son Tay (Tonkin) in 1851.

May 2nd

ST. ATHANASIUS (d. 373)

BOTH by his writings and his heroic conduct, Athanasius made an unequalled contribution to the defeat of Arianism. It can be said that the aim of his whole life was to achieve the triumph of belief in the divinity of the Saviour.

Born in Egypt about 295, Athanasius was ordained lector in 312 and deacon in 318; he soon became secretary of the bishop of Alexandria, whom he succeeded in 328. On that occasion the faithful acclaimed him saying: "He is a good man and an excellent Christian; he is an ascetic and a true bishop."

Athanasius' episcopate continued for forty-five years and was broken six times by exiles which amounted in all to nearly twenty-two years. They were instigated by the Arians and their allies, among whom the emperor usually was. Scarcely had he entered upon his episcopal duties, when Athanasius was dismissed by Constantine, to Trier; this first exile lasted from 335 till 337. The second lasted from 339 to 346; the proscription transferred him to Rome and replaced him as bishop of Alexandria by Gregory of Cappadocia who enjoyed the favour of Constantius.

After ten peaceful years spent among his flock, Athanasius was again exiled from 356 to 362, replaced this time by George of Cappadocia. He passed these six years in the deserts of Egypt, where the monks helped him to elude the imperial envoys. Among the works which he wrote there is *The Life of St. Anthony*, patriarch of the Thebaid and his great friend, who had just died. The two last exiles of Athanasius took place in 363 and 365, and were of eight and six months, respectively.

His works include writings about Christ, works of exegesis, spiritual works, official and doctrinal letters, as well as several personal apologia. These are often very bitter, but then what did his enemies not conceive to harm him? At the Synod of Tyre, for instance, they went so far as to accuse him of the assassination of Bishop Arsenius of Ypsele, whose hand, they alleged, he had previously cut off. Happily Arsenius was found alive and well in a monastery, and he appeared with both his hands before the members of the synod.

Among the writings wrongly ascribed to Athanasius there should be mentioned the creed, composed about a century after his death, known as the "Creed of St. Athanasius," *Quicumque vult.*

St. WALDEBERT or GAUBERT (d. about 665)

Abbot of Luxeuil; replaced the rule of St. Columbanus there by that of St. Benedict.

St. EXUPERIUS and St. ZOE, his wife; Sts. CYPRIAC and THEODULUS, their children

They were a family of slaves, tortured and put to death by their master because they were Christians (d. between 117–138).

Blessed MAFALDA

Joined the Benedictines at Arauca, after the annulment of her marriage with Henry I, king of Castile (1184–1252).

May 3rd

STS. EVENTIUS, THEODULUS, AND ALEXANDER (d. 119)

THESE three martyrs were put to death in the last years of Hadrian's reign. The interrogation put to them by Aurelian, an official of the Empire, has been preserved:

The first to appear was Alexander, aged thirty, and from him Aurelian wished to learn "the mysteries of the Christian sect"; " 'Christ has forbidden us to give holy things to the dogs,' replied Alexander. 'Am I then a dog?' demanded the judge. 'You are worse than a dog.' 'Good! then I am going to have you whipped.' 'I do not fear blows which last but a moment; eternal torments, which you do not fear at all, alone make me afraid. May God grant that you do not lose your soul!' " Aurelian ordered them to tie Alexander to a wooden trestle and to torture him with burning lamps and iron claws.

Eventius and Theodulus were priests. The first, aged eighty-one, declared that he had received baptism at the age of eleven, the priesthood at twenty, and that he had just spent a year in prison. Neither he nor his companion hesitated to proclaim their intention of remaining Christians.

Eventius and Alexander, bound back to back, were thrown into a furnace. It was intended, in order to break his spirit, to force Theodulus to be present at their torture, but of his own accord he leaped into the fire and perished with his companions. A pious matron, named Severina, recovered the remains of the martyrs and interred them in a *praedium* which she possessed. Their tomb could still be seen at Rome in 1586, under the high altar of St. Sabina.

Blessed EMILY BICCHIERE (1238–1314)

Born of a wealthy family of Vercelli, she persuaded her father to build a convent at the gates of the city, and thither withdrew at the age of eighteen with a few friends; together they followed the rule of the third order of St. Dominic.

Sts. ANTONINA and ALEXANDER (d. 313)

Condemned to premises of ill repute, Antonina saw a Christian soldier named Alexander come to her, who, dressed as a woman, took her place and allowed her to escape. The ruse was discovered and both were burned alive.

St. JUVENAL

Bishop of Narni in Umbria (d. 376).

St. AUSFRID

Count of Brabant and Ruy; became bishop of Utrecht (1008).

The INVENTION OF THE HOLY CROSS

This feast commemorates the discovery of the Saviour's cross; it will be mentioned on August 18th on the feast of St. Helena.

May 4th

ST. MONICA (333–387)

SHE was born at Tagaste, now Souk-Ahras, in the department of Con-stantine. Her parents, small landed proprietors, brought her up a Christian, and married her to a pagan older than herself, named Patricius. He was a man of spirit but irascible and debauched, by whose violence and in-fidelity she suffered a great deal. She also had to put up with the caprices of an ill-disposed mother-in-law. It was through prayer and her daily attend-ance at Mass that she found patience and gentleness. She herself used to say to women who complained of being unhappy at home: "If you can master your tongue, not only do you run less risk of being beaten, but perhaps you may even, one day, make your husband better." For her part she quickly tamed her mother-in-law; as for Patricius, she ended by loving him and, after thirty years, by converting him.

She had three children, of whom one was the future St. Augustine. He was first her pride because of the success he achieved in his studies and as a teacher; then he was her sorrow through his conduct. It is known that he lived for ten years with a mistress and was a Manichean. Hoping that dis-cussions would convert her son, Monica urged a certain bishop to debate with him, but the prelate considered him too presumptuous and too good a disputant to let himself be convinced: "Content yourself with praying for him," he replied to the mother. She returned to the charge weeping, and he sent her away saying: "Go. Continue as you have done till now; it is impossible that the son of so many tears should perish." She followed this counsel, and Augustine was touched by the grace of God when he was twenty-eight.

Widowed, Monica rejoined him in Italy. It was a question which, mother or son, would advance the most rapidly in holiness. However, Monica aspired to see God, and to leave this world. "What am I still doing down here?" she said to her son. She died at Ostia as they were both to re-embark for Africa, she being fifty-six and St. Augustine thirty-three.

Blessed LADISLAUS OF GIELNOW

Lithuanian Franciscan who preached throughout Poland (d. 1485).

St. FLORIAN

Veteran of the Roman army, condemned to death for his zeal, was drowned in the Enns, near Lorch (Norica) in 304.

St. GODARD (961–1038)

Was abbot of Niederaltaich in 996 before becoming bishop of Hildesheim in 1020.

St. TITIANUS

Bishop of Lodi (d. 477).

St. MALOU

Bishop of Senlis (6th century).

St. ETHELRED

Became king of Mercia (England) in 675, abdicated in his son's favour in 705, and died abbot of Bardney in 716.

The Blessed JOHN HOUGHTON, ROBERT LAWRENCE, AUGUSTINE WEBSTER, Carthusians; RICHARD REYNOLDS, Brigittine; and JOHN HALE, secular priest; put to death in London on Cromwell's order in 1535.

May 5th

ST. ANGELUS (d. about 1222)

OF Jewish origin, Angelus was born at Jerusalem in 1185. He had a twin brother named John. Their mother had them baptized when she became a Christian, and after their parents' death both entered the Carmelite order. At the age of twenty-six, Angelus was sent to Jerusalem for his ordination. Afterwards he went about Palestine, working many miracles, for which he became celebrated. To escape his popularity he withdrew into seclusion, until the day when God inspired him to depart for Italy. No writings confirm the tradition, evidenced in certain pictures, according to which he met St. Dominic and St. Francis in Rome at the Lateran Council. In Sicily, where his fame as a worker of wonders had followed him, he wished to convert a knight of Alicata named Berenger, who was scandalizing all that district by his conduct, but the latter became enraged and had him massacred before the Church of St. James. Angelus was placed by Pope Honorius II among the martyrs.

ST. PIUS V (1505–1572)

BORN at Bosco, not far from Alexandria, in the diocese of Tortonea, he entered the Dominican order after having been a shepherd, and took his perpetual vows at the age of but fifteen years. It was then that he changed his name of Michael Ghislieri for that of Michael Alexandrinus. He studied theology at the University of Bologna and for sixteen years taught the sciences there. He was prior of the monasteries of Alba and Vigevano, delegate of the Inquisition at Como, commissioner-general of the Holy Office, bishop of Sutri and of Nepi, cardinal of Minerva and St. Sabina, and finally inquisitor-general. His election to the papacy took place on January 7th, 1566. Maximilian II in Germany, Catherine de Medici in France, and Queen Elizabeth in England caused him many and grave difficulties. On October 7th, 1571, it was miraculously told him that the Christians had won the battle of Lepanto against the Turks. It was he who named St. Thomas Aquinas Doctor of the Church, and on his orders the university professors were obliged to teach the *Summa Theologica* to their pupils. He died on May 1st, 1572, after recommending to the cardinals to give him a successor who should "only seek the glory of God, having no other interest but the honour of the Apostolic See and the well-being of Christendom."

St. JUDITH or JUTTA

Patroness of Prussia, was born in Thuringia and went to live as a hermit in the territory of the Teutonic Knights of whom Hanno of Sangherhausen, her relative, was grand master. She died near Kulmsee on May 12th, 1260.

St. AVENTINUS (d. about 1189)

Born in England, lead a hermit's life near Tours.

St. GERONTIUS (d. about 472)

Bishop of Milan.

St. NICETIUS or NIZIER

Bishop of Vienne in Dauphiny (5th century).

St. HILARY OF ARLES (d. 449)

Relative, disciple and, as bishop of Arles, successor of St. Honoratus of

May 6th

ST. EVODIUS (d. about 69)

ALTHOUGH nothing is known about the life of St. Evodius, this is not the case with the surroundings of his last years.

Antioch had in those days half a million inhabitants. Built on the Orontes in an enchanting situation, this ancient residence of the Seleucid kings had become that of the imperial legate of Syria, and was acknowledged to be one of the most beautiful places in the world. By reason of its opulence, its climate, its civil and religious feasts, its public monuments, its sumptuous dwellings, its streets paved with marble, its elegant gardens, and a thousand other adornments, Antioch was the Oriental capital of sensuousness and of beauty.

In a secluded quarter of the town there subsisted, however, an isolated group of pious Jews descended from those whom the Seleucids had attracted. If, in the course of time, their monotheism had influenced some of the pagans, they themselves had not been untouched by the pagan influence, so that hybrid and intermediate groups had been formed, in which the "God-fearing pagans" were juxtaposed with "Hellenized Jews." Through these circles Christianity penetrated to the "Greeks" or "Gentiles." Antioch was thus the first great city where was founded a Christian community composed of former pagans. Immediately after the resurrection, Paul and Barnabas carried out their ministry among them; Peter became their bishop; it was for them that the name "Christian" was coined and they were the first in history to bear it.

However, the moment came when St. Peter departed for Rome. Evodius was his successor. It is doubtful whether he was martyred. That he remained in office till about 69, when the celebrated Ignatius of Antioch succeeded him, is more certain.

St. JUSTUS (d. 168)

Bishop of Vienne in Dauphiny.

St. MAURELIUS (d. 542)

Bishop of Imola in Emilia.

Blessed BONIZELLA PICCOLOMINI CACCIACONTI

A charitable widow, who died in 1300 and is still honoured at Trequanda in the diocese of Pieza.

Blessed PRUDENCE

An Augustinian nun, died at Como in 1492.

St. JOHN BEFORE THE LATIN GATE

In the year 95, says St. Jerome, John was arrested at the order of Domitian at Ephesus, brought to Rome and, before the gate leading to Latium,
thrown into a cauldron of boiling water. After emerging from it safe and
sound, he was exiled to Patmos and, the following year, Domitian being
dead, the apostle was able to return to Ephesus.

May 7th

ST. STANISLAUS (1030–1079)

STANISLAUS became bishop of Cracow in 1072. He was born in the
town of Szezepanow on July 26th, 1030, of pious and wealthy parents. He
had studied at the universities of Gnesen and Paris and, to the edification of
all, he ascended through the different stages of the ecclesiastical hierarchy.

At that time Boleslaus II was king of Poland, a mighty warrior but a
debauched prince. Violation and rape were his regular habits, and the
abduction of Christine, wife of Count Miceslaus, finally enraged the nobles
and clergy. The archbishop of Gnesen, primate of the realm, was begged to
intervene, and, since he refused, the task of admonishing the king fell to
Stanislaus. He threatened him with excommunication if he did not mend
his ways.

Boleslaus replied by forcing the heirs of one Peter to lay claim to the estate
of Piotrawin which Stanislaus had previously bought. This Peter had
received payment before witnesses, but now the witnesses kept silence in
terror, and people began to believe that the prelate was a thief. Then, as the
biographies tell, Peter rose from the grave and came to witness that he had
received just payment for the sale.

Then Boleslaus seemed to desire to bridle his scandalous behaviour. Nevertheless, after the campaign in which he took Kiev from the Russians, drunk
with victory and popularity, he renewed his debauches. Finally, after repeating his admonitions, Stanislaus excommunicated him. As the king, contrary
to canon law, did not cease attending services in the cathedral, the bishop
announced that in the future he would celebrate Mass in the Church of
St. Michael outside the city. Boleslaus followed him there with his guards
and ordered them to arrest the prelate. But a holy fear restrained them. Then

he himself, with a blow from his sword, cleaved open Stanislaus' head, so that his brains spattered the walls.

St. MAILLARD

Bishop of Séez (d. 670).

St. HERNIN (d. 540)

Was born in England and lived as a hermit near Carhaix in Brittany.

St. DOMITIAN (d. about 560)

Bishop of Maestricht.

Blessed VILLANO (d. about 1230)

Was a Camaldulite monk of Fonte-Avellana before he became bishop of Gubbio, his birthplace, about 1206. If the story of the wolf which was converted by St. Francis at Gubbio is historical, the event took place in Villano's time.

Blessed ALBERT OF BERGAMO

Humble labourer and Dominican tertiary, died at Verona in 1279.

May 8th

ST. DESIDERATUS (d. about 555)

WE know about the life of St. Desideratus from a chronicle compiled several centuries after his death.

There we read that he was born of a distinguished family, five miles from Soissons. His father, Auginus, and his mother, Agia, raised him in the good ways which they themselves practised. When he became chancellor to King Clotaire, son of King Clovis, Desideratus discharged his office to everyone's satisfaction, except of course the heretics, murderers, and simoniacs whom he pursued relentlessly. We owe to him the building of a number of churches and the founding of several monasteries. So much did the sight of the excesses and the cruelty at court repel him, that he wished to leave the world, but his sovereign forbade him to take holy orders, saying that he could not do without him.

However, about 545, Desideratus, on the death of Archbishop Arcadius, was appointed his successor as the head of the church of Bourges. In this capacity he attended the Council of Orléans in 547, where the errors of Nestorius and Eutyches were condemned. His authority and understanding of affairs often enabled him to play the part of peacemaker in the kingdom. Thus, returning from a journey to Rome, he was successful in reconciling the Angevins and the Poitevins who had quarrelled in his absence; so also, having gone to Cologne, he succeeded in restoring peace among the German peoples who were on the point of hostilities.

Among the miracles attributed to St. Desideratus are the cure by the laying on of hands of a demoniac of Verdun, the cure of an Anjou miller of a mortal wound, and of a dying man who remained in good health for twenty years afterwards.

St. ACACIUS (d. 303)

Was a Cappadocian centurion in the Roman army, tortured and beheaded at Byzantium under Diocletian.

St. DOMINICA and St. INDRACT, her brother

Of Irish origin, they withdrew to live in a retreat at Skapwith (England). They were killed by brigands in about 710.

St. AURELIAN

He is said to have been a collaborator or successor of St. Martial, bishop of Limoges, in the days of the early Church.

St. IDA or ITA or IDUBERGA

Wife of Pepin of Landen. Widowed, she became a nun at the abbey of Nivelles (Belgium), of which St. Gertrude, her daughter, was abbess (d. 652).

St. GUIRON or WIRON (d. about 700)

A Scottish monk, who withdrew to Mont Sainte-Odile, near Ruremonde, and was the director of Pepin of Heristal.

St. PETER OF TARENTAISE

Cistercian, founder of the abbey of Tamie and bishop of Tarentaise, took sides against Frederick Barbarossa and the anti-Pope Victor III. He accomplished numerous miracles and died at Bellevaux near Besançon (d. 1174).

Blessed AMATO RONCONI (d. 1266)

Was born near Rimini; cared for the sick, made some long pilgrimages and became a lay brother at the abbey of San Giuliano.

The APPARITION OF St. MICHAEL

On Mount Gargano in the kingdom of Naples in 492.

May 9th

ST. GREGORY OF NAZIANZUS (d. 389 or 390)

A CONTEMPORARY and compatriot of St. Basil, Gregory was born at
Arianzus about 330. He studied at Athens and there taught rhetoric for
a time. Towards 359 he returned to his native country, was baptized, and
rejoined Basil at his monastery on the banks of the Iris; the two friends spent
the best part of their lives there in ascetic practices and the study of Origen.

This kind of life precisely suited Gregory, whose leanings were all towards
withdrawal and contemplation. It was with reluctance that, about 362, he
allowed himself to be ordained priest by his own father who was bishop of
Nazianzus. However, directly after his ordination he regained his seclusion
on the banks of the Iris.

The Christian East at that time was rent by doctrinal disputes, by factions
and schisms. One such occurred at Nazianzus which the old bishop could
not settle, but Gregory quickly ended it. Still reluctant and only to keep out
an intruder, he gave way in 371 to pressure from St. Basil, who made him
bishop of Sasima. He seems not to have occupied his see but to have acted
instead as coadjutor to his father. In 374 his father's death allowed him to
abandon an active life and to enter the monastery of St. Thecla at Seleucia.
There he remained till 379 when, again sacrificing himself to the cause of
peace, Gregory consented to occupy the episcopal see of Constantinople.
In 381 he presided over some stormy sessions of the second œcumenical
council, held in that city. Then he came back to Cappadocia, where again
for a time he administered the bishopric of Nazianzus.

In 383 he withdrew to his estate of Arianzus which he did not leave again
until his death. The four hundred poems which he wrote date from that
time, and of them many are touching and sometimes beautiful.

St. Gregory of Nazianzus is the supreme theologian of the Trinity. His
forty-five discourses and two hundred letters still extant show that he was
a talented orator and by temperament a gifted writer.

St. PACOMIUS (d. 348)

Born in Upper Thebaid, is one of the greatest figures of Christian
asceticism. He it was who, with St. Anthony of the Desert, laid the
foundations of the cenobitic life and who first wrote its rule.

St. GERONTIUS

Bishop of Cervia near Ravenna, put to death in 501.

Blessed ADALGAR or AUGER (d. 909)

Monk of Corbie-la-Jeune, later bishop of Bremen and Hamburg.

Blessed HANS or JOHN WAGNER (d. 1516)

Lay brother at the Ittigen Charterhouse near Schaffhausen.

May 10th

ST. SOLANGE (d. 880)

THIS little shepherdess, born in the town of Villemont, three miles from Bourges, was one of those extraordinary beings on whom heaven showers its most beguiling gifts. She was lovable, hard-working and charitable, and, moreover, marvellously beautiful.

Bernard de la Gothie, son of the count of Poitiers, was the victim of a violent passion for her, and he made her an offer of marriage. But the heart of the young girl was no longer free, having, she declared, taken the vow of virginity. In vain the young noble told her how miserable her refusal made him and enumerated the advantages which she was renouncing for herself and her family. So he resolved to abduct her, and he was carrying her off, when Solange struggled with such violence that she threw herself from his horse while crossing a stream. Insane with jealousy and furious at seeing his prey escaping from him, the abductor followed the girl and cut off her head with a stroke of his sword.

The cult of the virgin martyr has remained popular in Berry. The Church of St. Martin at Villemont, where her head is preserved, has taken the name of St. Solange. At times of general calamity and during droughts in particular, this relic used to be taken in procession through the town of Bourges.

St. ANTONINUS OF FLORENCE (1389-1459)

Antoninus or little Anthony joined the Dominicans in 1405; he was renowned as a canonist, theologian, and spiritual director; in 1418 he became a prior of his order, vicar-general about 1435, and archbishop of Florence in 1446. He has left a valuable *Summa Theologica*.

St. ISIDORE THE LABOURER (d. 1130)

Born at Madrid of very poor parents, Isidore took a post as servant to John de Vargas, a Madrid landowner who afterwards made him bailiff of his estate of Lower Caramanca. By his marriage to Maria Torribia, he had a son, who fell into a well and miraculously escaped, thanks to the prayers of his parents. The angels, it is said, sometimes helped Isidore to pull the plough. His goodness was extended to all the poor and even to the little birds, which he fed with grain during the winter.

St. GORDIANUS

A Roman judge, who was converted through witnessing the patience of the martyrs, and was himself beheaded in 362.

St. JOB

Patriarch of the Old Testament (15th century B.C.?).

Blessed WILLIAM or ANTHELM

An Irish priest, became pastor of Pontoise. Philip Augustus held him in veneration, and Anthelm died in his palace in 1193.

Blessed BEATRIX D'ESTE (d. 1226)

Daughter of the Marquis d'Este of Ferrara, died as a Benedictine at the age of twenty.

May 11th

ST. MAMERTUS (d. 477)

ST. MAMERTUS occupied the episcopal see of Vienne in Dauphiny from 364 to 477. Like St. Avitus and so many other remarkable men of the time, he was a Burgundian. Claudian Mamertus, the poet, controversialist, and philosopher, whose treatise on *The Nature of the Soul* is still valued by theologians, was his brother.

The district of Vienne at that time was the centre of great calamities; in addition to Arianism and the barbarian invasions, it was racked, say the chronicles, by continual earth tremors, mysterious forest fires, to say nothing of the incursions of bears, boars, and wolves. In such difficult circum‑stances as these our saint carried out his ministry and spread his good works abroad. He has sometimes been reproached with claiming too loudly the privileges which the Church had earlier enjoyed. His knowledge, courage, saintliness, and the gift of miracles with which he was blessed were what his contemporaries most admired.

The name of St. Mamertus is still connected with those processions of penitence called "rogations," which he was the first to introduce among his harassed and unfortunate people, and the custom later spread to the universal Roman Church. The inspiration came to him one night at Easter when a fresh fire was threatening to destroy the town of Vienne. St. Avitus expressly tells how the flames were then put out in a miraculous way. A homily, often attributed to St. Mamertus, defined the object of rogations in these terms: "Let us pray God to cure our ills, to turn misfortunes from our heads, to spare us from hail, drought, pestilence, and the fury of our enemies; let us pray for good weather, health, peace, and the remission of our sins."

St. Gengou Gangulphus

A Burgundian nobleman, suffered much from his wife's flightiness, and was killed by her accomplice near Avallon. He is the patron saint of those who are unhappily married (d. 760).

St. Majolus of Cluny (d. 994)

Born in Avignon and a canon of Mâcon, he became a monk to avoid being appointed bishop of Besançon. He was abbot of Cluny for almost fifty years. The confidence of popes and princes enabled him to exercise a wide influence, and, notably, to reform a large number of monasteries.

St. Gauthier of Esterp (d. 1070)

Abbot of the regular canons of Esterp in Limoges diocese.

The Blessed John Rochester and James Walworth

Carthusians hanged at London in 1537, for their fidelity to the Roman Church.

St. Francis of Girolamo

An Italian Jesuit, who found scope for his zeal and worked miracles in the kingdom of Naples (1641–1716).

May 12th

ST. DOMITILLA (d. end of 1st century)

THROUGH her husband Flavius Clemens, Domitilla belonged to the Flavian dynasty which gave Rome three emperors: Vespasian, Titus, and Domitian. The two first merited St. Augustine's phrase "the most lovable of the Caesars." After appearing to follow in their footsteps, Domitian showed himself proud and cruel, and the last two years of his reign were a period of persecution for the Church. He was incensed to learn that Flavius Clemens, the consul, his cousin, had embraced Christianity. He had him executed in the very first year of his consulate. And Flavia Domitilla or Domitilla was banished to the island of Pantellaria.

Some believe in the existence of a second Flavia Domitilla, a niece of the above, interned on the island of Pontia.

STS. ACHILLEUS AND NEREUS (d. end of 1st century)

ABOUT St. Achilleus and St. Nereus only two things are known for certain, the fact of their martyrdom and the place of their burial, which is at Rome in the cemetery of the Ardestine Way.

The rest is conjecture. Paul Allard gives us his in the following terms: "These two saints appear to have belonged to the pretorian cohorts under Nero, and to have taken part in the bloody executions which the evil emperors more than once ordered this privileged corps to carry out. They were distinguished soldiers and held decorations awarded by the Romans for valour. One day the new faith touched their hearts. After having been baptized, Nereus and Achilleus resigned from the service. Were they, after the succession of the Flavian dynasty, attached in some capacity to Domitilla's household? This assertion of the *Acts* does not seem improbable and would account for their burial in the cemetery of the Flavian Christians."

St. PANCRAS (d. 304)

A youth of Phrygian origin, beheaded at Rome for his faith.

St. EPIPHANIUS

Doctor of the Church (d. 403). For thirty years a monk near Eleutheropolis (Beth-Saddouk), then bishop of Constantia (Cyprus), he was a violent opponent of Origenism; he died at the age of eighty-eight.

St. MODOALD (d. 640)

Uncle of St. Gertrude of Nivelles, councillor of Dagobert I, and bishop of Trier.

Blessed IMELDA LAMBERTINI (1320–1333)

Died aged thirteen at the Dominican house of Val di Petra, near Bologna.

May 13th

ST. SERVATUS (d. 384)

SERVATUS held the bishopric of Tongres (Belgium) at a time when the whole of Christendom had Arian tendencies. The all-powerful emperor, Constantius, was a heretic and supported the heresy; many bishops no longer believed in the divinity of Our Lord; St. Athanasius and St. Hilary, great champions of orthodoxy, were in exile.

The story of the Jewish origins of St. Servatus and his kinship with St. Anne appears legendary. It is not known when he became bishop of Tongres, but by 336, when St. Athanasius spent his exile at Trier, he had already occupied the see. The declaration which he made before the Council of Cologne in 346 informs us both of his meeting with the celebrated Alexandrian doctor and of his own orthodoxy. This is what he says in reference to the bishop of Cologne, deposed on that occasion: "It is not from hearsay that I know what he has been teaching, but from having myself heard it. Our churches are adjacent; many times I have had occasion to contradict him, when he has denied the divinity of Jesus Christ. It has even happened in the presence of Athanasius, bishop of Alexandria. . . . I judge that he can no longer be bishop of Christians; and those do not deserve to be considered Christians who remain in communion with him."

After failing in his efforts to reconcile the usurper, Magnetius, with the Emperor Constantius, Servatus made a pilgrimage to Rome. He returned convinced that Tongres would soon fall to the Huns. Hastily he carried the relics of the church to Maestricht, and there, shortly afterwards, he died. The towns of Tongres remained thereafter for nearly a century without a bishop.

St. ROBERT BELLARMINE (1542–1621)

Born near Florence, he entered the Jesuit order in 1560; was ordained priest at Louvain in 1570; taught at the Roman college from 1576 to 1588; became cardinal in 1599 and archbishop of Capua in 1602. He died at Rome on September 17th, 1621. He was a firm defender of the prerogatives of the papacy and an indefatigable writer; his best-known work is a volume of *Controversies* to refute and convert the Protestants.

Blessed GERALD OF VILLAMAGNA (d. 1245)

He took part in two crusades; for some time was a prisoner of the Turks; lived seven years at Jerusalem; became a Franciscan tertiary, and ended his days in a hut at Villamagna, near Florence, his native district.

St. ROLANDA

Daughter of a prince called Didier; she lived at Cologne and died at Villers-Poterie near Charleroi. Some say she lived in the 8th century, others in the 11th. She is invoked against colic and gravel.

St. AGNES

Followed Queen Radegunde into retreat at Poitiers and became abbess of the convent of the Holy Cross. The writings of the poet Venantius Fortunatus have made her famous (d. before 589).

St. JOHN THE SILENT (454–558)

Apart from some years as bishop of Taxara (Armenia), his long life was spent in the desert, in silence.

May 14th

BLESSED GILES (d. 1265)

WE find in the story of Giles references to the practice of Satanism. And it also contains not a little legend.

Compatriot, contemporary, and perhaps fellow disciple of St. Anthony of Padua, Giles of Santarém was the son of Rodriguez of Vagliaditos, governor royal of Coimbra. He studied at the university there, received rich benefices, and was made head of an opulent abbey. He was never seen in choir, but spent his time in the study of natural science. Soon he left the direction of his monastery to his prior, and set off for Paris in order to perfect himself in medicine.

On the way he met the devil, who offered to reveal the secrets of alchemy to him. Having accepted, he was carried away by him through the air to a cavern, which both entered and where Giles studied secret things for seven years. His master had made him sign a note of hand in the following terms: "I renounce my baptism and my claim to be a son of God, to become a servant of Satan, who in return will procure for me the honours and pleasures of this world."

In Paris, Giles was a leader in the acquisition of learning and in the practice of debauchery, but he could not find happiness. One night in a dream he saw himself carried into the cemetery of his abbey; spectres danced on the tombs and cried: "Woe to thee, if thou changest not thy life!" In terror he invoked the Virgin; then the spectres disappeared, crying: "Thou art saved!"

The next day he started for home. At Valencia in Spain he made his confession to a Dominican, who gave him absolution and caused him to join the Dominican order. In 1221 he made his profession; then he was sent to the monastery of Santarém in Portugal. There, after seven years of penance and tears, he one day found to his joy on the misericord of his stall in choir the frightful written pact with the devil he had signed years ago; the Blessed Virgin had at last snatched it from the demon.

After this, Giles was employed in the preaching ministry. His inner peace, it is said, became unshakeable, and he had the gift of converting the most hardened sinners.

St. Boniface of Tarsus (d. 306)

He was a big fine figure of a man, with a heavy shock of hair, much given to wine and debauchery, and extremely generous to the poor. Master of the revels of Aglae, a wealthy and dissolute Roman lady, who was converted, he followed her example, and in order to please her went to the East in search of relics. Having reached Tarsus, he saw some confessors of the faith being led to torture, took their part, kissed their chains, and for this was condemned to death. It was his relics that Aglae received, and she placed them in an oratory fifty stadia from Rome. At a later date the body of Boniface was placed in the Church of St. Alexis, on the Aventine hill.

St. Aglae (4th century)

Has just been mentioned. Her feast may be celebrated on February 25th, on June 5th, or today.

Sts. Justa, Justina, and Henedina

Martyred in Sardinia about 125.

Sts. Victor and Cournatus

Martyred in Syria in the 2nd century.

St. Michael Garicoïts

Born at Ibarra (diocese of Bayonne) in 1797, died at Betharram in 1863; founder of the Priests of the Sacred Heart of Betharram.

Blessed Maria-Dominica Mazarello

Italian nun, foundress of the Daughters of Mary Auxiliatrix (1836–1881).

May 15th

ST. DENISE (234-250)

DECIUS (249-251) succeeded Philip the Arab, who was friendly to Christianity and even allowed the Church to possess certain lands. Decius violently persecuted the Christians and put Pope Fabian to death. St. Denise, who was martyred at Lampsaca in Asia Minor, was a victim of the same persecution.

The proconsul Optimus, during a journey through the Troas, had three Christians brought before him: Andrew, Paul, and Nicomachus. This last had first professed his faith, but, on being tortured, he apostasized and asked to be allowed to sacrifice to the gods. Permission was given; he was released. He did not have long to enjoy his apostasy, for as he withdrew, he fell in convulsions, rolled for a few moments on the ground, and quickly drew his last breath. A young girl of sixteen, named Denise, seeing this, cried out: "Ah, most unfortunate of men, who for a few more moments in this world has risked eternal torments in the next!"

Arrested in her turn, Denise confronted the proconsul before whom she was taken. "God is greater than thou," she said to him, "and if I do not in the least fear your threats, it is because the divine might can help me to suffer every torment." Optimus handed her over to two young debauchees who wished to dishonour her, but they were miraculously prevented.

Meanwhile, Paul and Andrew, who had shown themselves firm in the faith, had been beaten with rods and then handed over to the crowd to be stoned. Hearing the clamour of the crowd, Denise escaped from her prison and ran to throw herself on the bodies of the martyrs. "I would suffer with you here below," she cried, "to merit reigning with you in heaven."

And her wish was granted instantly, for the proconsul Optimus had her beheaded on the spot.

St. ACHILLIUS

Bishop of Larissa and healer, was present at the Council of Nicaea and died in 330. Since 978 his relics have been at Prisbo (Achilli) in Bulgaria.

St. DYMPNA

Daughter of an Irish prince, founded the abbey of Gheel (Belgium), and was killed by her own father (6th century).

St. RETICIUS (d. about 334)

Bishop of Autun, taught Constantine the Great his catechism.

St. RUPERT or ROBERT (9th century)

Duke of Bigen, died at the age of twenty.

St. JEAN-BAPTISTE DE LA SALLE

Born at Rheims in 1651, had as director M. Tronson of St. Sulpice; became priest in 1678 and founded the Brothers of the Christian Schools; endured innumerable persecutions and died at St. Yon on April 7th, 1719.

May 16th

ST. UBALDUS (d. 1160)

A NATIVE of Gubbio near Assisi, Ubaldus first studied in the school attached to the Church of St. Marianus and St. James; he continued with the clerics of the Church of St. Secundus; then his parents wanted him to marry, but he refused; he was ordained priest and nominated prior of the chapter of St. Marianus and St. James. Ubaldus succeeded in reforming these canons whose fervour left much to be desired. This reform took place at the time when St. Francis often passed through Gubbio and, as we learn from the *Fioretti*, there converted a very bad wolf.

In 1226, the same year in which St. Francis died, the inhabitants of Perugia chose Ubaldus as bishop. After a strenuous resistance he agreed to undertake this task at Gubbio and carried it out to perfection for more than thirty years. Like St. Francis, his neighbour and doubtless his friend, he was humble, charitable, courageous, and patient. In order to become reconciled with him, he embraced an angry mason who had thrown him into a heap of fresh mortar. He went out to meet Frederick Barbarossa, who offered him gifts instead of sacking Gubbio as he had intended. He twice broke his leg and once his arm and rejoiced in being able to practise in his turn the patience he often preached in his sermons.

St. HONORÉ

Of the family of the counts of Ponthieu, and a bishop of Amiens at the end of the 6th century. In 1204, Renaud Chérée and his wife Sibylle had built in Paris a church in his honour, and it gave its name to a street still widely frequented today.

St. JOHN OF PONUK or NEPOMUCENE

Vicar-general of the archbishop of Prague, was thrown into the Moldau in 1393 by order of Wenceslaus the Idle, king of Bohemia, for having confirmed, contrary to the ruler's will, the election of a new abbot of Kladrau (1330–1393).

St. ANDREW BOBOLA (1592–1657)

A Polish Jesuit, evangelized Lithuania; was killed by Cossacks after fearful tortures.

St. SIMON STOCK

Born in England, entered the Carmelite order in 1213; became general of the order in 1245; died at Bordeaux in 1262. The Blessed Virgin gave him a scapular in a vision.

May 17th

ST. PASCAL BAYLON (1540–1592)

PASCAL was born at Torre Hermosa in the kingdom of Aragon on May 16th, 1540. His parents were humble and pious farmers named Martin Baylon and Elizabeth Jubera. He was always very fervent and austere and seems to have enjoyed from his childhood the realization of the presence of God. From the time he was twelve till he was twenty-four he was a shepherd, watching first his father's flock, then that of Martinez Garcia, a rich land-owner of Monteforte. Having no children, Martinez and his wife wanted to adopt Pascal as their son, but he declined the offer and joined as a lay brother the Franciscan friars of the Alcantarine reform. From 1544 until his death he lived at one time or another in the monasteries of Monteforte, Elche, Jumilla, Almanzura, Almanda, Villareal, and Valencia, being at the order of his superiors in turn cook, gardener, mendicant, and porter. It was chiefly in the last two occupations that he spread his immense kindness among the unfortunate and helped them by his healing powers. Few saints in fact have accomplished as many miracles as this humble lay brother. When there was a question of his canonization, St. Bellarmine, in presenting the case, cited miracles so many and so great that a cardinal cried out before the whole consistory: "*A saeculo non est auditum tale*" (The like has never been seen).

Everyone has heard of "St. Pascal's knocks"; the liturgy itself recalls them on his feast day. They are the knocks he gives as though to make his presence known to those about whose salvation he is particularly concerned. Sometimes strong and violent, these signs provoke terror; sometimes soft and gentle, they bring hope; sometimes they are simple and clear like awaited answers or friendly warnings. They have often called to order those who are lacking in respect for the consecrated Host. They say, too, that our saint never lets his friends die without warning them, three days in advance, by sounds coming from his relics or from his images. Pascal died at the monastery of Villareal the day he entered his fifty-third year. Pope Leo XIII named him "special patron of congresses and other Eucharistic associations."

Sts. SOLOCHON, PAMPHAMER, and PAMPHALON

Martyred in Chalcedon at the end of the 3rd century. They were Christian soldiers, of whom the first was stoned and the two others beaten to death.

St. ADRIAN, martyr of Alexandria, and St. VICTOR, Roman martyr (period unknown).

May 18th

STS. CLAUDIA, ALEXANDRA, JULITTA, PHANIA, THECUSA, MATRONA, AND EUPHRASIA (d. about 305)

THE martyrdom of the so-called "Ancyra virgins" took place during the persecution of Galerius, the cruel Theotecne being governor of Galatia. Three of them, Alexandra, Phania, and Thecusa, were members of a penitent sisterhood; the four others, Claudia, Julitta, Matrona, and Euphrasia, served God in the world. The circumstances of their deaths are known to us from the *Passion of St. Theodotus,* which, although its historical validity has been questioned, does not seem entirely negligible.

This document relates that Theotecne had the seven women arrested and sought to obtain their apostasy. As they refused, he condemned them to dishonour. Throwing herself at the feet of one of the profligates who came, Thecusa, the oldest, said to him: "Young man, think of your mother, whose hair is perhaps as white as mine. I do not know if she is still alive, but I pray her to intercede for me. Let us weep in peace; Jesus Christ will recompense you." Moved, the libertines burst into tears and went away.

Each year the statues of Diana and of Minerva were bathed in a lake near Ancyra. As it was the day before this ceremony, the governor decided that the Christian virgins should play an obscene role beside the pagan priestesses. Stripped of their clothing, they had to take their places before the chariot which carried the image of the goddesses. The shameful procession set out, escorted by flute and cymbal players, and the lewd dancing of dishevelled Bacchantes. When the cortège arrived at the traditional place for the immersion, they wished to clothe the poor women in the garb in which the pagan priestesses were attired, but they resisted. Then Theotecne had them flung into the lake, where they were drowned.

However, the following night their bodies were miraculously recovered by a holy man named Theodotus, who brought them back to Ancyra, and buried them near the Church of the Patriarchs.

St. Eric

Was elected king of Sweden in 1150 and killed at Ostra-Aros (Uppsala) in 1160 or 1161. The banner of St. Eric has played the same part in Swedish history as that of St. George in England.

St. Dioscorus

Son of a lector, was martyred at Cynopolis (Egypt) about 303.

St. Felix of Cantalica (1513–1587)

Capuchin lay brother, was for forty years mendicant in the city of Rome. When he met his friend, St. Philip Neri, he expressed the wish that he might endure the most fearful sufferings for the love of God; and on his side, St. Philip wished him the same.

May 19th

ST. PETER CELESTINE (1215–1296)

In the annals of the saints the case is unique of this hermit who donned the papal tiara at almost eighty years of age, laid it down five months later, and spent the rest of his life in prison.

Peter Celestine was born at Isernia, in the Abruzzi, eleventh child of a peasant family of twelve. From his early years he had lived in the supernatural world, and was not surprised at visits from angels or at being persecuted by demons, nor by the miracles which he strewed in his way. At twenty he became a hermit and spent three years in a cave. After a journey to Rome, where he was ordained, he settled on Mount Majella, where some disciples put themselves under his direction. He imposed upon them the rule of St. Benedict, reinforced by very austere statutes. This was the origin of the Celestines, who spread through Italy, France, and Belgium. In 1274, Peter appeared before Gregory X at the Council of Lyons, to ask approval for his order, which was accorded him.

Twenty years later, he received at his cell in Morone a delegation composed of a cardinal and four bishops. They informed him that, after two years of useless discussions, the conclave had just unanimously elected him pope. He entered Aquila, riding on an ass, and was consecrated in the cathedral of that town on August 20th, 1294. The following December 13th, he solemnly resigned and fled to regain his solitude. But, fearing intrigue and possible schism, Boniface VIII, his successor, had him arrested and shut up in the citadel of Fumone. Celestine there passed his last eighteen months in a narrow cell, guarded by six knights and thirty soldiers, declaring he had never in his life been as happy. He died in 1296, on the Saturday evening after Pentecost, and was canonized fifteen years later by Pope Clement V.

St. IVES (1253–1303)

Ives Helory of Kermartin was born at Minihy-Tréguier. After having studied theology at Paris and law at Orléans, he was named ecclesiastical judge at Rennes in 1280. He then held the same post in his diocese of Tréguier where, in addition, he was successively given the pastorate of Tredrez and of Louannec. When justice and charity required it, he ceased being judge and became lawyer; he was a lawyer of a very special kind, if the following well-known little verse is to be believed:

> *Sanctus Yvo erat Brito,*
> *Advocatus et non latro,*
> *Res miranda populo.*

(St. Ives was a Breton, a lawyer, and not a thief, and that is a remarkable thing in people's eyes.)

He lived like the Franciscan tertiaries whose rule he professed, dressed in coarse burlap, penitent, poor, and joyful, caring for the unfortunate, supporting up to seven orphans in his family manor of Kermartin. It was there he retired in 1298 and died on May 19th, 1303.

St. EMILIANA or HUMILIANA (d. 1246)

Franciscan tertiary who was born and died at Florence. She was married at sixteen and lost her husband five years later.

St. DUNSTAN (d. 988)

Reformed monastic life in England; was counsellor of kings and primate of Canterbury.

St. Pudentiana (d. 160)

Roman virgin, friend of martyrs; died at sixteen.

St. Theophilus of Corte (1676-1740)

Corsican Franciscan, reformer of his order in Italy; died at Fusecchio in Tuscany.

ST. BERNARDINE OF SIENA (1380-1444)

He is one of the most original personalities and, without doubt, the most delightful preacher of the Renaissance. His sermons lasted for hours; those which reports have preserved for us are remarkably lively.

He was born at Massa on September 8th, 1380, of the noble family of the Albizeschi. Having studied at Siena all that was then taught and given all his goods to the poor, in 1402 he joined the friars minor at Colombaio. The first of his many conversions was that of a Sienese lady, who accosted him for no good purpose; he dealt her such hearty disciplinary blows on the body that he drove the demon of impurity from her for ever.

Bernardine began preaching at Milan in 1418. From 1419 to 1423 he evangelized Bergamo, Como, Mantua, Placenza, Brescia, Venice, Vicenza, Belluno, Ferrara, Bologna, and Florence. His success was prodigious; crowds came, miracles took place, factions were reconciled, and devotion to the holy Name of Jesus, which he extolled, became widespread; in public places "bonfires of vanities" were built, whereon gamblers threw their cards and women their provoking gewgaws. At Siena, in 1425, he spoke every day for seven weeks; in 1427, cited as a heretic in Rome, he was exonerated and preached for eighty days; in 1431 he toured Tuscany, Lombardy, Romagna, the Marches of Ancona; then he returned to Siena to prevent his compatriots from going to war against Florence. St. John Capistran was his friend, and St. James of the Marches his disciple. Warned against him and urged to condemn him, Martin V in 1427, and Eugenius IV in 1432, almost immediately restored him to favour; the Emperor Sigismund was among those who sought his intervention.

After 1438 Bernardine was vicar-general of the Franciscans of the Observance in Italy. This did not put an end to his preaching activities. In 1439 he addressed the Fathers of the Council of Florence in Greek. He preached right up to his death, which took place at Aquila on May 20th, 1444, as he was on his way to Naples.

St. Theodore

Bishop of Pavia (d. 778).

St. Lucifer

Bishop of Cagliari, a virulent polemist and enemy of the Arians (d. 370 or 371).

St. Austregisilus

Bishop of Bourges (d. 624). While he graced the Burgundian court, he answered those who pressed him to get married: "If I found a good wife I would be too afraid of losing her; and if you want me to have a bad one, I would rather not."

St. Ivo of Chartres (d. 1116)

Fellow disciple and friend of St. Anselm; canonist and theologian, he played a useful and conciliatory part in the Conflict of the Investitures.

May 21st

ST. THIBAUT (d. 1001)

BORN at Tolvon near Voiron, Thibaut of Vienne was of Frankish race and through his mother, great-nephew of the king of Burgundy. He was brought up at court, where King Conrad treated him as a son. When Sobonius, archbishop of Vienne in Dauphiny, died, the lords and the clergy could not agree upon a successor, and the see remained vacant until May 957, when Thibaut was elected unanimously. He used his considerable fortune for the relief of the poor and in freeing the serfs. His episcopate lasted almost half a century. He it was who, in 994, convoked an important council in the town of Anse, which brought together the bishops of the provinces of Lyons, Vienne, and Tarentaise. There the abbeys of Cluny and Romans were confirmed in their landed estates; clerics were forbidden to hunt, and priests were reminded of their obligation to observe celibacy and to carry the Viaticum to the dying.

ST. GISELA or ISBERGE (d. about 807)

GISELA was the daughter of Pepin the Short and sister of Charlemagne. Pope Stephen II was her godfather, and when he came to France towards the end of 753, he was the guest of Pepin, in a town in Champagne.

Gisela passed the greater part of her life at Aire in Artois. There she met St. Venantius, a former warrior, who was living as a hermit. It was he, it is thought, who advised her to dedicate her virginity to God. She received, it seems, three offers of marriage: one from Constantine Copronyme, which her father's politics and the pope's wishes were enough to dispose of. Another came from a Welsh or Scottish prince; this time Gisela prayed to become ugly and her success put the suitor to flight; he thought better of it when he heard that she was lovely again; in a rage he had the hermit Venantius, to whom he attributed his disappointment, assassinated. On Pepin's death, Queen Bertha, his widow, urged Gisela to marry a son of the king of the Lombards, but still in vain.

Shortly after, Gisela founded at Aire a Benedictine abbey where she became a nun. There she lived thirty years, and sometimes Charlemagne came to visit her.

St. HOSPITIUS (6th century)

He lived till his death, loaded with chains, at the top of a walled tower, on the island of San Sospis at a league from the present town of Nice. He foretold the invasion of the Lombards, which, as far as he was concerned, left him in peace.

St. MAURELIUS

Abbot of the monastery of Isle, in the diocese of Troyes (d. 545).

May 22nd

ST. JULIA (6th or 7th century)

IT is believed that, taken at Carthage in the Persian invasion of 616, Julia was then sold as a slave to an Eastern merchant. This man, who had business in the West, took her with him on his journey. At Capo Corso they encountered Van or Saracen pirates. It is not known what these corsairs did to the merchant, but Julia they fastened to a cross, where she died, following the example of our divine Master. Her body was transported to the island of Gorgona, then to Italy. Later, Desiderius, king of the Lombards, gave it as a gift to one of his daughters, abbess of the Benedictines at Brescia. It was placed in the church there, which Pope Paul I came to consecrate in 763, and which became the centre of devotion to St. Julia in Italy.

ST. RITA (1381-1457)

BORN at Cascia in Umbria, baptized under the name of Margaret, Rita was compelled at the age of twelve to marry a young noble, who for a long time brutalized her, and whom in the end she tamed and loved. She mourned him greatly when he was assassinated after eighteen years of marriage. As soon as her two sons were of an age to bear arms, they resolved to avenge their father by killing his murderers. As she could not turn them from this fearful project, she prayed God to let them die in a state of grace, which was granted to her. She then entered the convent of the Augustinians in Cascia and there spent the rest of her life in suffering. A sermon of St. James of the Marches had inspired her to beg Christ to bring her, too, a crown of thorns. From that time her forehead was marked with a deep and fetid wound, and her superiors found themselves obliged to isolate her as a leper.

St. LUPUS

Bishop of Limoges from 614 to 637.

St. ATTO (d. 1155)

Born in Tuscany or in Spain, was abbot of Vallombrosa till 1130, then bishop of Pistoia. He is the author of a life of St. John Gualbert.

St. FULK

A pilgrim of English origin who died in the diocese of Aquin (12th century?).

St. HUMILITA or ROSANA (d. 1310)

The first of these names is that which she took when, after nine years of marriage, she entered religion at the same time as her husband Hugolotto. She was Benedictine abbess of Faenza, then at Florence.

St. ROMANUS (6th century)

A monk whom St. Benedict met on the road to Subiaco and who became, for a time at least, his companion.

May 23rd

ST. DESIDERIUS

THE feasts of two saints named Desiderius are kept today. One was bishop of Langres when the Vandals invaded Gaul in 407. Nothing is known of him except that he was massacred by the barbarians after his bishopric had fallen into their hands.

The other is Desiderius of Vienne in Dauphiny, about whom we are better informed. We possess five letters which Pope St. Gregory addressed to him between 596 and 601, some to recommend to him Augustine and his companions on their way to evangelize England, the others to urge the reform by him of various ecclesiastical abuses.

The age was very violent; murder and debauchery were common. At the Austrasian court, particularly, licence and murder were current. For his persevering efforts to remind Queen Brunehaut and King Thierry of their duties, Desiderius paid with his peace and his life. These sovereigns summoned him to appear at the Council of Châlon, where a plot had been laid to discredit and get rid of him. Protadius, chamberlain of Thierry, and Justa, alleged victim of the bishop, came to tell their tales of horror against him. Desiderius was condemned, deposed, and exiled. Three years later, Justa died suddenly and Protadius was killed. Shaken by this coincidence, the court recalled the exile, expelled his successor, and restored to him his bishopric. Desiderius again began to exhort Brunehaut and Thierry to observe Christian morality. His sermons so irritated them that they had him arrested in his cathedral. The soldiers charged with this mission perhaps exceeded their orders, for on reaching the place then called Priscianiacus, and today Saint⁄Didier⁄sur⁄Chalaronne (Rhône), they stoned their prisoner and beat him to death.

St. GUIBERT or WIBERT

Born about 892 in the district of Namur of a father called Lietold and a mother named Osburga, who remarried three times, Guibert became a professional soldier, then founded a Benedictine monastery on one of his properties at Gembloux. He himself became a monk at Gorze, in the diocese of Metz, and it was there that he died.

St. FLORENTIUS (d. 540)

He led a hermit's life and died near St. Vincent of Foligno. St. Gregory tells that he had five sheep and a tame bear to guard them.

St. WILLIAM (d. about 1201)

Born at Perth (Scotland), he was a baker and, to expiate some former sins, he set out on a pilgrimage to the holy places with his apprentice. The latter killed him near Rochester.

St. MICHAEL (d. 826)

Bishop of Synnada, today Tchifout-Kassaba in Phrygia.

St. JOHN BAPTIST OF ROSSI

Secular priest; born in the diocese of Genoa in 1698, died at Rome in 1764.

St. JEANNE-ANTIDE TOURRET

Foundress of a congregation of sisters of charity, which today numbers about ten thousand. She was born in the diocese of Besançon in 1765, and died at Naples in 1826.

May 24th

STS. DONATIAN AND ROGATIAN (d. 304)

THERE was a recrudescence of persecution of the Christians in 304; an edict was published by Diocletian which obliged them all to sacrifice publicly to the gods.

At that time there lived at Nantes two brothers of noble family, still young, of whom one, Donatian, had received baptism and was full of zeal, and the other, Rogatian, although having faith, had not yet been baptized. Denounced by their fellow citizens, they appeared in turn before the legate. He said to Donatian: "It appears that, not satisfied with refusing to adore Jupiter and Apollo, you propagate the cult of the Crucified and draw a great number of people after you."

"I wish," answered the accused, "to snatch them all from error and turn them towards Him who alone merits our adoration."

The judge had him put in a dungeon. He thought he would get on better with Rogatian. "Although converted by your brother," he said to him, "you have not yet been soiled by baptism; foreswear your error in order to preserve your life and merit the favour of our divine emperor."

Rogatian was no less steadfast than his elder brother. Then the legate said to the wardens: "Let this imbecile go and rejoin his master in folly; tomorrow a single blow of the sword will make them both expiate their insults to the princes and the gods."

The next day, after being tortured on the rack, the two youths had their heads cut off.

St. VINCENT OF LÉRINS (d. about 450)

Monk of the abbey of Lérins, he composed, about 434, a *Commonitorium*, or memorandum, highly valued by theologians. This work contains the famous "Canon of true faith"—*Quod ubique, quod semper, quod ab omnibus creditum est, hoc est enim vere, proprieque catholicum*—and, moreover, expounds the very fecund principle of "development of dogma."

St. SIMEON STYLITES THE YOUNGER (d. about 592)

Born at Antioch about 520, he lived from the age of seven years on columns or on pointed rocks and worked innumerable miracles.

St. MARTHA (6th century)

Wife of John of Edessa, mother of St. Simeon Stylites the Younger.

St. JOHN OF PRADO

Spanish Franciscan, martyred in Morocco in 1631.

May 25th
ST. URBAN (d. 230)

INFORMATION about this holy man is scanty. Son of an important personage of the city of Rome, Urban I succeeded Pope Callistus I on October 14th, 222. He ordained nineteen priests, seven deacons, and eight bishops; reigned seven years, eleven months, and twelve days; died May 19th, 230, and was buried, as were all the popes of the 3rd century, in the cemetery of St. Callistus.

ST. GERARD OF LUNEL (13th century)

GERARD first led a hermit's life with his brother Effernandus, in a grotto near the Pont du Gard. Both were born at Lunel, about three miles away. Together they embarked for the Holy Land at a Provençal port, but a storm surprised them in the Tuscan Sea and forced them to put in at Corneto. The idea then came to them of visiting the tombs of the apostles. After accom-plishing their devotions at Rome, they turned towards Ancona, where they reckoned to sail again and continue their journey towards Jerusalem. But Gerard fell ill on the way and died near the castle of Moncorsi. His body was buried at Montesanto, not far from Loreto, and is still venerated there in our day.

St. GREGORY VII (d. 1085)

Born in Tuscany of humble parents, he was Benedictine abbot of St. Paul, papal legate in France, and counsellor of six popes, before he himself donned the tiara in 1073. He prepared a crusade to take Jerusalem from the Turks, tried to end the Greek schism, and encouraged the conquest of England by William the Conqueror. In order to centralize the adminis-tration of the Church, he reduced the national primates to a purely honorary dignity and instituted papal legates in all countries. What historians have called the Conflict of Investitures and the struggle between the Papacy and the Empire, arose from his desire to exalt the idea of the supremacy of the Church over the temporal power. In the winter of 1077, he received the submission of Henry IV at Canossa. He died, a refugee at Salerno, on May 25th, 1085, at the time when the troops of the same Henry IV and those of Robert Guiscard were fighting over the possession of Rome.

St. JAMES PHILIPPI

Italian Servite; born and died at Faenza (1444–1483).

St. MADELEINE-SOPHIE BARAT

Foundress of the Religious of the Sacred Heart, born at Joigny (Yonne) in 1779, died at Paris in 1865.

May 26th

ST. PHILIP NERI (1515–1595)

HIS father was a notary in Florence who devoted himself to alchemy. His mother died prematurely, but she was replaced by an excellent stepmother, and Philip's childhood was happy and pure. He was born poet, musician, psychologist, and non-conformist. He was quick to seize the pleasing side of things and showed in everything an attractive freedom and originality of spirit.

When he was seventeen his father persuaded him to visit an uncle from whom he had expectations, who had a business at San Germano at the foot of Monte Cassino. Philip set out, but arriving at his destination, he neglected his business and expectations and devoted himself to piety under the guidance of a Benedictine from the nearby monastery.

Three years later, about 1536, he arrived in Rome. It appears that he lodged there for fourteen years with his compatriot, Galeotto Caccia, director of pontifical taxes. He gave lessons to the sons of his host, studied theology with the Augustinians and spent late nights in the churches and the cata, combs, preached in the streets, visited the hospitals and slums, converted rich and poor, made friends among the intelligentsia, and became affiliated with the confraternity of the "Oratory," whose name was soon to serve to designate his own work and his congregation.

This was formed between 1551, when Philip entered the priesthood, and 1572, when we find him at the head of an important group, including specifically Tarugi, later archbishop of Avignon, and Baronius, author of the *Annales Ecclesiastici*. It received its definitive approval in the bull of July 15th, 1575, spread to Naples in 1585, and later to France.

Philip Neri was one of the most popular saints; everyone loved and venerated him. God gave him a foretaste of celestial happiness during his lifetime. "Enough, Lord, enough!" he often said. "Hold back, I implore, the floods of Your grace." Or again, "Withdraw Thyself, Lord, I am but a mortal; I cannot bear so much joy." He was also heard to declare that "for one who truly loves God, there is nothing more difficult and painful than to remain alive."

St. Eleutherius

Pope (d. 189).

St. Mariana de Paredes (1618–1645)

Born and died at Quito; she was not able to realize her desire of becoming a Dominican nun and lived a contemplative life in the home of her relatives. During the earthquake at Quito in 1645 she offered herself as a victim to divine justice for the deliverance of her city. The Republic of Ecuador has conferred on her the title of "national heroine."

May 27th
ST. BEDE THE VENERABLE (673–735)

THE Venerable Bede was born at the time of the completion of the conversion of England begun about the year 600, as is well known, by St. Augustine of Canterbury. He himself, shortly before his death, outlined his life in the epilogue of his English history.

"I, Bede, servant of Christ and priest of the abbey of St. Peter and St. Paul at Wearmouth and Jarrow, have compiled this history, with the help of God, using for it old documents, ancient traditions, and what I have been able to see with my own eyes. Born in the neighbourhood of the said monastery, I was only seven years old when my parents confided me to the care of the Abbot Benedict (Biscop). Since then I have passed my whole life in the cloister, dividing my time between study of Holy Writ, regular observance and daily celebration of the Holy Office. My whole happiness was in studying, teaching, and writing. I was ordained deacon at nineteen, and priest at thirty, these two orders being conferred on me by Bishop John of Beverley. Since I became priest till the present time, when I have reached the age of fiftynine, I have employed my time in writing, for my own use and that of my brothers, commentaries on Holy Scripture, sometimes taken from the Holy Fathers, sometimes conceived in their spirit and according to their interpretation."

Setting out a list of his works, he enumerates fortyfive, some of which have been lost. Some treat of figures of rhetoric, cosmography, orthography, and even of thunder. The greater part are those works of exegesis which he has mentioned. In introducing into his country the patristic riches of former centuries, Bede did for England what Cassiodorus, Gregory of Tours, and St. Isidore did respectively for Italy, France, and Spain. His poems no longer exist. Among his letters, there are some which are veritable treatises. As for his *Ecclesiastical History of the English People,* which covers the period from their origins to 731, it is unanimously considered to be excellent, and to historians it is indispensable.

St. JULIUS
Christian soldier martyred at Durostorum in Mesia, at the end of the 3rd century.

St. JOHN I
Pope; victim, like the famous Boethius, of the cruelty of Theodore the Great, king of the Ostrogoths in Italy (d. 526).

St. Hildebert

Bishop of Meaux (d. 680).

St. Bruno

Cousin of Emperor Conrad II and bishop of Würzburg. He served the German emperors and wrote some commentaries on the Holy Scripture (d. 1045).

St. Eutropius

Was bishop of Orange towards the end of the 5th century.

May 28th
ST. GERMAIN (d. 576)

St. Fortunatus tells that Germain escaped death twice: first before his birth, when his mother tried to do away with him by criminal means, and afterwards when one of his aunts, whose guest he was, put poison into his drink.

Born in the Autun country, Germain pursued his studies at Avallon, passed fifteen years at the Burgundian property of one of his relatives called Scapillon, and was ordained priest by Agrippinus, bishop of Autun. St. Nectarius, successor of Agrippinus, then asked him to direct the abbey of St. Symphorian, where the monks followed St. Basil's rule.

It was about 555 that Germain was appointed by King Childebert to the bishopric of Paris. As bishop he continued to lead the rigorous life which had always been his, fasting, keeping vigils, and not permitting himself a fire at any time. One of the first miracles he accomplished was to restore King Childebert to health. Together they founded the celebrated abbey at Paris later known as Saint-Germain-des-Prés.

Germain exercised the good influence he had had on Childebert also on his successor Clotaire, and his wife, Radegonde. Widowed, she withdrew to Poitiers where she had as almoner the poet Fortunatus, who later became her biographer and that of St. Germain. The last years of the aged bishop were shadowed by the crimes and scandals of Clotaire's sons. He had, in fact, to excommunicate Charibert, king of Paris, an incorrigible adulterer. He died in his eighty-first year and was interred in the abbey he had founded.

St. Augustine of Canterbury (d. 605 or 606)

Began in 597 the conversion of England.

St. WILLIAM OF GELLONE

Duke of Aquitaine, cousin of Charlemagne, peacemaker of the Basque country, founder of the abbey of Gellone. He became a monk there in 806 and died there in 812. The troubadours often sang of him.

St. BERNARD OF MENTHON

Canon regular of St. Augustine, founded two hospices on the Alpine passes; died at Novara in 1081, according to some, in 1122, according to others.

Blessed LANFRANC (1005–1089)

Born at Pavia, he took his vows at Avranches, became a monk at Bec, and there conducted the celebrated abbey schools; was abbot of St. Stephen of Caen and died archbishop of Canterbury. He has left writings of exegesis and theology.

May 29th

ST. MAXIMINUS (d. 346 or 347)

BORN, according to some, in Aquitaine, according to others, in Dauphiny, Maximinus succeeded about 325 to Agritius, as bishop of Trier. This see was then of unequalled importance in the Church. Trier had become the capital of the Western Empire and the customary residence of sovereigns. St. Maximinus carried out his duties with wisdom and strength. He contributed by his counsel to keeping Constans orthodox when his brother Constantius allowed himself to be suborned by the Arians in the East.

It is known that they stopped at nothing to persecute the defenders of the true faith. In particular, they exiled Athanasius of Alexandria and Paul of Constantinople. These two patriarchs were warmly welcomed by Maximinus in Trier. Again back in Alexandria, St. Athanasius' praise for his benefactor knew no bounds, and he pointed him out to his colleagues in Egypt as one of the most reliable of the bishops in doctrinal matters.

Endless proceedings, discussions, and councils took place with the object of re-establishing unity in the Church. About 341, four Eastern bishops, led by Maris of Chalcedon, arrived at Trier bringing a formula which they put before the Emperor Constans. As this document was vague and ambiguous, Maximinus refused to receive the travellers into his communion. On the contrary, he immediately subscribed to the decisions of the Council of Sardica, which, in 343, exactly defined "the Procession of the Word."

The Arians, who had met at Philippopolis to counter the Council of Sardica, took care to anathematize the bishop of Trier, even fulminating a sentence of deposition against him. This was without the slightest effect, and Maximinus died soon after, revered by all his people.

St. BONNA

A Pisan virgin, she made one visit to the Holy Land, several to the apostles' tombs, and went nine different times to the shrine of St. James Compostela. She could read into hearts, lived as though accompanied by the apostle St. James, and accomplished prodigies. She died at Pisa in 1207.

St. MARY MAGDALEN OF PAZZI (1566-1607)

Florentine Carmelite, who endured unbelievable corporal and spiritual sufferings which she had asked of Our Lord.

May 30th

ST. FERDINAND (1191-1252)

FERDINAND III had as parents Alfonso IX, king of Leon, and Berengaria, daughter of the king of Castile, aunt of St. Louis.

The heir to Castile being dead, the masterful Berengaria had her son proclaimed king of Castile in 1217. Two years later, she chose a worthy wife for him in Beatrice of Swabia, by whom he had ten children. Later Ferdinand, after her death, married Jeanne de Ponthieu, whom Blanche of Castile had chosen for him. On the death of Alfonso IX in 1230, it was feared that the kingdom of Leon would fall into the hands of a daughter whom the king had had by a previous marriage, and whom he had named as his heir. Berengaria was fortunate enough to foil this plan by rallying the clergy to the support of her son, who united the two kingdoms under one sceptre.

In 1233 Ferdinand went to war with Islam, and in that year gained the victory of Xeres against Mohammed Ben Houd. Three years later he seized Cordova which the Moors had occupied for five centuries. In 1243 the kingdom of Murcia came under his sway. Finally, on December 22nd, 1248, after a siege of twenty-six months, he entered Seville, thus completing the downfall of Mohammedanism in Spain.

ST. JOAN OF ARC (d. 1431)

BORN at Greux-Domremy, about 1412, to Jacques d'Arc and Isabelle
Romée, Joan had one sister and three brothers. From the age of thirteen she
heard voices: those of St. Michael, St. Catherine, and St. Margaret. France
was then, to a large extent, in the power of the English who were in alliance
with the Burgundians. In May 1428 her voices told Joan to go and find the
king of France and to help him reconquer his kingdom. Her military
adventure lasted fifteen months, from February 23rd, 1429, when she left
Vaucouleurs, until May 23rd, 1430, when she was captured by the Burgundians at Compiègne. The twelve months which followed were those of her
Calvary.

The principal dates of her glorious career are the following: March 6th,
1429, Joan was at Chinon, where she saw the dauphin; March 28th,
theologians examined her at Poitiers; April 22nd, she left Blois to march
upon Orléans, which the English abandoned on May 8th; on June 10th,
she left for Jargeau, freed Tours, Loches, Beaugency, Patay; arrived at
Auxerre July 1st; entered Troyes July 10th; was present at the king's corona-
tion at Rheims July 17th; took Soissons July 22nd; then successively
Château-Thierry, Coulommiers, Crécy, Provins; made her entry into Saint-
Denis August 26th; was ennobled by the king, December 29th.

On July 14th, 1430, Cauchon, bishop of Beauvais, claimed her prisoner
in the name of the king of England as having been captured in his diocese.
The duke of Burgundy delivered her to him for 10,000 gold francs. She was
taken to Rouen, where, in obedience to England, Cauchon and about forty
priests, clerks, canons, and monks condemned her to the stake. She was
burned alive as a heretic and traitor, May 24th, 1431. Twenty-five years
later, at the request of her mother and brothers, her trial was reviewed and
she was cleared. Her beatification took place in 1909, and her canonization
in 1920.

St. FELIX I

Pope (d. 274).

St. VENANTIUS

Elder brother of St. Honoratus of Lérins, died at Modon (Peloponnesos)
in 374.

St. WALSTAN

Born at Norwich (England) of a wealthy family; became a servant in
order to live among and help the poor (d. 1016).

THE SAINTS OF MAY

May 31st

ST. PETRONILLA (1st century)

UNTIL the 17th century, St. Petronilla was regarded as a daughter of St. Peter and her name was held to be a diminutive of that of the prince of the apostles. In reality it derives from Petronius. A descendant of Titus Flavius Petronius, Aurelia Petronilla belonged to the imperial family of the Flavians. The emperors Vespasian, Titus, and Domitian were her relatives and contemporaries.

Some think that she was catechized and baptized by St. Peter. At least she had so much veneration and devotion for him that she deserved to enjoy his paternal affection and to be considered his privileged spiritual daughter. The *Acts* of St. Nereus and St. Achilleus relate that she was consecrated to his service. There came the day when, afflicted with paralysis, she was incapable of any work. "Why don't you cure her?" Titus asked St. Peter. St. Peter answered: "It is good for her to remain like that." God, however, restored her health and she ended her life as a martyr.

ST. ANGELA MERICI (d. 1540)

BORN about 1474 at Desenzano on the shores of Lake Garda, of a family of gentry, Angela died at Brescia on January 24th, 1540. At fifteen she had lost her parents. Taken by a maternal uncle to Salo, she entered the Franciscan third order and began to devote herself to the apostolate. For a long time this very beautiful girl fasted on bread and water, took the discipline, and slept on boards. She made numerous pilgrimages in Italy, visited the Holy Land in 1524, and was presented to Pope Clement VII the following year. In a vision at Brudazzo, God revealed to her that she would establish a "company" destined to promote the welfare of souls.

One of the effects of the Renaissance in Italy was, because of its insistence on pagan humanism, to encourage laxity of morals. It was in order to restore family morality by the Christian education of future mothers that St. Angela founded, in 1535, the Ursulines at Brescia. She wished her nuns to combine the monastic life with the education of young girls in the world. She gave them as patron the popular virgin St. Ursula who, at a time of passion and brutality, had affirmed through her martyrdom the rights of virtue in the face of wild barbarians.

St. SILVIUS

Bishop of Toulouse (d. about 400).

Blessed BAPTISTA VARANI

Born of a princely family at Camerino in 1458; died abbess of the Poor Clares of that town in 1527. She endured great sufferings, was granted revelations and, in helping Father Matthew Basci, contributed to the foundation of the Capuchin order.

St. GABRIELE DELL' ADDOLORATA

Born at Assisi in 1838, son of the pontifical governor of the city, Francesco Possenti entered the Passionists in 1856 and there took the name of Gabriel of the Virgin of Sorrows. He died of consumption during his theological studies at Isola, February 27th, 1864.

THE SAINTS OF JUNE

June 1st

ST. PAMPHILUS (d. 309)

 NATIVE OF Beirut in Phoenicia, Pamphilus studied Neoplatonic philosophy and sacred sciences at Alexandria under the learned Pierius. He was ordained priest at Caesarea in Palestine and passed the rest of his life in that centre of culture. A brilliant professor and a great booklover, he built up the library which Origen had founded there and which, according to St. Isidore, contained as many as thirty thousand volumes. It is said that he copied with his own hand the twenty-five books of Origen's commentaries on the minor prophets. St. Jerome, who rediscovered this manuscript, considered it a treasure. It was from the library at Caesarea that Eusebius drew the material for his famous *Ecclesiastical History*, and so great was his gratitude to his master that later he called himself Eusebius of Pamphilus.

Under Maximinus, Pamphilus was arrested by Urbanus, governor of Palestine, and, after various tortures, was thrown into prison half dead. There he remained, forgotten, for two years, Urbanus himself in the meanwhile having been disgraced and beheaded. Pamphilus profited by the delay to write with Eusebius, his companion in captivity, an *Apology for Origen* and was not executed until 309.

ST. CAPRASIUS (d. 430)

ON Caprasius falls the glory of having inaugurated religious life on the island of Lérins. The fame of his sanctity drew thither several disciples, notably St. Honoratus and St. Venantius. They were two brothers. In their company Caprasius left for the East, in order to learn what kind of life the monks of the Thebaid led. Venantius died in the course of the journey, in the Peloponnesos. Caprasius and Honoratus returned to establish themselves at Lérins; they died there within a short time of each other, and when later St. Eucherius of Lyons or St. Hilary of Arles praised the beauty of the solitary life, they joined the names of these two saints in their discourses.

St. CLAUDIUS
Bishop of Vienne in Dauphiny (5th century).

St. RONAN
An Irish hermit, who came to live and died in Brittany (5th or 6th century).

St. GERARD
Bishop of Mâcon from 886 to 926, died about 940 at the monastery of Brou, which he had founded.

St. SIMEON
A Greek monk, lived as a hermit in Palestine, travelled in the West, and ended his life as a recluse at the gates of the city of Trier (d. 1035).

St. THEOBALD (d. 1050)
Born of a family in comfortable circumstances near Mondovi; followed for the love of Christ the trade of shoemaker, street porter, and church sweeper.

Blessed HERCULANO DE PIEGARO
Celebrated Franciscan preacher; died at Castronovo (Tuscany) in 1451.

June 2nd

STS. BLANDINA, BIBLIS, POTHINUS, MATURUS, SANCTUS, PONTICUS, ATTALUS, AND OTHER MARTYRS OF THE GAULS (d. 177)

EUSEBIUS quoted in his *Ecclesiastical History* part of the letter of the church at Lyons where the circumstances of the death of these martyrs are related. There we read as follows:

"The servants of Jesus Christ who dwell in Vienne and Lyons to their brothers of Asia and Phrygia:

"They began by forbidding us to enter the public baths; then they followed us everywhere; finally all the brutalities of an infuriated mob were unloosed. Dragged to the forum, the believers professed their faith before an immense crowd. There were, alas, some ten defections. Soon, however, the most prominent people of the two churches were in prison.

"Among our slaves who were arrested, certain there were who, fearful for themselves, accused us of the worst monstrosities; there was a quite young girl about whom we were not at all certain; but she wore out the executioners, who took turns in torturing her, repeating only: 'I am Christian; we commit no wrongdoing.'

"To all the interrogations, the deacon Sanctus replied for his part: 'I am Christian,' refusing to indicate his status, name, and country in any other way. Copper sheets, red-hot from the fire were put on him; his body was nothing more than a heap of crushed limbs and charred flesh.

"Biblis, who had at first denied her faith, was put to torture to compel her to reveal the alleged crimes of the Christians. These torments made her remember the eternal torment; she recovered possession of herself, declared her faith, and even began haranguing the crowd.

"They threw the condemned into a dark dungeon; on their feet were placed wooden fetters tightened to the fifth hole. Many died by suffocation; others, contrary to expectations, survived.

"Taken before the tribunal, the blessed Pothinus, bishop of Lyons, an old man of ninety, answered the governor who asked him who was the God of the Christians: 'You will know Him when you are worthy to do so.' After having been kicked and stoned, he was dragged to prison, where he gave up his last breath.

"The first to be condemned to the beasts were Maturus, Sanctus, Blandina, and Attalus who were to provide the entertainment for a holiday. The two first were lacerated with rods as usual; then the crowd demanded that they should be seated in a chair made red-hot; till the evening they did not cease asking for new tortures for them; as in spite of all, they still breathed, they had to kill them in the amphitheatre.

"Blandina was hung by her arms to a post; but the beasts would not touch her, and she was taken back to prison. Attalus was also led back to the prison, because the governor, learning that he was a Roman citizen, declared that on this account he should be beheaded.

"Reserved for the last day of the show, Blandina and Ponticus saw all their brethren perish. Blandina never ceased exhorting her young companion, aged fifteen, who died with courage. As for her, after having been flogged, mutilated and burned, she was wrapped in a net and exposed to a bull, which played with her, tossing her into the air; then, finally, they finished her off with a sword. The pagans swore that never had they seen a woman suffer with such courage.

"For six days the bodies of the confessors of the faith were exposed to every outrage; then they were burnt and their ashes thrown into the Rhône."

St. Eugene I

Pope (d. 657).

St. Erasmus or Elmo (d. about 303?)

Is supposed to have been martyred in Campania. He is represented with his stomach torn open, tortured by executioners winding his intestines on a windlass; this has caused his invocation for intestinal maladies. Since this windlass recalled the ship's capstan, sailors took Erasmus for patron and invoked him under the name of St. Elmo. He is one of the Fourteen Holy Helpers.

St. Stephen

Bishop, martyred at Norrala (Sweden) about 1072.

St. Nicholas the Pilgrim

Also called St. Peregrinus (d. 1094), a Greek monk, whose strange ways sometimes made people mistake him for a madman. He was observed in the Pouilles preaching penitence, often surrounded by children and teaching them to sing with him the *Kyrie eleison*.

June 3rd
ST. CLOTILDA (d. 545)

AT that time three brothers divided the sovereignty of the kingdom of Burgundy: Chilperic, Godegisil, and Gundobad. When Chilperic died, Caretena, his widow, left Lyons, which fell to Gundobad, and, taking with her her daughters, Sedeleuba and Clotilda, she withdrew to Geneva where Godegisil lived. There was celebrated the betrothal by proxy of Clotilda, a Catholic princess, with Clovis, the Frankish king, still a pagan. Their wedding took place in 493.

Unfortunately, their first child died shortly after his baptism. The second, also baptized, seemed likely to succumb in the same way, but his mother's prayers saved him, and the Frankish king ceased to bear a grudge against the God of the Christians. Better still, his wife's influence over him grew to the point where at Tolbiac, expecting defeat, Clovis promised to receive baptism if Clotilda's God gave him the victory. He was, in fact, victorious and was baptized at Rheims on Christmas Day 496, with three thousand of his warriors. The conversion of the Franks to Catholicism contributed to the downfall of Arianism and the triumph of the true faith in the West.

Though Clotilda could not prevent her husband from being bloodthirsty, at least she brought him to occasional acts of generosity. The friendly relations she had with the most virtuous of her subjects, particularly with St. Genevieve for whom she built a church, are well known.

Her widowhood lasted thirty-four years and was full of sorrows. Five of her children survived, four sons and a daughter. The last was taken away from her to be married to the Arian king of Spain. Her sons committed horrible crimes: Childebert and Clotaire went so far as to stab the children of their brother, Clodomir, in her presence. Then Clotilda retired to Tours, near St. Martin's tomb, where she passed her last years in the construction of numerous churches and in prayer. After her death, her body was taken to Paris and placed in the Basilica of St. Genevieve beside Clovis and the patroness of Paris.

St. LIPHARDUS and St. URBICIUS (6th century)

Formerly a judge at Orléans, Liphardus founded a monastery at Meung-sur-Loire, of which he was the first abbot. Urbicius, his disciple, succeeded him.

St. GENESIUS

Bishop of Clermont in Auvergne, died about 660.

St. MORAND

Monk of Cluny, founder of the monastery of St. Christopher at Altkirch. It is said that he lived the whole of Lent on one bunch of grapes. Here and there wine growers have taken him as patron.

The TWENTY-TWO MARTYRS OF UGANDA

Charles Louanga, Mathias Marumba, Andrew Kagoua, Jamari Muzei and their companions, converted by the White Fathers, were put to death for the faith in 1880 and beatified by Benedict XV in 1920.

June 4th

ST. QUIRINUS (d. about 304)

THE present town of Sissek, on the Sava in Croatia, was already important when Quirinus occupied the episcopal see. Maximus, magistrate of the place, ordered his arrest. Having been warned, the bishop took flight, but his hiding-place was discovered and he was brought before the judge who reproached him with having fled.

"I did it in obedience to my Master," replied the accused, "for it is written: 'If they persecute you in one town, flee to another.'"

"You see that your God is powerless to save you from the hands of the divine emperors."

"Our God never abandons us. He was with me in my hiding-place; he was there when he allowed you to find me; he is with me now to help me proclaim my faith."

Maximus ordered him to sacrifice to the gods of the Empire; Quirinus refused; he was beaten. As he remained adamant, he was imprisoned until he could be taken before the governor of the province. Three days later, he was dispatched by Sopron to Sarvar, at the confluence of the Guntz and the Raab rivers. There the governor asked him if he agreed with the contents of the report sent by Maximus and if he intended continued violation of the imperial laws. Having confessed his faith anew, Quirinus was thrown into the Guntz, a rock tied round his neck.

ST. OPTATUS (d. after 384)

ST. OPTATUS, bishop of Milevis in Numidia, is ranked among the great defenders of orthodoxy. A native of Africa converted from paganism, he was gifted as a writer and polemist. This is shown in the work he composed, about 336, to refute Parmenianus, bishop of Carthage, author of a learned apology for Donatism.

This heresy, which lasted at least a century, was then general throughout Latin Africa and numbered among its adherents three hundred bishops. It had been propagated by Donatus, head of the church of Carthage, assisted by a very rich bigot named Lucilla. According to the Donatists, the Church should exclude sinners from her bosom, and these rigourists denied all validity to the sacraments administered by their adversaries.

In his refutation, Optatus showed that, in addition to their doctrinal errors, the Donatists were schismatics and rebels. He also used irony as when, for example, he scoffed at his opponents for the destruction of Catholic altars. "Since the Eucharist only touches the sacred linen, why do you break up and burn the altars where we have celebrated Mass? For, if it exists, our impurity passes through the wood as it does the linen! Then dig out the ground; search for a pure place to offer the sacrifice; but take care to dig as deep as hell, where you will find Core, Dathan, and Abiron, your true masters."

The year of St. Optatus' death is not known, but he was still alive in 384.

St. SATURNINE (period unknown)

It is said that she fled from Germany to avoid marriage but was caught near Arras by her suitor who killed her.

St. VINCENZA GEROSA (1784–1847)

Foundress with St. Bartolomea Capitanio, of the Sisters of Charity of Lovere, devoted to the education of girls and the care of the sick. This congregation, native to the diocese of Brescia, today numbers seven thousand nuns throughout the world.

St. FRANCIS CARACCIOLO (1563–1608)

Born of a noble family in the kingdom of Naples, he abandoned the world as the result of a sorrow, was ordained priest, devoted himself to helping those condemned to death, took part in the foundation of minor clerks regular, and became their superior-general. He had changed his name of Ascanio for that of Francis out of devotion to St. Francis of Assisi.

June 5th

ST. BONIFACE (d. 755)

HE was called Winfrid and was born about 680 in Wessex in England. At the age of seven he entered the abbey of Exeter, going later to Nursling, where he taught for several years. His dream had always been to convert Frisia and Saxony, "land of our fathers," he said, "whose inhabitants are of our own blood." After obtaining information about these countries, he went to Rome, where Pope Gregory II gave him full powers and changed his name to Boniface (he who does good).

In the Germany known as "Roman," comprising Thuringia, the Rhineland, and Bavaria, only vestiges of Christianity remained; that part of Germany known as "barbarian," Frisia and Saxony, had again become pagan. From 719 to 745 Boniface succeeded in re-Christianizing Roman Germany and in establishing an episcopal organization there which still exists. For this he secured the support of Charles Martel, founded monasteries, created bishoprics, trained missionaries, and obtained the help of a host of priests, nuns and schoolmasters who flocked from England. The influence he gained over Pepin the Short, and his own authority, enabled him, in addition, to reform the Frankish Church, then in a state of decadence.

At seventy-five, Boniface, believing that the moment had come to realize the dream of his youth, wished to undertake the evangelization of barbarian Germany. Leaving Mainz with about fifty priests and monks, he went down the Rhine towards Frisia. The flotilla anchored near Dockum in the early days of June 755, and there a band of pagans put the missionaries to death. Boniface was buried in the abbey of Fulda which he had founded. He never saw the conversion of Saxony; it was, as we know, achieved a little later by the rude sword of Charlemagne.

St. DOROTHEUS

Today is the feast of three saints of this name: DOROTHEUS OF TYRE, priest and martyr (d. about 362); DOROTHEUS OF THEBES, Egyptian anchorite and master of Palladius (d. about 395); DOROTHEUS THE YOUNGER, abbot of the monastery of Chiliocom on the Black Sea (11th century).

Blessed SANCTUS

Born in Gaul, martyred by the Moors at Cordova in 851.

Sts. FLORENTIUS and JULIAN

Martyred in an unknown period.

St. ZENAIDA

Martyred probably at Constantinople in the early centuries.

Sts. VALERIA, MARCIA, and CYRIA

Martyred at Caesarea in Palestine in the days of the primitive Church.

Blessed FERDINAND OF PORTUGAL (1402–1443)

Son of King John I of Portugal; died a prisoner at Fez, where the Moors held him as a hostage.

June 6th

ST. NORBERT (d. 1134)

BORN at Xanten in the Rhineland, about 1082, Norbert was related to the ruling families of Lorraine and Germany. His impressive good looks gained him speedy success. In his ordination as subdeacon he saw a means of opening the way to ecclesiastical honours. Up to the age of thirty-three Norbert led the life of a worldly cleric almost exclusively occupied with pleasure. Grace came to him one day when, riding towards Freten in Westphalia, he was struck by lightning and thrown from his horse. He became deacon and priest on Christmas Day 1115, gave away his possessions, and, dressed like a poor man, began to travel about the Rhineland preaching against the laxity of the clergy and the vices of Christians.

At first he was not taken seriously; he was even summoned before the Council of Fritzlar in 1118, accused of having slandered the clergy in his sermons and preached without permission. Then he went barefoot to Saint-Gilles in Provence, where Gelasius II had taken refuge. This pope authorized him to preach everywhere in the Latin Church.

Norbert again headed northwards. At Valenciennes he won over the young Hugh of Fosses, chaplain to Burchard, bishop of Cambrai. He found in him his most trusted disciple and friend, the collaborator of whom he had dreamed, his future successor at the head of the Premonstratensian order.

This name designates the institute of canons regular of which Norbert laid the foundations in 1120, in the diocese of Laon. Destined to promote the regeneration of the faithful and of the clergy, the new order spread rapidly, and in the lifetime of Hugh of Fosses numbered almost a hundred monasteries in twenty-nine provinces. Devotion to the Blessed Sacrament was especially encouraged by them. At Antwerp, in 1124, the Premonstratensians were able to answer Tanchelm's attacks against the priesthood and the Eucharist, and to convert most of the fanatical followers of this visionary.

In 1126 Norbert became bishop of Magdeburg. He died in 1134, having like St. Bernard, his contemporary, played a considerable role in the Church and done much towards ending the schism of Anacletus II.

St. CLAUDIUS (6th or 7th century)

Bishop of Besançon, or abbot in the diocese of Besançon; or, it may well be, simultaneously abbot and bishop.

Sts. ARTEMIUS, PAULINA, and CANDIDA

Roman martyrs of the 1st century.

Sts. GILBERT and PETRONILLA, and Blessed PONCIA

Shortly after his return from the second crusade, Gilbert, an Auvergne landowner, became a Premonstratensian and founded the monastery of Neuffontaines; his wife Petronilla founded that of Aubepierre of which she became abbess; Poncia, their daughter, also became a nun and succeeded her.

St. BERTRAND OF ANGOULÊME (1260–1350)

Born near Cahors, he was pastor of Creyssens and of Boulvé, canon of Angoulême (1316), cantor at the collegiate church of St. Felix of Caraman (1318), archdeacon of Noyon (1328), and patriarch of Aquileia (1334). He lived to the age of ninety without ever having a day's illness, and was assassinated between Sacile and Spilimbergo by the retainers of the count of Goritz, despoiler of the Church.

St. ALEXANDER

Bishop of Fiesole, was drowned in the Reno, near Bologna, by usurpers of church property in about 840.

June 7th
BLESSED MARIE-THÉRÈSE DE SOUBIRAN
(1834–1889)

LIKE many who founded orders, Mother Marie-Thérèse de Soubiran was disowned and persecuted by her own followers.

Born at Castelnaudary (Aude) on May 16th, 1834, she belonged to a family from which had already come St. Elzéar de Sabran, Franciscan tertiary, and Blessed Urban V, sixth pope of Avignon. At the age of fourteen she took a vow of virginity, dined off dry bread, and slept on a board.

After some time spent in a beguinage at Ghent, Marie-Thérèse tried to establish one in her own district. Gradually, the congregation of Sainte-Marie du Béguinage was transformed, called the Society of Mary Auxiliatrix, and in 1869, received pontifical approbation. Poor young girls were its special concern; perpetual adoration of the Blessed Sacrament was practised by it.

During the war of 1870, Marie-Thérèse took refuge in London. Her trials began after her return to France. Among her daughters was an arch-intriguer who succeeded in supplanting her, even preventing her from living in her own institution. The poor foundress had endless trouble in finding a religious house which would open its doors to her. Finally, in 1874, she was received at Notre Dame de Charité in Paris. There she made her profession in 1877. Four years later she was joined by her sister, Mother Marie-Xavier de Soubiran, also expelled from the Society of Mary Auxiliatrix.

Mother Marie-Thérèse lived for fifteen years more in the congregation which had received her, employed in small duties, humble, edifying, perfectly resigned. She said "Oh! richness of the present moment, thou art infinite, since thou containest my God! Why not love you? Why not enclose myself wholly in you?" She died June 7th, 1889, and was beatified in 1946 by Pius XII.

St. ROBERT (d. 1159)

Cistercian abbot of Newminster (England).

terrible voice !

St. COLMAN

There are not less than one hundred and twenty Irish saints of this name. Today we celebrate the feast of the bishop of Dromore, who seems to have died in the middle of the 6th century.

St. WOLFGANG

After having been a monk at Reichenau, became bishop of Ratisbon in Germany, and died at Pupping in Austria in 994.

St. GOTTSCHALK and his companions

These thirty Pomeranian apostles were put to death in 1066.

Blessed ANN OF ST. BARTHOLOMEW (1549–1626)

Companion of St. Teresa, brought the Carmelite reform to France and died at Antwerp.

June 8th

ST. MEDARD (d. about 560)

AMONG the missionaries of the Merovingian period who worked for the conversion of the Franks one of the most popular is St. Medard, bishop of Noyon. He was born not far from that town, in the village of Salency and studied at St. Quentin. It is from him that St. Radegunde received the deaconess' habit when she left King Clotaire, her murderer husband.

Several sayings are still current in France which make mention of the old bishop of Noyon:

"It is St. Medard watering his colts," say the farming people, speaking of the June rains which often vex them. And again:

> Should St. Medard's day be wet
> It will rain for forty yet;
> At least until St. Barnabas
> The summer sun won't favour us.

It appears that one day in the fields, Medard took one of his father's horses and gave it to a poor man who had lost his. A deluge followed which soaked everyone except Medard who, says the legend, was not even damp. He is credited with a host of other charitable and miraculous acts in aid of the small holders and poor of his diocese.

He is also supposed to have instituted the feast called "of the rose-queen." He had arranged, it is said, that every year the revenue of a dozen acres of his ground at Salency should be given to the most virtuous girl in the village. This example was imitated here and there; and in the course of centuries an annual ceremony took place in French churches of crowning with roses the girl who had most edified the parish.

St. CHLODULPH

Became bishop of Metz in 656 and died about 660.

St. GODARD (d. about 535)

Archbishop of Rouen. Legend makes him twin brother of St. Medard.

St. WILLIAM OF YORK

Was named bishop of York by Innocent II in 1143, deposed by Eugene III in 1147, reinstated by Anastasius IV in 1154, and died shortly afterwards.

Blessed PACIFICUS OF CERANO (d. 1482)

Piedmontese Franciscan, author of a treatise on moral theology which became famous under the name *Summa Pacifica* or "Compendium of the Peaceful Conscience."

June 9th

ST. PELAGIA (d. 304)

THIS young saint was like St. John Chrysostom a native of Antioch; what we know of her comes from two homilies which he delivered in glorification of her martyrdom.

Pelagia was fifteen. Her rare beauty attracted numerous admirers, but she sent them all away because she had resolved to remain a virgin. A magistrate who was seized with a violent passion for her, using the edicts of persecution as a pretext, attempted to have her abducted by soldiers.

"Behold this tender virgin," says St. Chrysostom, "she knew only her own maiden bedchamber; suddenly soldiers burst into it and summoned her to the tribunal. No father nor mother was at hand, nor nurse, nor servant, nor neighbour, nor friend; she was alone among these ruffians . . . it was a miracle that she could have answered them, found strength to look at them, to have opened her mouth, to have breathed. There must have been something there stronger than human strength, something which came from God, for her to have kept so free and tranquil. It was because Jesus was with her, Jesus her counsel, who spoke to her heart, who strengthened her soul and drove out fear.

"Often the devil takes pride in foretelling the future. Why did he not prophesy the confusion with which he was covered on that day; for never was he more grotesque than then! Behold this virgin snared in his nets. He could not even hold her. Pelagia thought of a ruse so unexpected and so wise that the soldiers were stunned. Calmly and gaily, feigning a change of mind, she asked them to let her withdraw a moment, just for long enough to put on the finery suited to a new bride. Not only had they no objection, but they declared they were pleased to be able to bring a girl nicely turned out to the judge. And she, walking with composure out of the room, ran up to the roof of the house and flung herself into space. . . .

"And so it was that St. Pelagia removed her body from impure attack; thus she delivered her soul for its ascent to heaven; thus she rendered innocuous her mortal remains and abandoned them to an enemy."

Blessed DIANA OF ANDOLO (d. 1236)

Beautiful, intelligent and sensitive, this young Bolognese, till then very vain, was converted by a sermon and joined the canonesses of St. Augustine in 1221. Her family removed her forcibly; on this occasion she fought so hard that they had to carry her away on a stretcher with a broken rib. Two years later she became a Dominican and died aged about thirty-five. She belonged to the illustrious family of the Carbonesi; Lodrengo, her younger brother, appears in Dante's *Inferno*.

Sts. PRIMUS and FELICIAN
Roman martyrs of the first centuries.

St. RICHARD
Bishop of Andria in the Pouilles (12th century).

St. COLUMBA OF IONA (521-597)

Is one of the great figures of western monasticism. Born in Donegal in Ireland, he founded a hundred monasteries, evangelized Scotland for thirty-four years, and died at Iona (Scotland).

Blessed ANNA MARIA TAIGI (1796-1837)

Born at Siena she became a housemaid in Rome; married at twenty-one a peevish servant by whom she had seven children, and for forty-seven years was a perfect wife, mother, and housekeeper.

June 10th

ST. LANDRY (d. 656?)

A CONTEMPORARY of the do-nothing King Clovis II, Landry succeeded Audebert as bishop of Paris in the year 650. He was so good-hearted he could refuse nothing to the sick or poor. During a time of famine he pawned his best furniture and some of the sacred vessels to feed the needy; therefore, he is usually shown with a basket in his hand distributing bread to the starving. Certain ancient traditions attribute to him the founding of the Hotel Dieu in Paris; his statue formerly adorned it as it still adorns the façade of St. Germain of Auxerre. Landry ordered Marculph to prepare a register of those acts of the chancery by which, at that time, privileges were granted to the monasteries; this monk dedicated his work to him, and it is apparently a register of Marculph's which the bishop used in 652 to exempt the new abbey of St. Denis from the episcopal jurisdiction.

It seems that even after his death our saint did not like irreverence shown in the house of God. The bellringer of St. Germain of Auxerre, to while away the time, had played dice in the church. The following night Landry appeared to him, a whip in his hand, and so soundly beat the bellringer that his skin showed the marks for a long time.

ST. OLIVIA (9th century)

St. OLIVIA is especially honoured at Carthage and at Palermo. Even among the Mohammedans she is held in veneration; the great mosque of Tunis is called the Mosque of Olivia; who speaks ill of the saint, say the Tunisian Moslems, is always punished by God.

Unfortunately, what is known of her seems legendary. It is said that she was a ravishing beauty and was perhaps thirteen when the Saracens seized her at Palermo and carried her off to Tunis. At first she was left in peace there, but when she began to work miracles and to effect conversions, she was abandoned in a forest alone with the wild beasts. Some hunters found her and she succeeded in converting them. The exasperated Moslems then arrested her, and, after having tortured her in every way, they cut her head off. At that moment, Olivia's soul was seen flying to heaven in the form of a white dove.

St. MARGARET (d. 1093)

Great-niece of St. Edward, wife of Malcolm III, king of Scotland, mother of St. Edith and St. David.

St. MAXIMUS

Bishop of Naples and martyr (4th century).

St. EVERMUND (d. about 720)

Abbot of Fontenay-les-Louvets (Orne).

St. BARDO (d. 1051)

Abbot of Werden on the Ruhr, archbishop of Mainz, and chancellor of Conrad, emperor of Germany.

June 11th

ST. BARNABAS (d. about 60)

JOSEPH surnamed Barnabas—that is to say, Son of Consolation—was a Jew of the tribe of Levi, a native of the island of Cyprus. He came to Jerusalem and shortly after Pentecost we find him one of the most influential members of the first Christian community. At that time he sold a field, placed the price of the sale at the feet of the apostles to serve the needs of the faithful and, like St. Paul, lived thenceforward by the labour of his hands.

It is possible that Paul and he were friends of long standing; it was, in any case, Barnabas who stood surety for the convert of Damascus when he had to present himself before the apostles at Jerusalem. Otherwise, all we know of his life dates from the time when he was in touch with St. Paul.

For a long time the town of Antioch in Syria, third in importance in the Roman Empire, was the scene of their apostolic works. From there they passed to the island of Cyprus, where they made converts at Salamis and Paphos. Then they reached Asia Minor; at Perge the young John Mark left them to return alone to Jerusalem; at Antioch in Pisidia sedition compelled them to flee. They had also to flee from Iconium and from Lystra to escape death. Derbe was the last stage of this four-year journey, at the end of which the friends, retracing their steps, returned to Antioch, their point of departure. In 49, they took part in the Council of Jerusalem at which the incorporation of Gentiles into the Church was approved; then they spent a short time at Antioch; later they parted to follow their own separate paths, which would lead them both to martyrdom.

While St. Paul took with him Silas as companion and went off towards Phrygia, Barnabas took with him John Mark, whom Paul no longer needed, and returned to Cyprus, his native island. After that we lose track of him, but a tradition tells that he died at Salamis, victim of his zeal, stoned and burned by Jews from Syria.

St. ADELAIDE or ALIX

Nun of the Cistercian abbey of Cambre, at Brussels. She became a leper and blind, and ended her life in sufferings which she herself compared with those of hell (d. 1250).

St. PARISIUS (d. 1267)

Camaldolite monk, almoner of the nuns of St. Christine at Treviso for seventy-seven years, died aged a hundred and seven.

Blessed PAULA FRASSINETTI (1809–1882)

Genoese by origin, founded the congregation of Sisters of St. Dorothy for the education of girls. Before her death she saw her daughters established in Portugal and Brazil.

June 12th

BLESSED GUY OF CORTONA (d. about 1245)

BLESSED Guy Vagnotelli of Cortona is generally identified with the gentleman from whom St. Francis, about 1213, received hospitality and about whom he pronounced his eulogy on good manners or courtesy.

The *Fioretti* tells us that when Messire Guy saw Francis and his companion enter, he could not have done more to greet the angels from paradise. He warmly embraced the two friars, washed and bathed their feet, had a great fire kindled and an excellent repast brought, and while his guests were eating, himself served them joyfully. He afterward said to Francis: "My father, I wish henceforth to care for your needs, for if God has showered the gifts of fortune on me, I ought to bear witness of my gratitude by sharing them with His poor. Also, when you again need tunics and cloaks, do not hesitate to purchase them; I will pay for them."

Alone with his companion again, Francis said to him: "In truth, I have rarely seen so civil a man, and nothing would please me more than to have him as a brother. He is grateful to God for his blessings, generous to the poor and perfectly courteous towards his neighbour. For courtesy, my brother, is one of the most beautiful attributes of God, who makes his sun to shine and his rain to fall on the evil and on the good. Truly, courtesy is the sister of charity, since it quenches hate and sustains love among men. Let us then come back here one day, just in case the Lord may wish to inspire this perfect gentleman to join with us in His service."

Messire Guy did, in fact, enter the Franciscan order. He passed the rest of his life at Celles, near Cortona, in a cave at the end of a valley on the banks of a stream; and he only rarely left this retreat to preach repentance to the local inhabitants.

Guy was sixty years old when St. Francis came down from heaven and said to him: "My son, you have worked enough; in three days at nones, I will come to fetch you to take you to paradise." And it turned out as St. Francis had said.

St. PLACIDUS (d. 1248)

Abbot of Val d'Ocre (Italy).

St. ODULPHUS

Formerly parish priest in Brabant, became a missionary among the Frisians and died at Utrecht about 865.

St. JOHN OF SAHAGUN

Celebrated Spanish preacher belonging to the order of the hermits of St. Augustine, died at Salamanca in 1479.

June 13th

ST. ANTHONY OF PADUA (1195–1231)

BORN at Lisbon in 1195, Anthony was canon regular at Holy Cross at Coimbra when, in 1220, the remains of the first Franciscan martyrs were brought back from Morocco to be buried in his church. Burning to follow in the footsteps of these heroes, he left his order to enter that of the Friars Minor and set out for Morocco; but he almost immediately fell sick, re-embarked, and was thrown by a storm on to the Sicilian coast. There he joined some brothers from Messina who were going to the Portiuncula, to the general chapter of 1221. Nobody at the Portiuncula bothered about him; and they would have even forgotten to make any provision for him but for the intervention of Brother Gratian, provincial of Lombardy, who agreed to take him under his charge. Anthony lived from that time on in a cave at the hermitage of San Paolo, near Forli, leaving it only to attend holy office and to sweep the monastery. But his theological knowledge and rhetorical talents were revealed one day of ordination at Forli, when an expected preacher failed them and his brethren obliged him to speak impromptu. From then on, except for time set aside for instruction which he gave at Bologna, Toulouse, and Montpellier, he preached until the end of his life, sometimes in Lombardy where he fought the Cathari with great resource of learning; again in France where his journeys to Brive, Arles, Bourges, and Limoges are remembered; again in Padua where he died at the height of his fame, aged thirty-six. He was canonized less than a year after his death. This remarkable orator spoke every tongue, it is said, and the *Fioretti* assures us that even the fish listened to him in delight.

St. Anthony of Padua is without doubt the most popular wonder-worker of the Latin Church; his devotees and his statues are found every-where; he is invoked in every need; St. Francis de Sales asserted that he had the power of finding lost articles; Pius XII declared him doctor of the Church on January 16th, 1946.

St. PEREGRINUS

Bishop of Amiterno, was drowned by the Lombards in the Pescara, falsely accused of having betrayed them (6th or 7th century). His family name was Cetheus.

St. RAMBERT (d. 680)

Ebroin, mayor of the palace, was made falsely to believe that Rambert wished to supplant him; Ebroin banished Rambert to Bugey, and later had him assassinated at Bébron, between Bourg and Belley.

St. AVENTIN

Hermit killed by the Arabs in the Labroust Valley (Haute-Garonne) in the 8th century.

Blessed GERARD

Brother of St. Bernard, died at Clairvaux in 1138.

June 14th

ST. BASIL (330-379)

HE is one of the three "œcumenical doctors" of the Greek Church, the two others being St. Gregory of Nazianzus and St. John Chrysostom. In him were united the most varied gifts: he was both a doctrinal and a political expert; he was philosopher, orator, and ascetic; he and Gregory of Nazianzus are considered the best writers among the Greek Fathers.

What remains of his oratorical work comprises nine homilies on the creation of the world, nine others on the psalms, and twenty-four discourses upon different religious subjects; his dogmatic works include two treatises against the Arians; his correspondence comprises no less than three hundred and sixty-five letters. His ascetical writings, the *Moralia*, the *Great Rules* and the *Little Rules* made him the monastic legislator of the East, as later St. Benedict was of the West.

He was born at Caesarea in Cappadocia, of a rich Christian family with ten children. His maternal grandfather was martyred; his father was a rhetorician and lawyer; his eldest sister, St. Macrina, founded the monastery of Annesi where she lived till her death; his younger brother is called St. Gregory of Nyssa.

After intensive study at Constantinople and Athens, Basil for some time taught rhetoric; then, about 356, influenced by Macrina, he resolved to embrace the religious life, and first had himself baptized. Before retiring to the banks of the Iris and there training disciples, he visited Egypt, Syria, and Mesopotamia to learn from the great solitaries of the desert. The kind of religious life which he instituted on his return comprised manual work, study, and prayer.

Basil spent no more than five years in his retreat. About 362, Eusebius, bishop of Caesarea, ordained him priest and from 366 entrusted him, so to speak, with replacing him in everything. The task was a difficult one; the Emperor Valens had just arrived in Caesarea, resolved to make Arianism triumphant everywhere; Basil resisted him with as much firmness and tact. He succeeded Eusebius in 370; it was then that he had to engage in thorny negotiations in Rome in order to re-establish the doctrinal unity in the Church.

Meanwhile his health, already suffering from penances, gave way completely under the burden of work, cares and worry. He died at forty-nine, on January 1st, 379, venerated by Christians, pagans, and Jews, who unanimously called him Basil the Great.

Sts. VALERIUS and RUFINUS

Roman officials in charge of the imperial granaries at Bazoches (Aisne); were drowned in the Vesle (d. 4th century?).

St. ELISHA

Prophet of the Old Testament. He was associated with Elias, whose work he carried on after receiving his mantle; he died at Samaria about 830 B.C.

Sts. ANASTASIUS, FELIX, and DIGNA

Martyred by the Moors at Cordova about 852. Anastasius was an old priest of Cordova; Felix was a monk, who was a native of Getulia in Africa; Digna was a young nun whose desire for martyrdom led her to reproach the judge for his cruelty.

June 15th
ST. GERMAINE COUSIN (d. 1601)

HER father, Laurent Cousin, was a poor labourer of Pibrac, near Toulouse; her mother, Marie Laroche, died shortly after having brought her into the world. The child was born sickly, scrofulous, and with a withered right hand. All her life she was made to tend the sheep. She never had her parents' love and was denied the affection which is found in the home. Her father had nothing but aversion for her, and the second wife whom he married persecuted her incessantly. She made her sleep in the stable or upon a heap of vine twigs, beneath the stairway. The stepmother forbade Germaine access to her children, whom Germaine loved.

It seems the little shepherdess did not know how to read. Her rosary, which she always carried in her hands, and heavenly inspiration took the place of books. Every day she went to Mass, leaving her flock in God's care so that she could go to the church; and God watched over them indeed, for never were her sheep touched by one of the wolves which infested the country. It was observed that they did no damage in her absence, respecting the boundary which she prescribed for them by sticking her crook into the ground. She was also seen to cross, dry-footed, a torrent swollen with rain.

And we shall have related all that is known of her life when we have added that she gave alms by depriving herself of part of the dry bread she was given to eat. She ended her life, as she had lived it, alone, in misery, beneath the staircase of the house where her father one morning found her dead upon her vine twigs.

St. YOLANDA or HELEN

Daughter of King Bela IV and niece of St. Elizabeth of Hungary. She married Boleslaus, duke of Kalish; widowed in 1279, she entered the order of St. Clare at Sandeck; later became abbess of the Poor Clares at Gnesen, where she died in 1299.

Sts. MODESTUS and GUY or VITUS

Martyrs of the 4th century about whose life and death almost nothing is known. St. Guy became very popular after the 7th century; he has been numbered among the Fourteen Holy Helpers; he is considered as the protector of epileptics and of sick people afflicted with the dance which bears his name.

St. LANDELIN (d. 686)

Celebrated brigand who, after his conversion, founded the abbey of Lobbes and finished his life in that of Crépin (Hainaut).

June 16th

ST. QUIRICUS or CIRYCUS (4th century)

IF we are to believe his *Acts*, which unfortunately are not very reliable, St. Quiricus was, next to the Holy Innocents, the youngest of all the martyrs. For many centuries his cult has been widespread. In Palestine and Syria, in Lydia, in Pontus, in Italy, France, and England, countless churches are dedicated to him.

He was, it is said, but three years old when, to escape Diocletian's edicts of persecution, Julitta, his mother, fled from Iconium to Seleucia, then from Seleucia to Tarsus, taking the child with her. At Tarsus she was arrested and brought with her little boy before the governor, Alexander. Called upon to apostasize, she refused, and was condemned to be flogged. As she was being beaten, she kept repeating: "I am a Christian," and the infant Quiricus, whom the magistrate held on his knees, also never stopped crying: "I am a Christian." These cries finally exasperated the governor Alexander, who took the child by one leg and flung him head first against the walls of the tribunal, and his skull was broken.

Julitta blessed God for having accepted the sacrifice of her son and ended her own trial courageously.

St. JOHN FRANCIS REGIS

Jesuit, travelled in lower Languedoc, Valais, and Vivarais, preaching by day, praying by night, converting many Protestants. He died at La Louvesc (Ardèche), where his tomb continues to draw pilgrims (1597–1640).

St. VORLÉ

Hermit in Champagne (d. about 591).

St. BENNO or BERNARD

Bishop of Meissen, died in 1106. He is the patron of fishermen and drapers; he is also invoked for rain.

St. LUTGARD (1182–1246)

Flemish mystic, born at Tongres, was first a Benedictine at St. Catherine near Saint-Trond (Belgian Limburg), then a Cistercian near Couture-Saint-Germain (diocese of Namur). She lost her sight eleven years before her death.

June 17th

ST. RAYNER (d. 1160)

BORN at Pisa, Rayner was first a strolling troubadour who sang to his own accompaniment on the viol, often passing nights without sleep, as his profession required. In the castle of a noble lady in whose house he was singing his ballads, he met one day a holy man named Albert of Corsica, whom he asked to pray for him. Albert promised to do so and obtained the conversion of the minstrel. Then Rayner threw his viol on the fire and shut himself up in his room to weep for his sins. He wept so much that he temporarily lost his sight, and his conduct changed so greatly that he was thought to have gone mad.

He set out for the Holy Land and became a trader in order to pay his expenses. His biographer and contemporary Beninseca shows him rowing with the sailors, amusing them by his joyous humour, and right away making a lot of money. But one day when he opened his purse, such a stink came out that Rayner scented the devil, and resolved forthwith to do without money. He embraced perfect poverty and lived from that time on the alms given him.

His pilgrimage completed, he returned to Pisa where, after staying with the canons regular, he entered the monastery of St. Guy. There his fame for wisdom and generosity made him the guide and consolation of a host of his fellow citizens. Innumerable cures were attributed to him, not to speak of his power of calming tempests, of freeing prisoners, and driving out demons. His reputation as a wonder-worker spread abroad and long survived him, for, two centuries after his death, Queen Joanna of Aragon still held it an honour to receive his relics in Spain.

St. AVITUS

Ruled a monastery at Orléans about 525.

St. HERVÉ (6th century)

It is said that his father was the bard Hyvarnion and his mother Rivanone, that he was blind from birth, and lived as a solitary in Brittany throughout his life.

St. BESSARION

Celebrated Egyptian anchorite of the 4th century. He seems to have belonged to no monastic group; he was a kind of vagabond of God, having no possessions but a copy of the Gospels. One day he sold it to succour a poor man; his disciple Douglas reproached him. Bessarion replied: "Are you scolding me for selling the book wherein it is written: Sell all that you have and give it to the poor?"

St. MANUEL (4th century)

He is said to have been of Persian origin and a victim of the persecution of Julian the Apostate.

June 18th

ST. EPHRAEM (306–373)

CHRISTIAN literature in the Syriac tongue claims no more illustrious representative than this doctor of the Church. As an exegete, Ephraem made commentaries on almost the whole Bible and showed himself almost as learned as St. Jerome. In addition to his hymns, homilies, and instructions, which he wrote in verse to please the poetic taste of his compatriots and to match the songs of the Gnostics, he composed works upon original sin, the Eucharist, the Incarnation, and other subjects of great theological importance. He was in addition a wonderful and irresistible orator, a mystic favoured with the gift of tears, one of those extraordinary men whose sanctity impresses and pleases all here below.

Born at Nisibis, in Roman Mesopotamia, where his father was a priest of the god Abnil, while he was still young his Christian sympathies caused his banishment from his father's house. He was taken in by St. James, bishop of Nisibis, who provided for his intellectual and religious education. He received baptism at the age of eighteen at Beit-Garbayâ; lived for some time at Amid, his mother's birthplace; to make his living, took a post at the Edessa public baths; then, on the advice of a monk, went to live in the desert.

It was the period of wars between the Romans and the Persians. When the latter besieged Nisibis in 338, Ephraem came back to take his place among his fellow citizens in their trials. As it happened, the city on this occasion held out. It only fell to the Persian might in 363; then Ephraem left it for ever and took refuge at Edessa, where the Romans remained in power. It was there that he passed his last years, giving himself up to teaching and writing. He died a deacon, having always refused to be ordained priest.

Sts. MARCUS and MARCELLINUS
Roman martyrs of the 3rd century.

St. LEONTIUS
Soldier martyred in Phoenicia in the 4th century.

St. AMANDUS (5th century)
Bishop of Bordeaux, baptized St. Paulinus of Nola.

Blessed MARINA OF SPOLETO (d. about 1300)
Founded a convent of Augustinian nuns in that town and there passed her last thirty years.

Blessed HOSANNA OF MANTUA (1449-1505)
Dominican tertiary, relative and friend of the Gonzagas, dukes of Mantua.

St. ELIZABETH OF SCHÖNAU (d. 1164)
Celebrated German mystic, was a nun of the abbey of Schönau (Rhine). Her visions are related in *The Book of the Ways of God* which she dictated to her brother, the canon Egbert.

June 19th
BLESSED MICHELINA OF PESARO (1300-1356)

NATIVE of Pesaro in the Marches of Ancona, Michelina Metelli was married at the age of twelve to Lord Malatesta of the dukes of Rimini. She became a widow at twenty, and shortly afterwards her only child died.

Meanwhile, a pilgrim named Siriana had passed through Pesaro, and she had installed herself at her home. Siriana belonged to the Franciscan tertiaries. Michelina joined them also, and helped by Siriana, from that time embraced the perfect life. She distributed her goods to the poor and, after St. Francis' example, begged her bread and sought humiliations. Great temptations awaited her in her new life, as well as many trials. One of the most cruel came from her family who, pretending to believe her mad, shut her up in a tower with irons on her feet, to cure her so that she might cause them no further embarrassment. Michelina won over her jailers by her mildness and recovered her liberty. She put it to good use in redoubling her penances and prayers. She also devoted herself to the care of lepers, tending them like beloved children and kissing their leprous sores, and sometimes, they say, miraculously restoring them to health.

Michelina wanted to make use of her remaining strength to visit the Holy Land. She died returning from her pilgrimage, on the feast of the Holy Trinity, June 19th, 1356.

Sts. GERVASIUS and PROTASIUS

Martyrs, whose bodies St. Ambrose found at Milan on June 19th, 386. Their cult afterwards extended everywhere in the West.

St. JULIANA FALCONIERI (1270–1341)

Niece of St. Alexis, one of the founders of the Servites, and herself the founder of the Servite Religious of Mary. Born and died at Florence.

St. DEODATUS

Former bishop of Nevers, became a hermit in the Vosges. Some attribute to him the foundation of the monastery of Jointures (7th century).

Blessed ODO OF CAMBRAI (d. 1113)

After having been professor at Toul and Tournai, he became a monk and founded the abbey of St. Martin of Tournai. He afterwards occupied the see of Cambrai which he twice was forced to abandon; he died at Anchin where he retired. In the dispute over the Universals, he defended the realists against the nominalist Raimbert of Lille. He has left a poem on the Trojan war, an *Exposition on the Canon of the Mass*, a *Treatise on Original Sin*, and various minor philosophical works.

June 20th

ST. FLORENTINA OR FLORENCE (d. 7th century)

ST. FLORENTINA, or Florence, was born at Cartagena (Andalusia) towards the middle of the 6th century. Her mother, who was called Turtur, ended her days in a cloister; her father, who was called Severianus, seems to have been of Graeco-Roman origin. Her brothers were St. Fulgentius, bishop of Ecija, St. Leander of whom we have spoken on February 27th, and the famous St. Isidore of Seville.

Nothing is known of St. Florentina except that she was a nun and that she received from St. Leander a long and beautiful letter which has been preserved. He said to her:

"Casting about, my dear sister, for what rich heritage I could leave you, I have thought of all kinds of things, but they have seemed vain to me, and

I have put them away from me as one brushes away with the hand importunate flies. Nothing that I have seen under the sun is worthy of you; I have found above the skies that great treasure which is the gift of holy virginity, ineffable and mysterious gift which I cannot possibly praise highly enough. You and your companion are already virgins of the Lord, as the saints hope one day to be, the fine flower of the Church and its truest leaven, the offering acceptable to God and consecrated on the celestial altars. Already in fact, well-beloved sister, Christ is your spouse, your father, your friend, your heritage, your Lord, and your God."

Leander recalls to Florentina that the nuns who were born as slaves have become her equals. "If their birth made them slaves, their profession has made them your sisters. May nothing remind them of their former lowliness. Those who fight with you for Christ under the banner of virginity should taste the same joyful liberty that is yours."

He recalls the memory of their mother, and with a play upon words, exhorts Florentina to persevere in her state. "Daughter of candidness and innocence, never fly away from the roof where the turtle dove (*turtur*), our mother, has placed her young. Rest now on the breast of the Church, that mystic dove, as you used to sleep upon the heart of her who tended your infancy. Believe my burning desire to see you Christ's; I groan at the thought that another might snatch away your crown, you the better part of myself, you my buckler in Christ, my cherished gage, holy victim on whom I count to rise from the abyss of my sins."

When she died, Florentina was placed to rest at the side of Leander in the cathedral of Seville, and they were later associated in the same veneration.

St. SILVERIUS

Pope for sixteen months, died a victim to political and religious intrigues on the island of Palmaria, in November 537.

St. INNOCENTIUS

Bishop of Le Mans (d. 559).

St. GOBAN

An Irish disciple of St. Fursey, converted East Anglia (England). It is said that he went to Gaul and led a solitary life between La Fère and Prémontré (d. about 670).

St. ADALBERT or ALBERT (d. 981)

Former monk of St. Maximinus at Trier, friend and counsellor of Otto the Great; archbishop of Magdeburg. He is one of those great prelates who were both missionaries and popular leaders and who contributed to the Christianization of eastern Germany and the Slavs.

St. JOHN OF MATERA

Founder in Italy of the Benedictine congregation called *de Pulsano*, non-existent today (d. 1139).

The Blessed THOMAS WHITBREAD, JOHN FENWICK, WILLIAM WARING, JOHN GAVAN, and ANTHONY TURNER

English Jesuits hanged at Tyburn June 20th, 1679, falsely accused of having desired to kill the king.

June 21st

ST. ALOYSIUS GONZAGA (1568-1591)

THROUGH his father, Ferdinand de Gonzaga, marquis of Castiglione, and his mother, Martha de Tana Santena, Aloysius was related to the reigning Mantuan dynasty and to many an illustrious prelate. He was born at the castle of Castiglione, near Brescia, on March 9th, 1568. His mother wished him to be a churchman; his father destined him for a career of arms and, when he was four, made him put on a soldier's clothing and sent him to mix with the troops which he was raising for the king of Spain in the fortress of Casal. The child picked up some guardroom expressions for using which he never forgave himself. It was this period which he called his "life of sin" and which ended when he was seven in what he called his "conversion."

In 1577, Aloysius was at the Medici court in Florence; there he pro-nounced the vow of perpetual chastity; in 1581 he was page to the heir to the Spanish throne at Madrid; there, after having sometimes tried and failed for three hours, he succeeded in meditating for the space of an hour without distraction. His father vainly tried to turn him from a religious vocation by forcing him then to appear at the courts of Mantua, Ferrara, Parma, and Turin; on November 25th, 1585, Aloysius said farewell to the world and entered the Society of Jesus. In it he spent six years, living in turn at Rome, Naples, and Milan, and died at Rome, June 20th, 1591, having always lived as an angel and mortified himself as a penitent.

He has sometimes been ridiculed for strange mortifications: his avoidance of looking at the face of his own mother, for example, has been found exaggerated, as though it were not better to remain pure by taking too many precautions than to fall into sin for lack of them. In any case, depravity was rife in the circles in which St. Aloysius grew up, so much so that he declared bluntly: "We have no right to pride ourselves on our birth; the great are dust like the poor; perhaps their dust stinks even worse, and that is all."

St. RODOLPHE

Son of the count of Cahors, became bishop of Bourges in 840 or 841; he took part in the foundation of the abbeys of Dèvres, Végennes, and Beaulieu-sur-Mémoire, and he died in 866.

St. ALBAN

Martyred at Mainz in the 4th century.

St. EUSEBIUS

Bishop of Samosata (d. 379). Cut on the head by a brick which an Arian woman had thrown at him, he died of the wound.

St. MEEN

Of English origin, he set sail for Brittany and founded monasteries there (7th century).

Blessed JOHN RIGBY (d. 1600)

Died in England, victim of the Reformation, at the age of thirty.

June 22nd

ST. PAULINUS OF NOLA (353-431)

HIS is one of the most attractive figures of Christian hagiography. A wealthy man, who for love of God and the poor, embraced poverty; a soul, delicate and crystalline, which lived in retreat lest it be defiled; a gracious humanist who yearly offered a festal poem to St. Felix of Nola; St. Paulinus was tender, faithful, and heroic in heart, truly modelled by the Gospel. None was more loved by his friends, nor had more glorious ones: St. Martin, St. Augustine, rugged St. Jerome, St. Ambrose, Ausonius, Sulpicius Severus, the Emperor Theodosius, the Pope St. Anastasius, and so many others whose names, thanks to him, have not perished. Paulinus sent them affectionate letters, composed verses to cheer and console them. They, too, wrote to him; and they sent their disciples to him that they might be edified by his example.

Meropius Pontius Anicius Paulinus was born at Bordeaux of one of the most illustrious Roman families. Possessor of immense estates in Gaul,

Italy, and also in Spain, his wife's native country, public and private affairs led him to make many journeys. At Alcala de Henares a son was born to him, who died a week later. This fearful grief, the counsels of St. Ambrose and St. Delphinus of Bordeaux, the miracles he witnessed at the tomb of St. Felix at Nola, in addition to the influence of his pious wife, Teresia, determined him to enter the way of perfection. He received baptism at the age of thirty-eight; four years later, in 394, he was ordained priest at Barcelona, somewhat against his will; he and his wife then retired to Nola near to the tomb of St. Felix; and they lived there until their death. In 399, Paulinus was almost forced to accept a bishopric. In his last days, on his bed of sickness, St. Januarius and St. Martin appeared to him, he said, to comfort him.

The greater part of the writings of Paulinus of Nola have been lost; many which are apocryphal are attributed to him; chief among those of his authentic works which remain are fifty-one letters and thirty-six poems.

St. ALBAN (d. 287)

Was a victim in England of the persecution of Maximianus Herculius. He lived at Verulanium, later called St. Albans.

St. FLAVIUS CLEMENS (d. 96)

Former Roman consul, cousin of the Emperor Domitian, who had him executed. He was married to Flavia Domitilla, his cousin.

Sts. JOHN I and JOHN IV

Two bishops of Naples; the first died in 432, the second about 849.

St. EVERARD or EBERHARD

Benedictine abbot of Biburg, became archbishop of Salzburg in 1147 and died in 1164.

Blessed INNOCENT V (d. 1276)

Was archbishop of Lyons (1272-1273), cardinal bishop of Ostia (1273-1276), and pope from January to June, 1276. A Dominican of French origin, he had been a professor at Paris. He has left a commentary on the *Sentences*, and minor works on the unity of form, the substance of heaven, the eternity of the world, the intellect, and the will.

June 23rd

ST. AUDREY or ETHELREDA (d. 679)

MODERN calendars mention on this day St. Felix or St. Jacob. Unfortunately nothing is known of the first, except that he is venerated as a martyr at Sutri (Tuscany); and of the second, it is only known that he was bishop of Toul (8th century) and that he died at Dijon on his return from a journey to Rome.

We are better informed on St. Ethelreda or Audrey, whose name is found in all ancient calendars. She was very popular in former times and the English especially dedicated many churches to her. Born at Exning (Suffolk) she was the daughter of Anna, king of East Anglia, and sister of Sts. Withburga, Sexburga, and Ethelburga. Although it seems she had vowed her virginity to God, she was made to marry Prince Tonbert, with whom, nevertheless, she kept continence for the three years that their union lasted. Tonbert having died, she retired from the world to lead the life of prayer which was her vocation. Considerations of politics compelled her, however, to remarry to Egfrid, prince of Northumbria. The couple had vowed in the presence of St. Wilfrid, archbishop of York, their spiritual father, to live like brother and sister. Egfrid kept his word for a long time but later thought about breaking it. From then on, St. Wilfrid urged the princess to embrace the religious life once and for all. About 672 she founded two abbeys on the island of Ely, one for men, the other for women, which she ruled until her death.

Her austerity was great; except upon the chief feasts she ate but once a day; she wore inconvenient and clumsy clothing; after matins she remained at prayer in the choir until morning. An abscess of the throat from which she suffered towards the end of her life has made her the patron of those who suffer similar ills.

St. WALTHER

Pastor of Onhaye (Walloon Belgium), was killed by blows from an oar while crossing the Meuse. His murderer was a profligate companion upon whom he was urging a more virtuous life (13th century).

Blessed MARY OF OIGNIES (d. 1213)

Walloon mystic, born at Nivelles (Brabant). She lived in continence with her husband and with him cared for the lepers. Later he allowed her to retire to a cell at Oignies where she enjoyed extraordinary graces.

Gregory IX and Jacques de Vitry, her contemporaries, held her in great veneration.

St. LIETBERTUS (d. 1076)

Brabançon noble who, after a lively pilgrimage to the holy places, became bishop of Cambrai.

June 24th

ST. JOHN THE BAPTIST (1st century)

THE Precursor of Jesus was the son of Zachary of the order of Abia, and of Elizabeth, of the descent of Aaron. Zachary was one of the priests whose duty it was to burn incense in the temple. As he was ministering there, the angel of the Lord brought him the news that Elizabeth would give birth to a child who would be filled with the Holy Ghost from his mother's womb. But Zachary doubted the angel's word and was struck dumb until the moment when the promise was fulfilled. Meanwhile, the Virgin Mary had also learned from the archangel Gabriel that Elizabeth was going to be a mother in her old age, and she visited her relative for three months.

John the Baptist began his ministry at the age of about twenty-seven. He wore a tunic of camel's hair and a leather girdle; his food was locusts and wild honey. From Jerusalem and from all Judaea people came to him to receive baptism, confessing their sins. "Brood of vipers," he said to the Pharisees, "yield the acceptable fruit of repentance . . . already the axe has been put to the root of the trees, so that every tree which does not shew good fruit will be hewn down and cast into the fire" (Matt. iii, 7–10). To the publicans he recommended not to extort from anyone; to the soldiers, to be content with their pay; to men of goodwill, to give to the poor half their food and clothing.

And above all, he announced Christ's imminent coming: "I am . . . the voice of one crying in the wilderness, Straighten out the way of the Lord. . . . I am baptizing with water; but there is one standing in your midst of whom you know nothing; he it is, who, though he comes after me takes rank before me. I am not worthy to untie the strap of his shoes." After baptizing the Saviour, John gradually sank back into obscurity. "This is the Lamb of God", he said, pointing out Jesus who was passing. "Look, this is he who takes away the sins of the world." And he later said: "This joy is mine now in full measure. He must become more and more, I must become less and less" (John i, 23–30; iii, 29–30).

John still baptized for a time at Aenon, near Salim, then his best disciples left him to follow Jesus. The last part of his life he spent as Herod's captive, chained in the prison of Machaerus, and died a victim of the vengeance of a dissolute woman. Everyone knows how Herodias had his head brought her on a dish. St. Jerome adds that for a long while Herodias savagely attacked the head of the prophet, repeatedly stabbing his tongue with a dagger.

Devotion to St. John the Baptist goes back to the 4th century. The various Christian churches have rivalled one another in showing honour and respect to him of whom Jesus said: "There is no greater . . . among all the sons of women" (Luke vii, 28), and they have set him in the front rank of the saints.

St. IVAN

Hermit in Bohemia (10th century).

St. THEODULF (d. 776)

Fifth abbot of Lobbes (Belgium).

St. BARTHOLOMEW

Missionary in Norway, monk of Durham, and at the end of his life, a hermit on Farne Island on the coast of Northumbria (d. about 1190).

St. RUMOLD (d. 775)

Some say he was of Irish origin, others Anglo-Saxon; he made a pilgrimage to Rome, then settled in a hermitage near Malines; founded a monastery in that town; and died murdered by two knaves he had admonished.

June 25th

ST. PROSPER (d. 463)

THE life of St. Prosper of Aquitaine is much less well known than his work. His entire activity seems to have been devoted to the study and defence of St. Augustine.

A native of Aquitaine, he received a most thorough literary and philosophical training. He seems to have been married and soon entirely to have consecrated himself, with his wife, to the service of God. Nevertheless, he did not become a priest.

The list of his writings in verse and prose, composed to refute the Semi-pelagians and in general those who on questions of grace and predestination did not profess the Augustinian doctrines, is a long one. He blames especially

St. Vincent of Lérins and the famous Cassian. Among his works we may cite the long *Epistle to Rufinus,* a poem of a thousand hexameters entitled *De ingratis,* one hundred and six little poems composed in distichs and combined under the title of *Epigrammata ex sententiis S. Augustini,* the *Pro Augustino responsiones* and the *Liber contra Collatorem.* In 431 Prosper went to Rome and obtained from Pope Celestine a letter confirming the orthodoxy of St. Augustine and begging the Gallican bishops to put an end to their campaign against him.

He was also connected with Pope St. Leo, was perhaps even his secretary. Furthermore, St. Prosper is author of the *Chronicle,* of which the first two books are repetitions of St. Eusebius and St. Jerome, but of which the last part, covering from 379 to 455, is original and interesting.

ST. WILLIAM (1085–1142)

ST. WILLIAM founded numerous monasteries in Italy under the rule of St. Benedict. His monks were habited in white and devoted themselves especially to manual labour.

Of Piedmontese origin, he had since the age of fifteen led a life of penance and had made barefoot the pilgrimage to St. James in Galicia. He was afterwards inspired to withdraw and lead a solitary life in the kingdom of Naples, between Nola and Benevento. This splendid site, formerly sacred to the gods, was called Monte Virgiliano, in memory of Virgil who, it is said, consulted the Sibyl there. William changed this name into that of Monte Vergine or Mount of the Virgin; and there it was that he built his first monastery. He died when visiting the nuns of the abbey of San Salvatore del Goleto, which he also founded.

St. MAXIMUS (d. after 465)

Bishop of Turin; one of the lights of the Church in the 5th century. The collection of his discourses which has come down to us is almost as important as that of St. Augustine.

St. ADALBERT (d. after 714)

Of English origin, he was a disciple of St. Willibrord and his successor as abbot of Echternach (Grand Duchy of Luxemburg).

St. GOHARD

Bishop of Nantes, killed by the Normans in 843.

St. LUCY

Is supposed to have been martyred at Rome in the 3rd century.

St. AMANDUS (d. end of 6th century)

Hermit of Limoges, founder of a monastery there, later Saint‑Amand‑de‑Coly (Dordogne).

June 26th
ST. MAXENTIUS (d. about 515)

MAXENTIUS, who was first called Adjutor, was born at Agde in Narbon‑naise Gaul or Languedoc. At that time there flourished in that town a monastery ruled by the Abbot Severus. It was at the school of Severus, himself educated at that of the Orientals, that Adjutor was initiated into the religious life. He made such progress and people began to speak of him so much that he was troubled and took flight. After two years of search, his family discovered his retreat and made him return. He came back to Agde at the moment when a drought had just ended. He was given credit for having brought back the rain, whereupon he disappeared for good and all and went to settle in Poitou. There, lest he be discovered, he changed his name of Adjutor to that of Maxentius, and entered the abbey ruled by Agapit. When the latter resigned, about the year 500, Maxentius was elected to succeed him. He, too, resigned several years before his death.

Although only sixty‑two, Maxentius was so dried up by fasting that nothing but skin and bones remained; he was bent double from prostrations; on his knees were great callouses, so many hours had he passed kneeling on the stones.

ST. DAVID (d. about 540)

DAVID led a hermit's life at Thessalonica, yet not in such retirement from the world as to prevent his becoming the guide of a great number of souls. This is what Palladius said about him:

"There was, living as a recluse in my country, an ascetic named David, full of compassion and of virtues. He was born in Mesopotamia and passed about seventy years in a cell. For fear of the barbarians, the walls of the town were then guarded by soldiers. One night, those who were on watch on that side, saw fire coming out of the window of the monk's cell. They first thought that it had been set on fire by the barbarians, but in the morning they were struck dumb to find the hermit safe and sound and his cell intact. The same phenomenon was repeated the following night. And I myself witnessed this prodigy, not only once or twice but many times. And then I thought: 'If God does so much for His servants here below, what glory will He not give them in time to come when their faces shall shine like the sun!' And I tell you, my children, that that is what made me become a monk."

St. VIGILIUS (d. 405)

Bishop of Trent, correspondent of St. Ambrose. It is said that he was martyred in the valley of the Sarca, north of Lake Garda.

Sts. JOHN and PAUL

Roman martyrs of the early centuries.

St. SALVIUS

Itinerant bishop who came from Auvergne and was killed in the Valenciennes country with his companion, St. SUPERY (8th century).

St. ANTHELM (1107–1178)

Seventh prior of the Grande Chartreuse; bishop of Belley; created prince of the Empire by Frederick Barbarossa.

St. PELAGIUS (d. about 925)

A young Spaniard, who, because he refused to deny his faith, was dismembered by the Moors at Cordova.

St. BABOLEN

Third abbot of Stavelot-Malmédy (d. about 671).

The Blessed MADELEINE FONTAINE, FRANÇOISE LANEL, THÉRÈSE FANTOU, and JEANNE GÉRARD

Sisters of Charity of Arras, executed as "pious counter-revolutionaries" at Cambrai in 1794.

June 27th
ST. LADISLAUS OR LAZLO (d. 1095)

SON of Bela I and younger brother of Geza I, Ladislaus was born and grew up at the court of Poland where his parents had taken refuge. When Andrew I became king of Hungary, he recalled his brother Bela to the country and, having no heir, designated him his successor. The unexpected birth of Salomon, son of Andrew, upset all plans. From then on there were intrigues, troubles, foreign interference, wars and much bloodshed. Ladislaus himself had to bear arms to uphold the cause of Geza and his own. Briefly, in thirty years, the throne of Hungary passed successively to Andrew, Bela, Salomon, Geza, and finally in 1077, fell to Ladislaus. After that date, however, Salomon again attempted to dethrone his cousin who had innumerable difficulties in pacifying the country. Ladislaus had also to drive the Tartars back to their steppes, to subjugate the Serbs and Bulgars, and to make war in Dalmatia and Croatia until, in 1089, these two districts were united to his territory.

The reign of Ladislaus was of the utmost beneficence. He used his power only for the good of his people and in order to accomplish what he judged to be the will of God. He is considered as continuing the work of St. Stephen who, a century earlier, had introduced Christianity into Hungary.

Head and shoulders taller than his soldiers, Ladislaus showed extraordinary bravery on the battlefield; in addition, he was wise, virtuous, and generous. So greatly was he admired in the West that, when the first crusade had been decided upon, the English, the French, and the Spanish begged him unanimously to head the expedition. He accepted, but a revolt of the Bohemians broke out which he had first to put down. While accomplishing this, he died at Neutra in Moravia, June 30th, 1095.

St. Zoilus

Martyr of the first centuries.

St. Crescens

Disciple of St. Paul and martyr (1st century).

St. Emilian

Bishop of Nantes and martyr (d. 725).

Our Lady of Perpetual Help

The devotion to Our Lady of Perpetual Help comes to us from the Greeks. It is especially the Redemptorist Fathers who, since 1866, have spread it in the West.

June 28th

ST. IRENAEUS (d. about 202)

ST. IRENAEUS, called by Tertullian "a careful explorer of all doctrines," was a native of the Roman province of Asia. It is believed that he was born at Smyrna about the year 130. Certain it is that in his youth there he knew St. Polycarp. "I can tell," he wrote thirty years later, "where the blessed Polycarp sat to talk, how he came in and went out, how he lived, what he was like, how he spoke to his people, and what he told of the contacts he had had with John and other people who had seen the Lord."

About the year 177, Irenaeus was at Lyons as collaborator of Bishop Pothinus, and for this reason the Gallic Christians entrusted him to carry a message to Pope St. Eleutherius with the object of re-establishing peace. It is without doubt due to this journey and to his absence that he was not a victim of the persecutions at Lyons in which St. Pothinus and St. Blandina perished. Later, about 190, having in his turn become bishop of Lyons, Irenaeus begged the pope not to excommunicate those in the East who refused to celebrate Easter on the same day as in the West. St. Jerome affirms that he ended his life in martyrdom; he must in this case have been a victim of the massacre of the Christians of Lyons which took place in 202 under Septimius Severus.

St. Irenaeus has left to us the *Account of Apostolic Doctrine*, a simple and direct presentation of Christian beliefs, and the celebrated *Refutation of Knowledge Falsely so called* (*Adversus baereses*). This false knowledge was chiefly that of the Gnostics. Their system of related eons contained some quite comic items. Instead of constantly ridiculing his adversaries, Irenaeus often treated them most charitably. He wrote: "There is no God without goodness"; and again: "It is through love that the Word has become what we are, in order to make of us what It is"; and to those against whom he fought: "We hold out our hand to you with all our hearts, and will never cease to offer it to you."

Irenaeus wrote in Greek; he excused himself for not having at all an elegant style because, he said, "we are living among the Celts, and what a barbarous tongue it is we speak with them."

St. ALICE or ALETH OF BOURGOTTE (d. 1466)

Cared for the poor in the Parisian hospital of St. Catherine; then lived as a recluse for forty-six years near the Church of the Holy Innocents.

Sts. PLUTARCH, SERENUS, HERACLIDES, HERO, HERAIS, POTAMIANA, and MARCELLA

Disciples of Origen who were martyred at Alexandria about 202.

St. IRENE

Rather than marry Michael III, emperor of Constantinople, preferred to become a nun (9th century).

June 29th

ST. PETER (d. 64)

SIMON lived in Bethsaida on the north shore of the lake of Tiberias and there followed the calling of fisherman with his father, Jona, and his brother, Andrew. He married and for some time was a disciple of St. John the Baptist. When, having left all, he came to join the Saviour, "Jesus looked at him closely, and said, Thou art Simon, the son of Jona; thou shalt be called Cephas (which means the same as Peter)" (John i, 42). He at once took his place at the head of the apostolic college; from that time he appeared in all the Gospel scenes and almost always played a leading part in them.

He was present at the marriage at Cana, at the feeding of the five thousand, at the miraculous draught of fishes, at the cure of his mother-in-law and of a host of other sick people. With James and John, the sons of Zebedee, he witnessed the Transfiguration on Thabor and the Agony in the Garden. He heard, and sometimes provoked, the most important statements of the divine Master. Before anyone, he professed belief in the divinity of the Saviour: "Thou art the Christ, the Son of the living God." Jesus then replied: "Blessed art thou, Simon son of Jona; it is not flesh and blood, it is my Father in heaven that has revealed this to thee." Then he added: "And I tell thee this in my turn, that thou art Peter, and it is upon this rock that I will build my church: and the gates of hell shall not prevail against it" (Matt. xvi, 16-18).

During the passion, Peter also showed his courage in striking Malchus with a sword, but he ended by abandoning his Master and even denied Him thrice in the high priest's courtyard. He was the first of the apostles to see Jesus risen and, after the ascension, took leadership of the little Christian community. On the day of Pentecost, he spoke in the name of all and converted three thousand people. His authority constantly grew; miracles took place along his way; his shadow, cast upon the sick, sufficed to cure them.

About the year 43, Peter was at Jerusalem where Herod Agrippa had him imprisoned; he was there again about the year 50, presiding over the council and deciding, with Paul and Barnabas, on the entry of the Gentiles into the Church. He had first established his episcopal see at Antioch; it is believed that he occupied it for seven years and gave place, about 42, to St. Evodius. He stayed afterwards at Corinth; then was bishop of Rome, where he died, crucified head downwards, during Nero's persecutions.

St. PAUL

The Roman Church always celebrates his memory at the same time as that of St. Peter. Tomorrow, June 30th, it consecrates a special feast to him, known as THE CONVERSION OF ST. PAUL.

Sts. SALOME and JUDITH

Mysterious recluses who lived at Niederaltaich (Bavaria); it is believed that they were two high-born princesses and they are thought to have lived in the 9th century.

St. EMMA (d. 1045)

Countess of Sanngau, foundress of the monastery of Gurk (Karinthia).

St. BEATA or BENEDICTA

Two virgins of this name were martyred in the Senonais in the 3rd century.

June 30th
ST. PAUL (d. 67)

BORN at Tarsus in Cilicia, in the first decade of our era, St. Paul belonged to an important and devout family of Jews. He possessed the status of a Roman citizen by birth. He received the Hebrew name of Saul, which he later Latinized to Paulus. He spoke Aramaic and Greek. At the school of the Rabbi Gamaliel of Jerusalem, he studied exegesis, Jewish dogma, traditional law and casuistry, and became a model Pharisee.

In the eyes of enlightened Jews an inglorious Messias did not make sense. To worship the Crucified of Calvary was to betray the religious ideal of Israel and the very reason for her existence. Paul persecuted the Christians with a sort of rage until the day when the risen Christ appeared to him and transformed him. From that moment he was wholly devoted to spreading the knowledge and love of Our Lord.

During the years following his baptism we find him preaching at Damascus and "in Arabia"; twice making the journey to Jerusalem; staying at Caesarea, at Tarsus, at Antioch in Syria. From 45 to 48 he was at Cyprus, in Pamphylia, in Pisidia, and in Lycaonia. In 49, he conferred with St. Peter and St. James at Jerusalem. From 50 to 52, he journeyed through Phrygia, Galatia, Macedonia; preached at Philippi, Thessalonica, Beroea, and Athens; stayed many months in Corinth, and returned to Antioch, having passed through Caesarea and Jerusalem. In the spring of 53, Paul again departed for Ephesus; then he visited all the churches in Macedonia, went to Achaia, passed the winter of 57–58 at Corinth, stayed in the Aegean Islands and in the ports of the Asiatic coast, and returned to Jerusalem for Pentecost in the year 58. There the Jews attempted to kill him; they succeeded only in having him arrested by the Roman authorities who kept him captive at Caesarea for two years. As he had appealed to Caesar, in the end they sent him to Rome, where, after two more years of captivity, he was set free in the spring of 63.

It is known that the apostle again visited Crete, Ephesus, Troas, Macedonia, and Epirus; perhaps he also stayed for a short time in Spain. It was in Asia, apparently, that the police of Nero arrested him; and it was at Rome that, after renewed imprisonment, he was beheaded. According to Eusebius his martyrdom took place in 67, three years after that of St. Peter.

St. MARTIAL

Bishop of Limoges. According to Gregory of Tours, he came to Gaul during the consulate of Decius and Gratus, that is in 250.

St. LUCINA

According to the Roman martyrology, she was a disciple of the apostles and died at Rome.

St. BERTRAND

Bishop of Le Mans from 586 to 623.

Blessed ARNOUL CORNEBOUT (1180–1228)

Born at Brussels, lay brother of the abbey of Villers in Brabant.

St. THIBAUT (d. 1066)

Born at Provins, he belonged to the family of the counts of Brie and Champagne. His father was called Arnoul; his mother Guillemette or Gisèle. He lived as a hermit and in voluntary poverty, first near Rheims, then at Pettingen (diocese of Trier), and then near Vangadizza (diocese of Vicenza). There his mother Guillemette rejoined him, and he instructed her in the anchorite's life.

THE SAINTS OF JULY

July 1st

ST. THIERRY OR THEODORIC (d. 533)

HE DOCUMENTS which give information about St. Thierry or Theodoric probably date from three centuries after his death and are not to be taken very literally.

According to them, Thierry, born at Aumenancourt near Rheims, came from a rather poor background; his father Marquart lived by plunder and highway robbery; his mother was a little better. However, the child from the cradle was given signs of special favours from heaven. Although he later was involved in an ill-assorted union, St. Remigius helped him break it off; afterwards he ordained him priest and entrusted him with building a monastery on Mont d'Hor in Champagne, and frequently visited him there. Among the numerous disciples who came to Thierry we must mention St. Theodulf, who was his successor, and Marquart, his own father, who had been given grace to forsake his evil ways.

The chief miracle attributed to St. Thierry is one he accomplished for the benefit of the king of Austrasia, Thierry I, eldest son of Clovis. This ruler suffered from ophthalmia, and the doctors wished to remove an eye, asserting that he would surely die if he did not submit to this operation. The king refused, alleging that if he had but one eye he would lose his prestige among his warriors. It was then that the abbot of Mont d'Hor was called to the palace, and anointed the eyes of the king, completely curing them. Afterwards the sovereign often used to visit his healer. Perhaps this was the origin of the custom among the French kings of going on the day after their consecration to dine at the abbey of St. Thierry.

The Precious Blood of Our Lord

This feast, celebrated in Spain in the 16th century, was introduced in Italy by Blessed Gaspare Bufalo and extended to the whole Church by Pius IX in 1849.

St. Thibaut (1017–1066)

Noble of the Champagne country, who died a hermit, his body covered with ulcers, at Salanigo near Vicenza (Italy). The curriers have taken him as their patron.

St. Gallus (d. 551)

Paternal uncle of Gregory of Tours, became bishop of Clermont after having lived at the court of Thierry I, king of Austrasia.

St. Esther or Edissa

Niece of Mardochai, who took Vasthi's place as wife of Assuerus and was responsible for the death of a great number of enemies of the Jews (5th century B.C.).

St. Regina

Wife of Count Albert of Ostrevant, one of the founders of the monastery of Denain, near Valenciennes, whose daughter, St. Renfroie, became its abbess (d. end of 8th century).

July 2nd
ST. OTTO (1060–1139)

So great was his rectitude and his selflessness that at the height of the Conflict of the Investitures, St. Otto kept the friendship of both the popes and the emperors.

Born in Swabia of a noble and impoverished family, he early applied himself to study and soon embraced the ecclesiastical calling. He was twenty when, in 1080, three years after Canossa, he dared reproach Henry IV with creating an anti-pope in the person of Clement III. The emperor nonetheless took his critic into his service. In 1088, his sister Judith having married Ladislaus I, duke of Poland, he gave her Otto as chaplain. On Judith's death he recalled Otto and made him chancellor of the Empire; in 1102, he named him to the episcopal see of Bamberg. Emperor Henry V, who had sometimes to listen to his reproaches, had also a friendly veneration for him.

When Boleslaus, king of Poland, had completed the conquest of Pomerania, he called for missionaries to convert these pagan districts. Otto was then sixty-four. With some companions he left Bamberg in 1124, crossed Poland and evangelized the towns of Pyritz, Julin, Kamin, Stettin, Wollin, Kolberg, and Belgard; in one year he built eleven churches and baptized 20,000 persons. He was well received in general, except at Julin, where he was knocked down and dragged in the mud, and only escaped death by a hair's breadth. Three years later, learning that some of the new converts had fallen back into idolatry, he returned and went about confirming them in the faith. These things account for Otto being called the apostle of Pomerania.

The Visitation of the Blessed Virgin Mary

This feast recalls the visit which Our Lady made to her relative Elizabeth (Luke i); it was instituted by Urban VI in 1389, in order to obtain the end of the Great Schism.

St. Monegunde

Native of Chartres, led the life of a recluse in her native town, and then at Tours, near the tomb of St. Martin (6th century).

St. Bernardino Realini

Italian Jesuit, preacher and spiritual director, born at Carpi (Emilia) in 1530, died at Lecce (Apulia) in 1616.

Blessed Peter of Luxemburg (1369–1387)

Born at Ligny-en-Barrois, he belonged to one of the greatest families of the West. Of extraordinary precocity, he pronounced the vow of chastity at ten, became a brilliant student at the University of Paris, and at fifteen was made, against his will, bishop of Metz and a cardinal; he died shortly before he was eighteen, having always shown great wisdom and piety, and lived in continual austerity. One of his claims to fame is having fought

against those who denied the Immaculate Conception. Although he had
been of the Avignon obedience, Clement VII beatified him in 1527. We
have some minor works and letters from his hand.

July 3rd

ST. ANATOLIUS OF LAODICEA (3rd century)

ST. ANATOLIUS is honoured today by both the Greeks and the Latins,
but we are dealing with two different persons. St. Anatolius of the Latin
Church was bishop of Laodicea in the 3rd century. The one of the Greek
Church was bishop and patriarch of Constantinople in the 5th century.
Both were born at Alexandria which, at the beginning of our era, was the
greatest city in the world, after Rome.

Before becoming a light of the Church, Anatolius of Laodicea enjoyed
considerable prestige at Alexandria, and was credited with a rich knowledge of arithmetic, geometry, physics, rhetoric, dialectic, and astronomy; he
taught Aristotelian philosophy and was called upon to fill important civic
posts. It was in 263, it appears, that he rendered an outstanding service to his
fellow citizens by gaining permission during the Roman siege of Alexandria
for noncombatants to pass freely out of the town. He himself then left for
Caesarea in Palestine, where the bishop made him coadjutor and promised
him the succession. Some years later, going to the Council of Antioch,
Anatolius stopped in Laodicea. The Laodiceans, whose bishop had just
died, saw in our traveller the man exactly fitted to replace him and kept him
there by force. According to St. Jerome, Anatolius occupied the see of
Laodicea from 276 to 283. There remain some fragments of one of his works
on arithmetic.

ST. ANATOLIUS OF CONSTANTINOPLE
(5th century)

HE was elected bishop of Constantinople in 449, when the town had been
the capital of the Roman Empire for more than a century. There arose
theological disputes caused by Nestorius and Eutyches, which led at times
to bloodshed. It was out of a sense of duty that Anatolius then accepted the
most prominent episcopal see of the Orient. Unlike many of the prelates of
that region, his faith in Christ remained always pure and his attitude
towards the Roman pontiff most respectful. He tried to make his colleagues

accept the letter in which Pope St. Leo defined the true Christological doctrine; at the Council of Chalcedon (451) he subscribed to the condemnation of Eutyches and signed the formulary of faith elaborated in agreement with the papal legates. He was fervent and charitable, an ardent defender of the most austere forms of the anchorite life. The Greeks still honour him as one of their most powerful wonder-workers.

Blessed RAYMOND LULLY

Franciscan tertiary, a sort of legendary hero, one of the greatest geniuses of the middle ages. His writings have not yet been completely catalogued: they comprise works on theology, philosophy, apologetics, science, and pedagogy; philosophical novels, marvellous lyric poetry, mystical works of great beauty, and a host of occasional pieces. He has been credited with some treatises on magic and alchemy, which are not his. In May 1311, he thus epitomized his life: "I have been married and have had children; I have been rich and loved pleasures and the world. I have left all with a good heart for the glory of God, for the service of my fellow men, and to spread the holy faith. I have learned Arabic and often visited the Saracens; for my faith I have been beaten and imprisoned; for forty-five years I have endeavoured to interest the heads of the Church and Christian rulers in the public good. And now, here I am old and poor, but my ideal is always the same and such it will remain until my death, please God." It was at an age of more than eighty that after several vain attempts he succeeded in becoming a martyr. At Bougie, the Saracens stoned him and left him for dead. He died in sight of Majorca in 1316, on the Genoese boat which had rescued him.

July 4th
ST. BERTHA (d. about 725)

IF a life of St. Bertha, not wholly legendary, is to be believed, she was born in Artois, married to a noble of the Merovingian court, and had several children. Widowed, she founded the abbey of Blangy, where she withdrew with two of her daughters, and it was to one of them that the rule of the monastery fell when Bertha resigned as abbess. She spent the rest of her days immured in a cell beside the abbey church. The ceremony of enclosure was very solemn; several bishops took part in it who, having blessed the cell, withdrew, confiding Bertha to the care of the angels. However, this cell was pierced by a window giving on to the altar, and it was opened each day to allow the saint to assist at Mass and to address a few edifying words to the community.

ST. ULRICH (890–973)

ULRICH or Udalrich through his mother, Ditberga, belonged to the family of the dukes of Swabia. Brought up at the abbey of St. Gall, he was confided at sixteen to the care of his uncle, St. Adalbero, bishop of Augsburg, who at once made him his ecclesiastical chamberlain. Later, when the time had come, he ordained him priest and gave him a canonry.

It was in 924 that Ulrich took over the episcopal see of Augsburg. During the half-century that he occupied it he gave innumerable proofs of his zeal in promoting the welfare of the faithful and in correcting abuses among the clergy. He himself lived austerely, rising at three and eating only once a day. It is known that at this period bishops were often held responsible for the raising of troops and the defence of their territory. Ulrich acted with wisdom and courage; he fortified the town of Augsburg, thus sharing in the victory which Otto won in 955 over the Hungarian invaders; otherwise he personally fought as little as possible, and his nephew usually replaced him in his military obligations.

In 971, tired and ill, he handed in his resignation as bishop and obtained permission from the emperor for his nephew to succeed him. The Council of Ingelheim adjudged this act to be uncanonical, and cited the aged bishop for trial. Otto admitted his fault, did penance, and died a saintly death shortly afterwards. He was ranked among the saints, on February 3rd, 993, by John XV; his was the first recorded canonization made by a pope.

St. FLORENTIUS

Bishop of Cahors (5th century).

St. AURELIAN (d. 895)

Was the forty-eighth bishop of Lyons and the first to whom a council gave the title "primate of the Gauls."

St. ANDREW OF CRETE (d. 740)

Archbishop of Gortyna (Crete), celebrated orator and poet of the Greek Church. There have come down to us some of his *idiomata* or hymns which are of the greatest beauty.

July 5th
ST. ZOE

FOLLOWING the ancient martyrologies, church calendars inscribe today the name of St. Zoe. She was, they say, married to a certain Nicostratus and had a great devotion to the apostle St. Peter. One day when she was praying at his tomb she was arrested by the police of Diocletian, who hung her from a tree and lit a fire under her feet, so that she died by suffocation. Unfortunately, all this appears controvertible, and nothing is known about this St. Zoe.

That is not true of another saint of the same name, whom the martyrologies place on May 2nd, but who is never mentioned by the lay calendars, which reserve this date for St. Athanasius, the great Alexandrian doctor. She is well known, as is her husband, Hesperius, and her children, Cyriacus and Theodulus. They lived in Pamphylia in the first half of the 2nd century and were a slave family belonging to a Roman citizen, a devout worshipper of the gods. Even though slavery had begun to be a little less severe, female slaves were still often taken away from their husbands. For a long time this was the case with Zoe, whose husband worked in the far-off countryside, while she and her sons remained in the town. Her *Acts* describe her as exercising in her lowly state the virtues of patience and charity. One of her duties was to care for the dogs, and to prevent those which guarded the gate from biting visitors. One of her charitable customs was to set aside from her own food something for the poor and for hungry vagabonds. One day, on the occasion of a domestic celebration, she was reunited with her husband and her two sons when the master of the house sent them some meat which had been used in sacrifice. As they refused to eat it, the master came in in a rage and had them all, parents and children together, thrown into a fire.

St. PHILOMENA
Venerated at San Severino, near Ancona.

Blessed ARCHANGELUS OF CALATAFIMI (d. 1460)
A Sicilian hermit who lived in a cave until Martin V abolished the eremitic life in Sicily. He then became a friar minor at Palermo, was made provincial of his order, and died at Alcamo, April 10th, 1460.

St. ANTONIO MARIA ZACCARIA (1502-1539)
Born at Cremona, he became a doctor of medicine, was ordained priest in 1528, and soon founded the clerks regular of St. Paul. Their name of

Barnabites comes from the Church of St. Barnabas to which they minis-
tered in Milan. He is also considered as the founder of a congregation of
women called the Angelicals. He died at Cremona, July 5th, 1539.

Blessed ELIE DE BOURDEILLES (d. 1484)

Franciscan originally from Périgord, he was bishop of Périgueux from
1438 to 1468 and archbishop of Tours from 1468 to his death. In 1483 he
had been named cardinal. In 1452 he made a report intended to vindicate
Joan of Arc and he defended the rights of the Church against the French
kings on many occasions. Specifically he reproached Louis XI for keeping
Cardinal Balue in prison; but such was his sanctity that the king, far from
bearing a grudge, desired to be prepared by him for death.

July 6th

STS. PHILEMON, APOLLONIUS, AND ARRIAN
(d. 306)

IN 306, when religious peace reigned in the West, Galerius and Maximinus
began a persecution in the East. They made victims among the hermits of the
Thebaid, of whom one, Apollonius, was arrested and imprisoned. Among
the pagans who had full liberty to go and deride him in his dungeon was
a flute player named Philemon. He heaped mockeries on the old man. "May
God have mercy on you," replied the prisoner gently, "and may He not
impute your words to sin." This affectionate language touched the musician's
heart; he was converted and soon went to the governor Arrian to reproach
him for his cruelty. The latter at first thought that Philemon, a public favourite,
was perpetrating some new joke. When he saw that the artist spoke in
earnest, he tried to win him over by gentleness and persuasion. But Philemon
continued all the more to reproach the magistrate with putting so many
innocent people to death.

While this was taking place, Arrian learned that the conversion of
Philemon was Apollonius' work. He then condemned both to torture by
fire. "Lord," said the old hermit, mounting the pyre, "do not lose the souls
which trust in you." He had no sooner pronounced these words than a cloud
descended on the pyre and its flames were put out by the rain. Many saw in
it a sign from heaven, and Arrian himself was converted. Meanwhile,
Hierocles, prefect of Egypt, soon heard about what had passed; he summoned the two condemned men to Alexandria, and with them the governor

Arrian, who came within his jurisdiction, and he had all three thrown into the sea.

Certain of the calendars and martyrologies place the feast of these martyrs on March 8th, others on November 16th.

St. DOMINICA

Virgin martyred in the East under Diocletian. She is venerated at Tropea (Calabria). This is probably the same saint who is honoured by the Greeks on July 7th under the name of Kyriaké (*Kyrios, Dominus*).

St. ISAIAS (d. 6th century B.C.)

Prophet of the Old Testament.

St. MECHTILD (d. 1160)

Bavarian Augustinian, relative of Frederick Barbarossa, sister of Blessed Euphemia, died at the abbey of Driessen.

St. ANGELA

Daughter of a king of Bohemia, author of some admirable *Contemplations* and *Revelations*, died at Prague about 1230.

St. JUSTUS (d. 6th century)

Monk of the abbey of Condat (St. Claudius).

St. MARIA GORETTI (1890–1902)

Daughter of a farm worker of Latium (Italy), she was stabbed while resisting a young man who attacked her.

July 7th

THE BLESSED ROGER DICKENSON AND RALPH MILNER (d. 1591)

To practise and spread the Catholic religion the English in those times risked prison and death. Ralph Milner and Roger Dickenson were the victims of their devotion to the Roman Church. The first was an illiterate farmer who had abjured Protestantism; the second was a secular priest, a native of the county of Lincoln, who had studied at Rheims, and was then exercising his ministry secretly in the Winchester district. Ralph Milner was seized on the very day of his first Communion and was imprisoned. But he was paroled from time to time, and he took advantage of this to succour his companions in captivity and to help itinerant missionaries in their work. It was thus that he allied himself with Roger Dickenson. The latter had already been once arrested, but on that day his guards had been drinking and had parted company with him. The second time he was arrested with Ralph Milner. The judge took pity on the latter who was getting old and had eight children; seeking a pretext to set him free, he said that if Milner would consent to say his prayers in the nearby parish church, it would be taken as a gesture of reconciliation with the Church of England, and he would be left in peace. But Ralph Milner refused to make the least deceitful gesture, wishing to share the lot of his friend Dickenson; and both were executed at Winchester on July 7th, 1591.

Sts. CYRIL (d. 869) and METHODIUS (d. 885)

For a long time their feast was set on July 5th; it is at present celebrated on the 7th. Cyril, who called himself Constantine till the eve of his death, ended his days in Rome at the age of forty-two; Methodius died in Moravia, over seventy. They were two brothers of Greek origin, sons of a high official of Thessalonica, and had themselves filled high civil posts. In 863 the basileus of Constantinople and the patriarch Photius entrusted them with a political and religious mission in Moravia. They took with them an alphabet which enabled them to have a translation of the Bible and a Christian liturgy made for the Slavs; this was an important landmark in the conversion of the Slavic world to Christianity.

The TWENTY-NINE MARTYRS OF CHINA

They were tortured and died in 1900, victims of the Boxer Uprising. Almost all were Franciscans. Among them were three bishops, GREGORY GRASSI, apostolic vicar of Chansi, FRANCIS FOGOLLA, his coadjutor, and ANTHONY FANTOSATI, apostolic vicar of Hunan; five Franciscan priests; seven nuns, Franciscan Missionaries of Mary; five seminary students. The others were servants of the Mission or Christians in the entourage of the missioners.

St. WILLIBALD (d. about 790)

Son of St. Richard, king of the Saxons, was a monk at Monte Cassino when, about 738, St. Boniface took him as a helper into Germany and made him bishop of Eichstätt.

St. ETHELBURGA (d. 7th century)

Daughter of Anna, king of East Anglia (635–654), emigrated to France and became abbess of Faremoutiers in Brie.

July 8th

ST. ISABELLA or ELIZABETH OF PORTUGAL
(1271–1336)

DAUGHTER of Peter III, king of Aragon, great-niece of St. Elizabeth of Hungary, at the age of twelve Isabella married Denis, king of Portugal, by whom she had two children: Alphonso and Constance. The behaviour of the king was at first irreproachable; but later, he became unfaithful; Isabella suffered much, but showed no bitterness, and carried her heroism to the length of bringing up and loving the illegitimate children of the king.

Lending ear to a nobleman's slanders, Denis began to suspect the fidelity of the queen. He commanded the owner of a limekiln to come to the palace and secretly ordered him to throw into the fire the courtier he would first send to him. The next day he ordered the secretary and alleged accomplice of the queen to go to the kiln, but before reaching his destination, the secretary, as was his wont, heard two Masses. This delay saved him, for his denouncer, ordered to verify the outcome of the operation, arrived before him and was thrown into the kiln in his stead.

Numerous were Isabella's other trials. She was exiled to Alemquer on the pretext that she had aroused Alphonso to take arms against his father. When the king saw that she was innocent, he gave her Torres Vedras to govern, a task she ably fulfilled. On two other occasions she succeeded in reconciling the rebellious son with his father. In the same way she settled the disagreement which had risen between Denis and Ferdinand of Castile, his son-in-law. The latter died young, closely followed to the tomb by Constance. The king died in 1325, entirely transformed by the virtues and goodness of his wife.

Isabella then cut her hair to enter the order of St. Clare. But as it was represented to her that her role in the world was by no means ended, she limited herself to living in the habit of a tertiary with the Poor Clares of Coimbra. She fell ill at Estremoz in the course of a journey undertaken to reconcile her son and grandson. To Queen Beatrice, who looked after her, she said: "Draw up a chair for the radiant lady in white who is coming." It was the Blessed Virgin who entered; the dying woman murmured: "*Maria, mater gratiae*"; then gently gave up her soul.

Blessed PETER THE HERMIT (d. 1115)

A native of Picardy, great orator to the masses, preached the first crusade, came back from the East about 1100, and ended his days in an Augustinian monastery near Huy (Belgium).

Sts. KILIAN, COLOMAN and TOTNAN

Irish missionaries, who attempted to evangelize Thuringia and were assassinated there about 689.

July 9th

ST. THOMAS MORE (1478-1535)

A GOOD example of an "honest man" and Christian humourist, this great humanist, a friend of Erasmus and Holbein, refused to recognize his sovereign as spiritual head of the Anglican Church and died with a heroism full of good humour and simplicity. He wished to be helped up on to the scaffold ("I can manage to get down alone"); protested his fidelity to God and to the King; recited the *Miserere*; embraced his executioner and gave him a piece of gold ("Courage, my good man, don't be afraid; but take care, for I have a short neck and you have to look to your honour"); bandaged his eyes himself, put out of the way his beard, which, in his opinion, "did not deserve to be cut off since it had betrayed nothing"; put his head on the block; and the executioner cut it off with a blow of his axe.

ST. JOHN FISHER (1459-1535)

ST. JOHN FISHER had been chaplain of the mother of Henry VII and chancellor of Cambridge University before becoming, in 1504, bishop of Rochester. A great admirer of the classical writers and a distinguished humanist, like Thomas More he numbered Erasmus among his friends. He opposed the divorce of Henry VIII and Catherine of Aragon, as also the constitution of the English Church. In 1534 his refusal to take the oath which the king required of the English bishops led to his arrest and imprisonment in the Tower of London; there he received in 1534 the cardinal's hat from Paul III. The following month he was taken from the Tower to his execution.

The Blessed MARIE ROSE, MARIE CLAIRE, MARIE ANNE, and the other MARTYRS OF ORANGE

These blessed persons were part of a group martyred during the Terror of 1794 in France, and beatified by Pius XI in 1925.

St. ANATOLIA

Martyred in Italy in the 3rd century.

St. VERONICA GIULIANI (1660–1727)

Poor Clare at Città di Castello; was favoured with extraordinary graces and received the stigmata.

The HOLY MARTYRS OF GORKUM

There were nineteen of these (eleven Franciscans, two Premonstraten, sians, one Dominican, one canon regular of St. Augustine, and four secular priests) who were hanged at Brielle, near Gorkum (Holland), on July 9th, 1572, for their "papism" and their belief in the Real Presence.

July 10th

ST. FELICITAS
AND THE SEVEN BROTHER MARTYRS (d. 162?)

THE first years of the reign of Marcus Aurelius were marked by all kinds of public calamities. Very superstitious, the Romans sought those responsible for these calamities in order to sacrifice them to the gods. As Tertullian wrote, speaking of this epoch, which was that of his childhood: "Were not the Christians the cause of all these disasters? If the Tiber inundated Rome, if the Nile did not inundate the countryside, if there were war, famine, or pestilence, a cry was immediately raised: 'The Christians to the lions! Death to the Christians!'"

An ancient *Passion* places Felicitas and her sons among the number of the victims then chosen. Felicitas was a very pious widow, whose social situation placed her very much in the public eye of Rome. The pagan priests told the emperor that her example was most dangerous, that if she was not made to venerate the gods they would be so irritated that it would be impossible to appease them. The emperor charged the prefect Publius with obliging her to sacrifice. Publius summoned her and in a private conversation endeavoured to obtain her abjuration. Failing in this, he cited her to appear for regular trial in the forum of Mars, together with her sons.

The sons of Felicitas were called: Januarius, Felix, Philip, Silvanus, Alexander, Vitalis, and Martial. All seven made admirable and super, natural replies to the magistrates whose duty it was to secure their apostasy. Their mother inspired them with her own faith: "Lift your eyes to heaven; look up, my children; there Christ awaits you; fight for your souls; stay firm in His love." Since none of them gave way, the emperor condemned them all to death. Januarius perished under the blows of a whip loaded with lead;

Felix and Philip were beaten to death with staves; Silvanus was thrown from a high rock; Alexander, Martial, and Vitalis were beheaded, as was also Felicitas.

This is, indeed, a good story. Certain historians, however, have contested its exactness. In their opinion the author of the *Passion* which we have summarized was carried away by the story of the Machabee brothers and made the seven above-mentioned Christians into brothers and gave them Felicitas as mother. There may be no bond of blood between these eight martyrs.

St. PASCHASIUS

Bishop of Nantes (7th century).

St. ULRICH

Born at Ratisbon about 1018, was page to the Empress Agnes, novice master at Cluny, and founded the abbey of Zell (Black Forest) where he died, blind, in 1093.

Blessed PACIFICUS (d. about 1230)

Former troubadour, surnamed "king of verses"; became one of the companions of St. Francis and introduced the Franciscan order into France.

The Blessed MARTYRS OF DAMASCUS

Eleven in number, namely, eight Franciscans and three Maronite brothers from among their friends, they were massacred at Damascus by the Druses and Turks on July 9th, 1860. Among them may be mentioned Blessed EMMANUEL RUIZ, born in the province of Santander in 1803, who died with his throat cut; CARMEL VOLTA, born in the province of Valencia in 1803, beaten to death; ENGLEBERT KOLLAND, born in 1827 in the diocese of Salzburg, killed with blows of an axe; JUAN JAIME FERNANDEZ, born in 1808 in Galicia, thrown from a cliff and killed, after a night of suffering, by a blow from a scimitar.

July 11th

ST. OLGA (d. 969)

IT was under St. Vladimir that the Russian nation was converted to Christianity. But this event was as though foreshadowed by the baptism of St. Olga, this king's grandmother.

Of lowly birth, Olga had married Prince Igor, grand duke of Kiev, in 913. After his assassination in 945 by the Dravidians, she became regent and severely punished this insurgent people. Her regency lasted until 955, when she gave the power to Sviatoslav, her son. She was over seventy when she went to Constantinople and was baptized under the name of Helen. Returning to her country, she bent her efforts to spreading the Christian religion. Doubtless she had asked the Eastern emperor to send her missionaries; in any case she requested them of Emperor Otto the Great, who for his part was anxious for the conversion of the Slavs, the Magyars, and all the Eastern peoples who were exerting pressure on his frontiers. The mission sent in 952 by Otto and led by St. Adalbert, a monk of St. Maximinus at Trier, was completely wiped out, only the leader escaping. However, after the reign of Sviatoslav and Yaropolk, son and grandson of Olga, Vladimir, brother of Yaropolk, mounted the throne, and was baptized in 987. He imposed the new faith on his peoples, thus assuring the triumph of Christianity in Russia.

BLESSED OLIVER PLUNKET (1629-1681)

THE martyrdom of this blessed person is a symbol of Irish resistance to the political and religious persecutions of England. Oliver Plunket was born at Loughcrew on the day after the death of James I, who had organized the immigration of the English Protestants into northern Ireland; and he was a contemporary of Cromwell, who, by ruining this country, tried to reduce it to apostasy.

He had been sent to Rome at the age of sixteen. There he made his theological and canonical studies. He was ordained priest in 1654, and until 1669, when Clement IX named him archbishop of Armagh and primate of Ireland, he exercised various and important functions in the pontifical city.

There only remained two bishops in Ireland when Oliver landed there in 1670. His ministry was pursued sometimes with success, sometimes with set-backs caused by British conspiracies and the treason of his own people. In 1678, the discovery of an alleged papist conspiracy aggravated the situation of the Irish Catholics. Plunket was taken to London, accused of having plotted a landing of 20,000 French in English territory and attempting to arm 70,000 soldiers against England through taxes raised from his clergy. He remained in prison many months. Two renegades, former monks, bore witness against him. Deemed guilty of "false religion and high treason," he was condemned to be hanged. "It is good," he declared, "for me at this time to give an example to the Irish people, since I have already given them so much good advice." He thanked the jury and died, begging God to pardon his enemies.

St. Pius I

Pope (d. 155?). It was in his time that Marcion came to Rome and broke with the Church.

St. Cyprian

Bishop of Brescia (period unknown).

St. Aleth

Bishop of Cahors (5th century).

St. Leontius the Younger

Bishop of Bordeaux (d. about 570).

July 12th

ST. JOHN GUALBERT (d. 1073)

One day as he was going to Florence, followed by his squire, John Gualbert reached a narrow pass and suddenly found himself face to face with the man who had killed his brother. To act as a self-appointed judge and to apply the law of retaliation was the custom among the Italian lords of that time. Even if feelings of revenge did not arise in Gualbert, family honour demanded that he take this opportunity to kill his enemy. This man knew it; he was alone; he could not flee. Believing that his last hour had come, he threw himself from his horse and, his head bent and his arms making a cross, he commended his soul to God. Gualbert was by no means pious nor had his conduct hitherto been edifying; this spectacle, however, moved him; the man with his arms extended, trembling and praying, brought before his eyes the image of the crucified Saviour. John put up his sword, forgave him, and went on his way.

Having dismissed his squire, he took himself to San Miniato and donned the Benedictine habit. He thought to end his days in that monastery, but when a new abbot paid in gold for his election, he left; nor did he stay long with the Camaldolese of Camaldoli in the Apennine mountains. Making his way back to Florence, he stopped midway in a valley planted with beeches and pines. This place, which was called Vallombrosa, became the cradle of the Benedictine reform which John Gualbert founded and over whose destiny he presided until the day of his death.

At Vallombrosa, luxury, simony, ambition were unknown; the priests chanted the holy office with devotion; the lay brethren gave themselves up to manual work; all practised penance and humility. Gualbert himself never became a priest. He even refused to receive the rank of porter; in the morning when he was first to arrive before the sanctuary, he waited patiently for the monk whose duty it was to open the gate. He is said to have been almost eighty when he died. His congregation still counts more than six monasteries.

Sts. NABOR and FELIX

Martyrs honoured at Milan from the beginning of the 4th century.

Blessed JOHN JONES

Welsh Franciscan, hanged at London in 1598 "for having been ordained abroad and having, without cause, re-entered the kingdom."

July 13th
ST. EUGENE (d. 505)

AFTER the Vandals had conquered Roman Africa, the Arian king Genseric declared war on the Catholics of that country, closing their churches, exiling their bishops, and forbidding them to appoint successors under pain of death. Although Huneric, Genseric's successor, at first showed himself less rigorous, the church of Carthage, capital of the kingdom, remained without a bishop. A deal was eventually made between the emperor of Constantinople and the Vandal king, permitting the Catholics of Carthage to elect a leader provided that the Arians could do the same in the East; otherwise, added the royal edict, Huneric "would exile to the Moors the whole African Catholic clergy without exception." And thus it was that in 481 the church of Carthage, deprived of a shepherd for almost thirty years, was able to elect St. Eugene.

His zeal and his talents soon accomplished marvels. The Arian prelates took alarm, raised loud protests against him, and Huneric went back on his word. He forbade Eugene to exercise his ministry; five thousand of the faithful were deported to the country of the Moors; religious persons were mistreated.

However, the emperor of Constantinople exhorted the king to exercise greater moderation, and the latter invited the heads of the two parties to meet and, as far as possible, to agree. A conference was fixed for February 1st, 484. Four hundred and sixty-six Catholic bishops attended, but only ten were permitted to take part, and of these not one spoke anything but Latin. Cyril, patriarch of the Arians, presided and, pretending to know only Gothic, refused to listen to them. After some futile discussions the king issued an edict on February 20th again proscribing the Catholic religion. The four hundred and sixty-six bishops who had come to Carthage were despoiled of their goods; forty-six of them were deported for forced labour to Corsica and three hundred and two to southern Tunisia. Eugene was exiled to the shores of Lake Trito in Byzacena.

He reappeared in Carthage in 487 under Gunthamund, successor of Huneric. In 494 he obtained from this tolerant king the recall of his exiled colleagues and the reopening of the Catholic churches. But in 496 Gunthamund was replaced by Transemund, who resumed the persecutions and sent several bishops into exile. Eugene was deported into Languedoc, ruled by the Arian king, Alaric II, and he died at Albi in 505.

St. ANACLETUS I

Pope, appears to have occupied the see of Rome between 79 and 90.

St. SARA

Led, for more than sixty years, the life of a hermit on the banks of the Nile, between Pelusium and Scete (4th century).

Blessed JACOBUS DE VORAGINE (d. 1298)

Born at Casanuova near Varezze, he entered the Dominican order, taught theology, was twice provincial of Lombardy, and became archbishop of Genoa in 1292. He has left some sermons, a *Chronicle of the Town of Genoa*, and above all, *The Golden Legend*, which enjoyed enormous success before the advent of Protestantism; it recounts, in an edifying manner and citing many miracles, the life of about a hundred and seventy saints honoured in his time.

July 14th
ST. BONAVENTURE (1221–1274)

ST. BONAVENTURE, surnamed the "Seraphic Doctor," is often cited, with Duns Scotus and St. Thomas Aquinas, as one of the three most celebrated philosophers and theologians of the middles ages. He is also a spiritual author of great power and authority. His works fill not less than ten thick volumes in quarto.

He was called John Fidanza and was born at Bagnorea, near Viterbo, in 1221. He entered the order of friars minor about his twentieth year, studied at Paris, and taught theology and Holy Scripture there from 1248 to 1257. Appointed in the latter year general of his order, he governed it in difficult circumstances until 1274. It was in order to try to re-establish peace among his brothers that he wrote his exact but incomplete *Life of St. Francis,* which the general chapter of 1266 imposed to the exclusion of all others. He did much to give a definitive rule to the Franciscan order, encouraged study, and developed devotion to the Blessed Virgin.

A friend of the popes and often begged by them to accept an episcopal see, St. Bonaventure had to resign himself to becoming a cardinal and bishop of Albano in 1273. Gregory X, who had prevailed on him to do this, counted on his help to put an end to the Greek schism. Bonaventure sent monks to Constantinople to negotiate with the Orthodox; the reunion of the Eastern and Western Churches was realized at the Council of Lyons on July 6th. We know, unfortunately, how precarious was this agreement. Our saint died eight days later at Lyons on July 14th, 1274.

St. FELIX

Bishop of Como (d. about 390).

St. DEUSDEDIT (d. 664)

Archbishop of Canterbury.

St. FRANCIS SOLANUS (1549–1610)

Spanish Franciscan, a great missionary, he evangelized Peru, Chile, and the north of Argentina; he died at Lima.

July 15th

ST. HENRY II (972–1024)

NEPHEW of Otto the Great, founder of the Holy Roman Germanic Empire, St. Henry succeeded his father, Henry the Peaceful, duke of Bavaria, in 995. Shortly afterwards he married Kunegunde, daughter of the count of Luxemburg. He had been brought up at the abbey of Hildesheim and had come deeply under the influence of St. Wolfgang, bishop of Ratisbon. He was consecrated emperor in the cathedral of Mainz on June

16th, 1007; his sovereignty extended to the greater part of Germany, Austria, Switzerland, the Low Countries, and the north of Italy.

Henry II passed the greater part of his life in making war against his brothers-in-law and other vassals anxious to cast off the yoke or to encroach on his possessions. He also had to appear many times in Italy, notably in 1021 when Benedict VIII asked him to take arms against Basil II, emperor of Constantinople, whose progress was imperilling the pontifical possessions. Henry had received the crown of Italy in the cathedral of Pavia in 1004 and that of the Holy Empire at St. Peter's in Rome ten years later. He died at the castle of Grona on July 15th, 1024, and was interred in the cathedral he had built at Bamberg. St. Kunegunde, with whom he had lived in continence, was also buried there fifteen years later.

It is generally agreed that St. Henry is one of the most Christian princes who has reigned in the West; none was more desirous of procuring the glory of God or the honour of the Church; none understood better the excellence of the monastic life and the need for reform of the clergy. He himself gave an example of the evangelical virtues, notably humility and the forgiveness of injuries.

ST. VLADIMIR (d. 1015)

ST. OLGA, his grandmother, had removed Vladimir from the court, and at the death of his father he possessed only the little estate of Novgorod. But seven years sufficed for him to reconquer all his paternal inheritance, and a few years later he had retaken Galicia from the Poles, vanquished the Eastern Bulgars on the Volga, and conquered the territories of the North as far as Finland. He was baptized in 987, and thereafter worked to Christianize his subjects. Missionaries came from Byzantium and from Germany; idols fell; whole populations received mass baptism; at his death the Christian religion had spread from Rostov to Volhynia. Vladimir had obtained the hand of Anna, sister of Basil II and Constantine VIII, for having helped these emperors at a difficult time. When he lost her, he married a granddaughter of Otto the Great, and he left twelve children at his death.

St. DONALD OF FORFAR (Scotland)

Had nine daughters who formed by themselves a little community of nuns (8th century).

Blessed ANGELINA OF MARSCIANO (1377–1435)

Was born in Umbria; became a widow at seventeen; founded in 1397, a congregation of Franciscan tertiaries at Foligno.

St. POMPILIUS MARIA PIROTTI (1710–1756)

Clerk regular of the Piarist fathers, native of the diocese of Benevento, died at Lecce. A talented professor and preacher, he was slandered, imprisoned, and finally vindicated.

July 16th

OUR LADY OF MOUNT CARMEL

IT is mainly the Carmelites, devoted servants of Mary, who have led to her invocation under this title. As is well known, they themselves take their title from Mount Carmel in Syria. After the 14th century they celebrated a feast of Our Lady of Mount Carmel in memory of the approval given to their rule by Pope Honorius III in 1226. At the beginning of the 17th century, this feast of July 16th became that of the Scapular which, according to Carmelite tradition, had been given in 1251 by the Blessed Virgin to the Carmelite Simon Stock. In 1726, Benedict XIII extended the celebration of this feast to the universal Church.

Let us note in passing, that the so-called Sabbatine bull, attributed to Pope John XXII, is a controversial document. In it those who carry scapulars are assured that they will be delivered from Purgatory on the Saturday after their death.

Certain appellations of the Virgin have given rise to various first names: it is thus that Dolores or Lola, Conception or Conchita, Mercedes, Soledad, Socorro, Paloma, evoke respectively, Our Lady of Sorrows, the Immaculate Conception, Our Lady of Mercy, Our Lady of Solitude, Our Lady of Good Help, and Our Lady of the Dove. Our Lady of Mount Carmel is in the same way the origin of the Spanish first names, Carmel, Carmen, and Carmela, as well as the Italian first names, Carmine and Carmelo.

St. REINELDA

Venerated at Saintes in Belgium (d. about 680).

St. HÉLIER

Said to have been a native of Tongres; he was assassinated on the island of Jersey (6th century).

St. EUSTATHIUS

Bishop of Antioch, great adversary of Arianism, died exiled by the Emperor Constantine about 338.

St. MARIE MADELEINE POSTEL

Born at Barfleur, Normandy, in 1746, died aged more than ninety at Saint-Sauveur-le-Vicomte, after having practised penance all her life and having always enjoyed good health. She became directress of a girls' school in 1774, a Franciscan tertiary in 1798, and founded in 1807, at Cherbourg, under the name of "Poor Daughters of Mercy," a teaching and nursing congregation which at the time of her death had thirty-seven houses.

July 17th

ST. ALEXIS (5th century)

ST. ALEXIS has been popular in the West since the 10th century at least. However, his biography, such as it has come down to us, is less historic than legendary.

He is said to have been the only son of a Roman senator named Euphemian, who was related to the emperor and possessed of an immense fortune. With his wife Aglae he practised all the Gospel precepts and they brought up their child in a perfect fashion. When they judged the moment had come, they betrothed him to a girl of the highest rank. The nuptial ceremony was held, but before its end Alexis gave back to his betrothed the gold ring which was to be the symbol of their union. Having made this gesture, he fled from his paternal home, set sail for Syria, and from there he reached the town of Edessa on foot. Mingling with the mendicants on the porch of the Church of Our Lady, he held out his hand for alms and lived for seventeen years by begging. His holiness having been recognized and divulged by a sacristan, he fled, taking passage on a ship which was sailing to Tarsus, but which was driven back by contrary winds to Italy.

Alexis returned to Rome; his parents were still living; his betrothed had remained faithful to him. He did not make himself known and asked for lodging under the staircase of his father's palace. "I consent," said the senator Euphemian, "on condition that you pray God to bring us back our child." Alexis did not reveal his identity but promised his prayers and lived for seventeen years, begging his bread in the streets, visiting the churches, and at evening regaining his poor quarters. All this time he was exposed to ill treatment by his father's slaves who even went so far as to fling dirty water on his head.

One day when Pope Innocent I was celebrating Mass in the presence of the emperor, a celestial voice was heard saying: "Seek the man of God; he will pray for Rome and the Lord will favour you!" The voice then revealed that this man was to be found in the house of Euphemian. The pope and emperor betook themselves thither, and Alexis was discovered dead in his rags beneath the staircase, holding in his hand a parchment which gave his name and history.

ST. MARCELLINA (4th century)

ON the death of her father who was pretorian prefect of the Gauls, Marcellina returned to Rome with her mother and her two brothers; one was named Satyrus; the other was the future St. Ambrose. On the feast of the Epiphany in 353, she received from Pope Liberius the virgin's veil in the Church of St. Peter. Exhorting her to serve Christ courageously, the pope cited as an example the Alexandrian page who, in order not to disturb a pagan ceremony by shaking off the melted wax which fell upon him, allowed his hand to be burned to the bone. And Marcellina, said St. Ambrose, did far more than Liberius had counselled her.

In order to free her from all temporal care, Ambrose left her the rents of all his lands. To encourage her in the practice of all the monastic virtues, he addressed to her, about 376, his treatise *De Virginibus*. The brother and sister kept up a lively correspondence; the archbishop's troubles gave grave concern to the nun, and when she suffered, her brother hastened to her rescue. Marcellina assisted Satyrus in his last illness; she also outlived St. Ambrose, and it was she who gave Paulinus of Milan documents for his life of the great doctor.

St. BENIGNUS

Abbot of Vallombrosa, relative of St. John Gualbert (d. 1236).

St. FREDEGAND

Native of Ireland, was abbot of Deurne, near Antwerp (8th century, it seems).

St. GENEROSUS and the eleven other SCILLITAN MARTYRS

They died by the sword under Commodus at Scillium (Tunis), July 17th, 180.

The Blessed CARMELITES OF COMPIÈGNE

Executed at Paris under the Terror, July 17th, 1794.

July 18th

ST. CAMILLUS DE LELLIS (1550-1616)

HE was born at Bacchianico (kingdom of Naples) of a noble family and lost his mother at the age of thirteen. In 1569, he enlisted with his father in the service of Venice; he was then almost six feet six in height. Both fell ill and the father died; Camillus, who had contracted an incurable disease of the feet, presented himself at the Franciscan monastery of Aquila but was dismissed. Ill himself, he entered as infirmarian the hospital of St. James at Rome, but his passion for gambling and his violent character soon resulted in his dismissal. He again enlisted in the Venetian army for three years, left for Corfu, and fell ill on the eve of the battle of Lepanto. He then went into the pay of Spain; but the royal galleys were decommissioned, the crews were paid off, and Camillus soon found himself at Naples with no fortune but his equipment. He lost at cards his sword, his arquebuse, his powderhorn, his campaign cloak, and even his shirt. For a time he begged at the church doors, then found employment as ass-driver in the service of the Capuchins of Manfredonia. He was bringing back a barrel of wine on his donkey when, on February 2nd, 1575, an old monk accosted him and whispered a few words into his ear. This, with the grace of God, was all that was needed to convert him. From then on he tried on four occasions to become a Franciscan and each time met with failure. In the intervals he was infirmarian of the hospital of St. James at Rome.

It was there, in order to remedy the frightful state of sick people in the hospitals, that Camillus thought in 1582 of founding the Ministers of the Sick. Encouraged by St. Philip Neri, he became a priest in 1584. Two years later Sixtus V approved his congregation; it became an order in 1591 and spread from Rome to Milan, Genoa, Florence, Messina, Palermo, Ferrara, and other places. Until the last, although afflicted with serious infirmities, Camillus cared for the sick; he loved them like children, seeing in them Christ suffering and abandoned. When a cardinal asked to see him while he was taking care of one of them, he said: "For the moment I am with Our Lord; I will see His Excellency when I have done."

St. ARNULF

Grandson of the duke of Swabia, bishop of Metz (d. 640).

Blessed BERTHA DE MARBAIS (d. 1247)

Relative of Joan of Constantinople, became a nun at the abbey of Aywières, then abbess of that of Marquette (Nord).

St. EMILIAN (d. 362)

Christian soldier burned alive at Drisna (Rumania) for having overthrown some pagan altars.

St. FREDERICK

Bishop of Utrecht (d. 838). Some aver that he was assassinated on the orders of the wife of Louis the Débonnaire.

St. HERVÉ or HERVAEUS (d. 1119)

Was in turn monk of the Trinity at Vendôme, anchorite in the forest of Craon, recluse near Angers, pilgrim to the Holy Land, and hermit on an island of the Loire opposite Chalonnes.

July 19th

ST. VINCENT DE PAUL (d. 1660)

BORN at Pouy in the Landes, about 1580, Vincent de Paul was third child of a family of labourers comprising four sons and two daughters. He seems to have received at birth those qualities which characterize the best of the French peasantry: good sense and perspicacity, tenacity, some ambition, a happy facility for expressing ideas clearly, and the faculty of adapting himself to men and circumstances. After having tended sheep, he was sent to the college of the Grey Friars of Dax; then his father sold two oxen to pay for his theological studies at the University of Toulouse.

Ordained priest in 1600, Vincent opened a school at Buzet, tried without success to obtain a good ecclesiastical benefice, and went as far as Marseilles to collect three hundred crowns due to him. Taking sail to return to Narbonne, he was captured by Corsairs who led him captive to Tunis. Nevertheless, he managed to escape and returned to France. In 1610 we find him in Paris, almoner of Queen Margot, first wife of Henry IV. The king had received him on his return from captivity, as he carried a secret message from the court of Rome, and became his protector. Vincent was made pastor of Clichy in 1611, became a tutor in the Gondi family in 1613, obtained various advantageous benefices; then suddenly, in 1617, he resigned all honours and from that time his behaviour became that of a saint.

Apart from some months passed as a country priest at Châtillon (Doubs) in 1617, and numerous journeys throughout France, it was at Paris that he lived from that time until his death. Made almoner of the galleys in 1619, in 1625 he founded the congregation of Priests of the Mission or Lazarists, to evangelize the poor of the countryside; this name of Lazarist came to them from the priory of St. Lazarus where they were established. In 1634, Monsieur Vincent, as he was called, founded the congregation of Sisters of Charity, as we have told on March 15th, on the occasion of the feast of St. Louise de Marillac. To him is also due the charity for the care of foundlings, established with the idea of collecting infants abandoned at street corners or on the church porches. It is scarcely an exaggeration to say that his influence extended to all religious France of his day.

It is, however, as a man of heart and a friend of the disinherited that his name has come down to posterity. He did so much for the poor, the sick and for children, that his name is still known and respected everywhere. Since his day it is less easy than before to pass for a Christian without showing an interest in the unfortunate and doing works of charity.

Sts. Justa and Rufina

Potters at Seville. It is said that they were put to death about 272 for having destroyed a statue of Salambo.

St. Arsenius

A Roman noble who withdrew into the desert of Scete after the capture of Rome by Alaric (410). He lived there to an advanced age, favoured with the gift of tears.

July 20th
ST. MARGARET (3rd century)

THE Greeks invoke her under the name of St. Marina. Her cult spread to the West following the crusades, and what is told of her seems legendary.

It is said that she was born at Antioch in Pisidia; her father, named Aedesius, occupied a high rank among the pagan priests; she was converted by her nurse and vowed to remain a virgin for the love of Christ. When her father learned this, he drove her out of the house and Margaret became a shepherdess in the countryside. One day when she was watching her sheep, she was seen by the prefect Olybrius, who, attracted by her beauty, said to a servant: "Go and find that maid; if she is free I will marry her; if she is a slave, I will take her as concubine." She was led to him; he interrogated her; and the maiden declared to him her noble birth, her name, and religion. "Of those three things," remarked Olybrius, "the two first become you; all is noble in you and there is not a pearl (margarita) in the world that equals you in beauty; but the third does not suit you at all, for it is unworthy in you to adore a crucified God." Whatever the girl answered to this so displeased Olybrius that he had her imprisoned. What she went on to say in audience the next day threw him into such a fury that he had her tied to the rack, beaten with rods, and torn with iron hooks.

One miracle after another took place in the prison where Margaret spent the rest of the day: she put to flight a dragon which tried to devour her; she seized the demon himself by the throat and trod him underfoot, forcing him to say why he so persecuted and tempted Christians. "It is", he replied, "because I hate virtue and wish to deprive Christians of the happiness I have lost." The next day, after new tortures and new miracles, and having prayed for her torturers and for those who would afterwards invoke her, Margaret had her head cut off with a blow of the sword.

St. ELIAS

Prophet of the Old Testament, born at Thisbe in Galaad (9th century B.C.).

St. AURELIUS

Bishop of Carthage and primate of Africa from 393 to 430. He is said to have had under him several provinces and almost five hundred bishops.

St. FLAVIAN

Bishop of Antioch. His zeal for orthodoxy caused his exile to Petra (Arabia) where he died in 512.

St. JEROME EMILIANI (1481–1537)

Venetian noble, who, after a military and profligate youth, devoted himself to the poor, sick, and orphans. He founded at Somasca, near Bergamo, a congregation which is called the Somaschi. He died of the plague in caring for the stricken of that city.

Blessed GREGORY LOPEZ (1542–1596)

Former page of Philip II, went to lead the solitary life in Mexico. An original, sympathetic, and remarkably gifted person.

July 21st

STS. VICTOR, LONGINUS,
ALEXANDER, AND FELICIAN (d. about 287)

ALTHOUGH its former splendour had declined, Marseilles still occupied at that epoch a place apart among the cities of the West. An autonomous republic, a great shipping port, the centre of Hellenic culture in Gaul, it was a rich, fine, and well-populated city. Greek was as much spoken there as Latin and Gaulish; all the religions of the Empire were represented there. Christianity had been implanted there two centuries before; its adherents were many and faithful.

If we are to believe the *Passion* of St. Victor, the Christians in Marseilles were stricken with terror when Maximianus Herculius arrived in the district on his way to Trier. If we accept the story, given here on September 22nd, this bloody tyrant had just massacred the whole Theban legion in the Valais.

An officer named Victor took it upon himself to comfort his trembling co-religionists. Denounced or taken by surprise, he was led before the prefects of his legion. They urged him kindly to remain faithful to the gods of Rome and to the friendship of the emperor rather than to adore a dead man called Jesus. In a loud voice Victor cried: "Your gods are demons. I am a soldier of Christ, the true God, crucified for us, arisen from the dead. What do military service and the friendship of the emperor mean to me, if for them I must betray my best beloved?" The prefects sent him to Maximianus before whom he continued to proclaim his faith. Wishing to make an example of him, the emperor ordered him to be dragged through the streets of the city. The populace heaped insults and blows upon him. He was then put in prison, where he converted three soldiers, Longinus, Alexander, and Felician, who immediately declared themselves Christians and were beheaded. As for Victor, after having been beaten by the lictors and tortured on the rack, he was crushed under a millstone on the public threshing floor, "like wheat chosen of God."

St. PRAXEDES (period uncertain)

Virgin honoured at Rome; her history is obscure.

St. DANIEL

Prophet of the Old Testament.

Blessed ODDINO BAROTTI (1334–1400)

Former pastor of Fossano (Piedmont), became a Franciscan tertiary, made great pilgrimages and died in his native town of Fossano in the course of an epidemic, a victim of his own charity.

July 22nd

ST. MARY MAGDALEN (1st century)

DEVOTION to St. Mary Magdalen has been widespread in the West since the 11th century. Few historians still defend the story of her sojourn in Provence, but the exegetes continue to question whether what the Gospels say of Mary of Bethany and of the harlot who anointed Our Lord must be applied to her. This is the problem and how it has been resolved:

The Gospel three times mentions Mary, sister of Martha and Lazarus, who lived at Bethany in Judaea. In St. Luke she is seen sitting at the Saviour's feet, while the busy Martha reproaches her for not bothering about the meal. "Martha, Martha," said Jesus, "how many cares and troubles thou hast! But only one thing is necessary; and Mary has chosen for herself the best part of all, that which shall never be taken away from her" (Luke x, 41–42). Mary of Bethany reappears throughout the chapter in which the resurrection of Lazarus is recounted (John xi); she is finally found with Martha and Lazarus at a repast which Simon the leper offered to Our Lord. That day she poured a pound of spikenard on the head and feet of the Saviour. "Why should not this ointment have been sold?" said Judas. "It would have fetched two hundred silver pieces, and alms might have been given to the poor." "Why do you vex the woman?" said Jesus. "You have the poor among you always; I am not always among you" (Mark xiv, Matt. xxvi, John xii).

Elsewhere the Gospel mentions, without giving her a name, a harlot who, at the house of Simon the Pharisee, came to kneel before Our Lord, anointing His feet with perfume, covering them with kisses and tears, and drying them with her hair. To the scandalized Pharisees, Jesus declared: "If great sins have been forgiven her, she has also greatly loved," and He sent away the harlot saying: "Thy faith has saved thee; go in peace" (Luke vii).

Finally the Gospel tells us of a woman called Mary Magdalen or Mary of Magdala in Judaea. She was of those women whom Jesus had delivered from evil spirits and who now were following Him and assisting Him with their goods. She was "the woman out of whom he had cast seven devils," which does not necessarily mean that she was or had been a sinner, since diabolical possession does not in any way imply a state of sin. We find Mary Magdalen again at Calvary, watching from afar; she was present at the burial, coming back to the sepulchre on Sunday before dawn; she was the first witness of the resurrection; it was she whom Jesus charged to announce His resurrection to the disciples. "Jesus said to her, Mary. And she turned and said to him, Rabboni (which is the Hebrew for Master)." Jesus added, "Do not cling to me thus; I have not yet gone up to my Father's side. Return to my brethren, and tell them this; I am going up to him who is my Father and your Father, who is my God and your God" (Matt. xxviii, Mark xvi, Luke xxiv, John xx).

What can be concluded from these texts? Must we see, with the Eastern liturgists and a number of Western exegetes, three different people in these women to whom Our Lord showed so much goodness? In this case, Mary Magdalen would not necessarily be a former sinner. Must we see one and the same person? Or must we see two, distinguishing on one hand Mary of Bethany, and on the other hand identifying Mary of Magdala with the anonymous sinner of St. Luke? In the last two cases, Mary Magdalen would certainly be such as she is represented in popular belief—the woman to whom many faults had been forgiven before she entered so intimately into the Saviour's circle.

St. WANDRILLE (d. 668)

Born in the neighbourhood of Verdun and related to Pepin of Landen, founded several abbeys, one of which was in the forest of Jumièges in Normandy.

St. LORENZO DA BRINDISI

Celebrated Capuchin, born at Brindisi in 1559, died at Lisbon in 1619, general of his order from 1602 to 1605. He preached throughout Europe, was the instigator of a crusade against the Turks which resulted in the victory of 1601, and was entrusted with important diplomatic missions.

July 23rd
ST. APOLLINARIS (d. about 200)

RAVENNA was in the 2nd century a commercial and strategic port to which merchants, soldiers, and sailors came in great numbers. It was among them that St. Apollinaris for a long time exercised his ministry and died. He was doubtless one of those poor itinerant priests, burning with the love of Christ, who had no other desire than to make Him known and loved among men. Perhaps he came from the East.

It is known that after 404, Ravenna replaced Rome as the capital of the Western Empire; from that time its bishops often set themselves up in rivalry to the Roman pontiff, attempting to extend their spiritual jurisdiction at his expense. It was natural that they should attempt to bring forth for their church origins in keeping with their claims. Thus there arose under Arch-bishop Maurus (642–671) the legend of a St. Apollinaris, a disciple at Antioch of the apostle St. Peter, who accompanied him to Rome and was charged by him with evangelizing Ravenna. This legend, embellished with a host of miracles and exploits, ended in the spectacular and anachronistic martyrdom of our saint, and helped incidentally to spread his cult in Italy and on the banks of the Rhine.

St. LIBORIUS

Probably lived in the 4th century; he was, it is believed, the second or third bishop of Le Mans.

St. ANNE or SUSANNA

Born at Constantinople of noble parentage, refused to marry a favourite of the Emperor Basil (867–886); she was persecuted for this until the death of this suitor permitted her to enter a convent of Leucadia; there she lived some fifty years and died in 918.

St. JOHN CASSIAN (d. 435?)

Born perhaps in Rumania, he became a monk at Bethlehem, spent some fifteen years in Egypt in the company of Antonine monks, was ordained deacon by St. John Chrysostom at Constantinople about 400, came to Rome in 405, reached the south of France in 415 and founded two monasteries, one for men, the other for women, at Marseilles. It was at the request of Castor, bishop of Apt and a founder of religious communities, that he drew up, from his experiences in Palestine and in Egypt, the twelve books of *Cenobitic Institutes and the Remedies for the Eight Capital Sins*. He also composed twenty-four *Conferences* from his recollections of his visits to the great monks of Lower Egypt. These works have had an immense influence on monastic life in the West and make Cassian one of the classic writers of Christian asceticism.

July 24th

ST. CHRISTINA THE ASTONISHING (d. about 1224)

BORN of a peasant family at Brusthem, in the diocese of Liége, about 1150, Christina became an orphan at fifteen. The facts which the Dominican Thomas de Cantimpré (d. 1270) and Cardinal Jacques de Vitry (d. 1244) report about her are almost incredible. Thomas de Cantimpré, former professor of theology at Louvain, certainly affirms that what he has to say of her comes from accounts of people who knew her, but he is extremely credulous; as for Jacques de Vitry, he is a very serious chronicler, and he assures us he knew Christina personally. "In her," he writes, "the divine operations were truly marvellous. She had been dead a long time and had obtained the grace of resuming her flesh in order to suffer her purgatory here below. Thus for many years she underwent extraordinary trials, sometimes rolling in the fire, sometimes remaining in icy water in the middle of winter, sometimes going as though despite herself into the tombs of the dead. In the end she was favoured with sublime graces and enjoyed profound peace. Often, her spirit in ecstasy, she led the souls of the dead to purgatory; sometimes she even lead them out of purgatory to paradise."

Her existence was filled with miracles and mysterious phenomena. The smell of sin nauseated her, and after contact with it, some time was necessary before she could stand her fellow men. She ended her life in the convent of St. Catherine at Saint-Trond, whose prioress testified that Christina had always been perfect in her submission.

St. CHRISTINA

There existed a St. CHRISTINA OF TYRE, highly honoured among the Greeks, and a CHRISTINA OF BOLSENA (Italy), who like the preceding was martyred towards the end of the era of persecution.

St. BORIS or ROMAN and St. GLEB or DAVID

Sons of St. Vladimir, assassinated by their brother Sviatopolk in 1015.

Blessed CUNEGUNDES (1224-1292)

Franciscan tertiary, wife of Boleslaus V, king of Poland, with whom she lived in continence.

Blessed ANTHONY TURRIANI (1414-1484)

First a surgeon, then an Augustinian hermit, born at Milan and died at Aquila. All his life he practised medicine successfully.

Blessed LOUISE OF SAVOY (1461–1503)

Daughter of Blessed Amadeus of Savoy, granddaughter of Charles VII, niece of Louis XI, cousin of St. Jeanne de Valois. She married Hugh of Châlons in 1479, lived happily with him until 1490 when she lost him, entered the Poor Clares at Orbe (Switzerland) in 1492, and died there July 20th, 1503.

July 25th

ST. JAMES THE GREATER (d. about 42)

HE is called "the Greater" in order to distinguish him from James the Less, "brother" of the Lord, whose feast is on May 1st.

Like St. John the Evangelist, James the Greater was a son of Zebedee, who possessed a fishing boat on the lake of Genesareth. One day when all three were repairing their nets, Jesus came by; He invited James and John to follow Him, and they did so. The Gospel shows James present at the cure of St. Peter's mother-in-law, at the raising of Jairus' daughter, and at the Transfiguration. James and John were surnamed by Jesus, Boanerges, "sons of thunder," on the day when they wanted to make the fire of heaven come down on a village which had refused to receive them. As the passion drew near they sent their mother to ask Jesus for a place of honour in His future kingdom. In the Garden of Olives, like Peter, they gave way to sleep during their Master's agony.

James the Greater must have been the first of the apostles to shed his blood for Christ. Having accompanied Peter to Jerusalem to celebrate Easter, he was arrested by Herod Agrippa who had him executed.

For eight centuries, the tomb of St. James was considered to be in Palestine or Marmarica. From the year 830 it was believed to have been in Galicia, and after the pilgrimages to Jerusalem and Rome that to Compostela became the most popular in Christendom.

ST. CHRISTOPHER (d. 251?)

ACCORDING to the Greek legend, Christopher was a barbarous cannibal; he suffered martyrdom in Lycia during the persecution of Decius which is known to have lasted only eighteen months but which was of incredible severity and extended to the whole Empire.

According to the Latin legend, Christopher was a giant. He measured twelve cubits, and when he walked he carried a tree as a staff. Not being a man to serve the first comer, he sought out the most powerful king on earth and entered his service. One day when a minstrel was singing before the king a song in which a good deal was said about the devil, Christopher noticed the king cross himself at the end of every verse. "Why so?" he said. The king replied: "It is so that the demon will not gain power over me." "Is the devil much stronger than you? If so, I shall leave you to enter his service." The giant met the demon and enrolled in his army. Passing with his master before a cross he noticed that Satan was trembling. "Are you afraid?" said Christopher. "Yes," answered the devil, "I fear Christ." "Then I am going to leave you in order to serve Christ." A holy hermit offered to instruct him. "What must I do?" asked the giant. "Fast, my son." "That will be difficult for me at first." "Then you must pray; always pray without ceasing." "But until I know my prayers, can I not begin with something else?" The hermit showed Christopher a turbulent river in which many people had been drowned. "If you stay here," he said, "to take the travellers across for nothing, it will be a charitable work for which Christ will be grateful." Christopher then became a ferryman, and thus it happened that one night he was hailed by a child who was the Infant Jesus, and he had the happiness of carrying Our Lord on his shoulders. In the middle ages it was believed sufficient to have seen an image of St. Christopher to be preserved all day from misfortune.

St. VALENTINA (d. 308)

A young virgin of Caesarea in Palestine, who reproached the governor of Gaza for torturing Christians and was flayed and then burned alive.

St. CUCUFATIS

Was martyred, it is said, at Barcelona in the 4th century.

July 26th

ST. ANNE (1st century)

THE name of the mother of Our Lady is known to us only through tradition; the Holy Scriptures do not in fact mention St. Anne at all; on the other hand the apocryphal gospels speak of her abundantly. *The Protevangelium of James* tells us that she was, like Joachim her husband, of the tribe of Juda, that both led a saintly life, possessed great herds, but unfortunately had no children. Among the Jews this was the worst ignominy; for Joachim it meant that at times the offering he brought to the temple was refused. But the day came when, after many prayers and humiliations, Anne gave birth to Mary, most perfect of human creatures, who was in turn to give birth to the Saviour.

The cult of St. Anne spread at first in the East; in the year 550 the Emperor Justinian raised a basilica in her honour at Constantinople; today the Greeks still have not less than three annual feasts to honour the grandmother of Our Lord.

In the West devotion to St. Anne seems to have gained popularity at the time of the crusades. Her feast, suppressed by St. Pius V, was re-established by Gregory XIII in 1594; Gregory XV in 1622 ordained it a public holiday; since Leo XIII it is celebrated in the Latin Church as a rite of the second class.

Nowhere in the world is St. Anne honoured and invoked as in Brittany where, from 1623 to 1625, she appeared to Yves Nicolazic de Keranna near Auray.

St. ERASTUS (1st century)
   Helper of St. Paul.

St. SIMEON
   Led the eremitic life in the country near Mantua (d. 1016).

St. BARTOLOMEA CAPITANIO (1807–1833)
   Born and died at Lovere in the diocese of Brescia; assisted St. Vincenza Gerosa in the founding of the Sisters of Charity of Lovere.

July 27th

STS. NATALIA, AURELIUS, LILIOSA, FELIX, AND GEORGE (d. 852)

So long as Cordova was dependent on the caliphs of the East, Christians who kept the peace were generally unmolested. The same was not the case after the kingdom became independent; from that time the Moors often took to persecution. Shortly before becoming their victim (in 859), St. Eulogius, archbishop of Toledo, devoted a few pages of his *Memorial* to martyrs we venerate today and who were his contemporaries.

Natalia, who was first called Sabagotha, had been a Moslem. Aurelius, her husband, was the son of an Arab and of a Spaniard of the best society.

Although they were both Christians, they hid the fact and conformed to Moslem customs. Aurelius had a relative named Felix who, with his wife called Liliosa, also abstained from all external practices of the faith. One day Aurelius, going through the streets, met a Christian perched nude astride an ass, facing the tail. The public criers went before him mocking; executioners were flogging him till blood ran. This was all that was required to send Aurelius home a changed man. From that moment, far from dissimulating, he and his wife openly lived a penitent and fervent life; foreseeing what would happen to them they gave their goods to the poor, except as much as was needed to assure their daughter's future. Won over by their example, Felix and Liliosa compromised themselves in the same way.

All were arrested under the pretext that Liliosa and Natalia had appeared in the street without the veil which Moslem women wear in public. With them was arrested a beggar named George, to whom Aurelius was giving hospitality at that time. George hailed from Palestine and, fearing that since he was a stranger he would be deprived of martyrdom, before the cadi he set about insulting Mohammed, dubbing him a son of the devil, a minister of Antichrist, and labyrinth of all vices. The cadi sentenced him to death with his companions, and they were executed in the following order: Felix, George, Liliosa, Aurelius, and Natalia.

St. Pantaleon (d. 305)

Said to have been a doctor and to have suffered martyrdom at Nicomedia.

St. Desiderius

Bishop of Besançon (5th century).

St. Celestine I

Pope (d. 432).

St. Ursus

Native of Cahors, founded monasteries in Berry and Touraine (5th-6th centuries). Today is also the feast of a St. Ursus, seventh bishop of Troyes, who died about 426.

The Seven Sleepers of Ephesus

About 250, says the legend, seven Christians died immured in a cave near Ephesus. A century later they awoke to confound those who denied the resurrection of the body; then they sank back into sleep.

July 28th

ST. SAMSON (6th century)

A NATIVE of Wales, Samson was brought up in the abbey of Llanwit, then ruled by St. Illtyd. By his virtue and gaiety he won all hearts except that of the nephew of St. Illtyd, who tried to poison him. But the poisoned brew which he gave him by good luck proved innocuous, and Samson was able to pursue his religious studies in peace. He was ordained priest by Dubric, bishop of Caerleon. We then find him as bursar, later abbot of the monastery of Caldey; he left it to visit and evangelize Ireland. He returned to Wales where he persuaded his father Ammon and his mother Anna to enter a monastery and a convent; lived for some time as a hermit near the mouth of the Severn; went to preach in Cornwall, then passed over to Armorica, landing at the mouth of the Guyoult on the spot where the town of Dol was to rise.

It was chiefly in Brittany that Samson gave rein to his zeal and his gift for organization. He built a monastery-bishopric on lands which a Gallo-Roman named Privatus had granted him. It rose from the marshes and was easy of defence, and had in its dependence numerous other abbeys and centres of religious life in Domnonia. Dol thus became the spiritual metropolis of the Breton country.

The bishop-abbot of Dol made two journeys to Paris to win Childebert to the side of Judwal, legitimate king of Domnonia, from whom the usurper and assassin Conomor had snatched the throne. Due to the support of St. Germain of Paris, Samson obtained Conomor's eviction; on the same occasion he received from the king of Neustria a territory at the mouth of the Seine where he founded an abbey, and he was accorded jurisdiction over the "Anglo-Norman" Channel Islands.

Immediately after his death, Samson was honoured in England, Normandy, and Brittany; his cult has spread to Italy; today sixteen parishes in France bear his name.

Sts. NAZARIUS and CELSUS

Martyrs of the primitive Church, honoured at Milan.

St. VICTOR I

Pope (d. about 200). St. Irenaeus of Lyons succeeded in dissuading him from excommunicating those of the Oriental Church who persisted in celebrating the feast of Easter on the 14th of Nisan.

St. INNOCENT I

Pope (d. about 417), witnessed the capture of Rome by the barbarians of Alaric in 410.

St. GÉRAN (d. 914)

Bishop of Auxerre, was born at Soissons, fought the Normans, sword in hand, and inflicted many defeats upon them.

July 29th

ST. MARTHA (1st century)

SISTER of Lazarus and Mary of Bethany (*see July 22nd*), St. Martha is known to us only by the Holy Scripture; in it three references are made to her.

The first is on the occasion of the repast she prepared for Jesus; on that day Our Lord addressed the following words to the too-restless mistress of the house: "Martha, Martha, how many cares and troubles thou hast! But only one thing is necessary; and Mary has chosen for herself the best part of all, that which shall never be taken away from her" (Luke x, 41–42).

Martha appears a second time after the resurrection of Lazarus. "Jesus," says St. John, "loved Martha, and her sister, and Lazarus." Learning that Jesus was come, Martha said to Him: "If thou hadst been here, my brother would not have died; and I know well that even now God will grant whatever thou wilt ask of him." Jesus said to her: "Thy brother will rise again." Martha said to Him: "I know well enough that he will rise again at the resurrection, when the last day comes." Jesus said to her: "I am the resurrection and life; he who believes in me, though he is dead, will live on, and whoever has life, and has faith in me, to all eternity cannot die. Dost thou believe this?" She answered Him: "Yes, Lord, I have learned to believe that thou art the Christ; thou art the Son of the living God; it is for thy coming the world has waited" (John xi, 1–28).

Finally, Martha is referred to by the evangelist when he tells of the meal of which Jesus partook at the house of Simon the Leper. He simply tells us, this time, that Martha took care of the service (John xii, 1–9).

Relics of St. Martha are believed to have been found at Tarascon in 1187. In the following century, the Franciscans assigned her feast a date in their breviary, and from that time her cult took on a certain importance in the West. Hotelkeepers have chosen her as their patroness.

St. BEATRIX

Roman martyr (d. 304).

St. LUPUS

Bishop of Troyes (d. about 478).

St. OLAF

King of Norway (d. 1030).

St. WILLIAM

Bishop of Saint-Brieuc (d. 1234).

St. CONSTANTINE

Patriarch of Constantinople (d. 677).

St. SERAPHIA

Roman virgin, is supposed to have been the friend of St. Sabina (*see August 29th*) and to have been put to death with her.

July 30th

ST. JULITTA (d. about 305)

IT is from a homily of St. Basil that we know the circumstances of the martyrdom of St. Julitta of Caesarea in Cappadocia.

This Christian widow had formerly been possessed of great wealth, but taking advantage of her weakness one of the notables of the town had almost entirely despoiled her. He was making ready to filch the rest of her property, when she resolved to sue him. The suit was going badly for the despoiler; the witnesses suborned by him were ill at ease; the judges were preparing to rule that he make restitution. Suddenly he sprang towards the tribunal in the middle of the forum. "This woman," he declared, "ought not to appear in court, for she is a Christian; and those who refuse to adore the gods of the emperors enjoy no civil rights." The imperial edict of 303 did indeed put the Christians outside the law, even depriving them of the right to claim damages for harm done to them.

At once withdrawing Julitta's plea, the president of the tribunal had an altar and incense brought before him. As he pressed the plaintiff to sacrifice, she cried: "May my body perish rather than deny God, my Creator!" To the insistence of the magistrate, she confined herself to saying that she was Christ's servant. He condemned her to the stake. She walked to it consoling with a smile her friends who wished to give her consolation, and urging them to suffer for Christ if occasion required it. She flung herself on the pyre, says her panegyrist, as though upon a glorious bed, and the fire choked her without destroying her body.

In Basil's time the body of Julitta was venerated in a church in Caesarea; at the place of her torture still flowed a spring which sometimes healed the sick.

St. ABEL

Son of Adam and Eve, killed by Cain.

St. RUFINUS

Has been honoured at Assisi since the earliest times.

St. DONATILLA

Martyred at Tebourba, south of Carthage, during the persecution of Maximinus (d. 304).

Blessed MANES

Brother of St. Dominic and one of the first Dominicans (d. about 1230).

Sts. ABDON and SENNEN (date uncertain)

Their legend represents them as Persian princes who distinguished themselves by their zeal for burying the martyrs. Decius is thought to have brought them to Rome where they died in torture.

July 31st

ST. IGNATIUS LOYOLA (d. 1556)

NATIVE of the province of Guipuzcoa, in the Spanish Basque country, youngest of a noble family of twelve children, Ignatius received a military education and led, it seems, a youth that was far from edifying. Defending Pampeluna against the French, he was struck on May 20th, 1521, by a bullet which broke his leg and put his life in danger. On June 24th, at the castle of Loyola where he had been taken, the last sacraments were administered to him; then a turn for the better took place. Many months of convalescence were to follow; he asked for novels to pass the time; the only books that could be found for him were *The Golden Legend* and *The Life of Christ* by Ludolph the Carthusian. These books transformed him and he resolved to imitate the saints. After being restored to health, he pronounced the vow of chastity, hung his sword before the altar of the Virgin at Montserrat, bought a pilgrim's outfit, and prepared to depart for the Holy Land. He passed the last months of 1522 lodged in the hospital at Manresa and retiring during the daytime to a cave. From his meditations, prayers, scruples, penances, revelations, visions, graces, trials, and spiritual experiences at Manresa came the works which, together with the *Constitutions* of the Society of Jesus, have won St. Ignatius his fame as a psychologist and trainer of men. This little book, approved by Paul III in 1548, and so highly recommended by Pius XI, is entitled *The Spiritual Exercises*. After a pilgrimage to the holy places (1523), sojourns in Spain (1524-1527), in Paris (1528-1535), in Venice (1535-1537), and journeys to England, Flanders and elsewhere, Ignatius arrived in Rome about the end of 1537. He lived there until his death, directing the institution which he had formed eight years before. The Society of Jesus received the pontifical approbation by the bull *Regimini Ecclesiae militantis* of September 27th, 1540. At the founder's death it comprised twelve provinces and seventy-seven houses. Suppressed by Clement XIV in 1773, it was re-established in the kingdom of Naples in 1804 and in the entire world in 1814. Today it possesses more than five hundred universities and colleges, gives instruction to more than 200,000 pupils, and has nearly 30,000 members.

St. FABIUS

Christian soldier martyred at Caesarea in Mauretania in 303 or 304.

St. PETER II

Bishop of Ravenna (d. 519?).

St. JOHN COLOMBINI (d. 1367)

Rich Sienese merchant who at the age of fifty was converted by reading, for lack of anything else, the story of Mary of Egypt in *The Lives of the Saints*. He founded the order of the Jesuati, suppressed in 1668 by Clement IX.

St. GERMAIN OF AUXERRE (d. 448)

Born at Auxerre, became bishop of that town after having been a high Roman official; made two journeys to Britain to fight Pelagianism; died at Ravenna where he was interceding for the Bretons at the imperial court.

THE SAINTS OF AUGUST

August 1st

ST. BAUDARINUS or BAUDRY (d. 545)

ONLY ONE biography of St. Baudarinus is in existence, that of Nicolas de Beaufort who lived six centuries after his hero. According to this author, it was about the year 500 that Baudarinus succeeded St. Lupus in the episcopal see of Soissons, at that time the residence of Clotaire, son of Clovis.

Our saint's misfortunes came from the slanders which were spread about him, and because he refused to the king goods of the Church coveted by him. Clotaire drove Baudarinus from his see and to avoid prison, or something worse, he set off in quick time for the Atlantic coast, embarking for England after writing his name and the date of his departure on a rock. He spent seven years in that country working at the cultivation of a monastery garden. Into this he put so much hard work and ability that never, Nicolas de Beaufort assures us, had the monks eaten such excellent vegetables. He also grew simples, and used them to cure a great number of sick people.

Meanwhile the people of Soissons mourned his absence, especially when a famine, following a drought, lay waste the country. These things were considered to be a punishment from heaven and the king was begged to recall the exile. Clotaire consented and the search began. They were helped by the inscription which Baudarinus had written on the rock on the coast. However, he did not give an altogether warm reception to the envoys from Soissons. "You would like me to come back," he said to them, "from the peace I have found to the people who drove me away like a mad dog?" Then he became convinced that God wished him to return to Soissons. He was received there in triumph, and the drought ended as did also the famine. And Baudarinus so completely forgot the ill treatment he had received that he cured, with simples brought from England, the king's daughter and various relatives of his former enemies.

St. EXUPERIUS or SPIRE

Lived, it is believed, in the 4th century. In the 9th century we know that he was regarded as the first bishop of Bayeux.

St. ARCADIUS

Bishop of Bourges for about fifteen years, died before 549.

St. JONATUS

Abbot of Marchiennes near Douai, died about 690.

Blessed JOHN OF RIETI (d. 1347)

Augustinian of the monastery of Amelia; the sight of the beauties of nature moved him to tears.

St. PETER ADVINCULA

This is the title of a Roman church already in existence in the 4th century, where there are still venerated two links of the chain which the apostle wore in prison.

August 2nd

ST. ALPHONSUS LIGUORI (1696-1787)

BORN at Naples, September 27th, 1696, of Don Joseph Liguori, a distinguished gentleman, and Donna Anna Cavalieri, a very fervent Christian, Alphonsus led from childhood a pious and pure life. Of his six brothers and sisters, two became priests and two nuns. He himself was first a precocious and brilliant barrister; a lawsuit which he lost at the age of twenty-seven turned him away from the bar. Ordained priest three years later, he exercised his ministry among the poor of his native town and the surrounding mountains until 1762, when he founded at Scala the Congregation of the Most Holy Redeemer.

The rule of the Redemptorists was approved by Benedict XIV in 1748. These monks were then about fifty in number, confined to the districts of the kingdom of Naples; today they number about six thousand, spread throughout the whole world. Their founder wished them to leave aside literary and theoretical discourses, and to preach practical sermons, retreats, and missions. This was the example he himself gave them, speaking of the Holy Eucharist, of the Virgin Mary, of prayer, and of the last things in such a way as to move the most barren hearts.

The miracle of bilocation which he accomplished to transport himself to the bedside of the dying Clement XIV is well known. It took place on September 21st, 1774. That day, after Mass, Alphonsus sat down in his armchair and remained there, mute and inert, until the following morning about seven o'clock. On awakening he declared that he had been to Rome to help the pope, who, in fact, as was soon known, had just died. At that time Alphonsus was at Sant' Agata de' Goti, an episcopal see he occupied from 1762 to 1775. His last years were filled with sufferings, temptations, and trials. He died at over ninety, and to a certain extent in disgrace.

His books had a great influence on the piety of his period and two of them, *Visits to the Blessed Sacrament* and *The Glories of Mary*, continue to edify innumerable souls. By his *Moral Theology*, compassionate and wise, halfway between the doctrines of the rigourists and the laxists, St. Alphonsus caused to prevail the system called "probabilism," today generally accepted in the Church.

St. SERENUS

Bishop of Marseilles, died at the beginning of the 7th century. Among the letters written to him by Gregory the Great, there is one in which the pope reproaches him with having despoiled his churches of their statues and images.

St. ALFRIDA or ETHELDREDA

Daughter of Offa, king of Mercia, lived for some forty years as a recluse on the island of Croyland and died about 840.

St. STEPHEN I

Pope from 254 to 257, died a martyr. He formulated the axiom against innovations and in favour of the apostolic tradition: *Nil innovetur nisi quod traditum est.*

August 3rd

ST. LYDIA (1st century)

ST. LYDIA was converted by St. Paul towards the year 55, in the course of a voyage he was making in Macedonia. St. Luke accompanied the apostle at that time, and it is he who speaks in the following passage of the Acts, reporting these events:

"So we put out from Troas, made a straight course to Samothrace, and next day to Neapolis. Thence we reached Philippi, which is a Roman colony and the chief city in that part of Macedonia; in this city we remained for some days, conferring together. On the sabbath day we went out beyond the city gates, by the river side, a meeting-place, we were told, for prayer; and we sat down and preached to the women who had assembled there. One of those who were listening was a woman called Lydia, a purple-seller from the city of Thyatira, and a worshipper of the true God; and the Lord opened her heart, so that she was attentive to Paul's preaching. She was baptized, with all her household; and she was urgent with us; Now you have decided that I have faith in the Lord, she said, come to my house and lodge there; and she would take no denial" (Acts xvi, 11-15).

Apart from this nothing is known of St. Lydia.

St. NICODEMUS

Doctor of the Law, came to Jesus by night and heard from His mouth the sublime discourse reported by St. John (iii, 1-21). A member of the Sanhedrin, he was able temporarily to prevent the Saviour's arrest (John vii, 50-52). After the passion he obtained the custody of His body, and, with Joseph of Arimathea, he embalmed it and laid it in the sepulchre (John xix, 39-40).

Blessed GEOFFREY DE LOUDOUN

Bishop of Le Mans, died at Anagni in 1255, buried in the charterhouse of Parc-Saint-Denis which he founded.

Blessed PETER JULIAN EYMARD (1811-1868)

Born and died at La Mure (Isère). First a member of the Marist congregation, he left it in order to found another called the Fathers of the Blessed Sacrament.

August 4th

ST. DOMINIC (1170-1221)

THE founder of the Order of Preachers was born at the castle of Calaruega, in Old Castile, June 24th, 1170. His father was called Felix de Guzmán; his mother, Juana of Aza, has been beatified by the Church. From his childhood Dominic applied himself to study and the practice of virtue; about the age of twenty-five, he became canon regular at the cathedral of Osma; but it was only in the course of a journey to Rome in 1205, with his bishop, that his true vocation became apparent.

Innocent III, who had just designated the Cistercians to convert the Albigenses, invited the two Spaniards to join them. The Cistercian methods were unavailing; seeing the pontifical legates come forth in fine array, the populace only admired the more the austerity of the Catharist apostles and allowed themselves to be indoctrinated by them. The Cistercians quickly left the field to them; the bishop of Osma soon succumbed under the task; and Dominic took the head of his mission. He recruited some priests who had decided to live up to their principles and with them continued his preaching. These "preachers" practised rigorous penances, went barefoot, and organized debates which sometimes lasted several days. Nevertheless, the Cathari refused to listen to reason, and it was decided in 1209 to conquer them by force of arms. In 1215, Dominic temporarily left the theatre of war and came to Rome where the approbation of his order was given him. Meanwhile he had established at Prouille, not far from Carcassonne, a convent of cloistered nuns, cradle of the future Dominican nuns.

St. Dominic died at Bologna in 1221. With the encouragement of the Roman Curia, he had strongly urged upon his brethren the necessity of study, "whether on journeys, at home, by day or night"; and he had succeeded so well that half a century after his time the Dominicans possessed about seven hundred doctors in theology, whereas in 1220, there were not twenty-five to be found in Europe.

St. ARISTARCHUS
Fellow apostle and brother in captivity of St. Paul (1st century).

St. RAYNERIUS
Camaldolite, bishop of Cagli in 1154, archbishop of Spalato in 1175, stoned to death by the Slovenes in 1180.

August 5th

ST. ABEL (d. 8th century)

AT that time Gaul was still nominally governed by the descendants of Clovis, but their dynasty was soon to disappear and to give place to the Carolingians. Already the mayor of the palace, Charles Martel, was acting as virtual ruler. His victory over the Saracens at Poitiers conferred new prestige on him, and from that time the pope himself considered him to be the saviour of Christianity. Charles, moreover, favoured the Church by supporting the apostolic efforts of St. Willibrord in Frisia, St. Pirmin in Alemannia, St. Boniface in Thuringia and in Bavaria, and these apostolic conquests increased Charles' own influence on the far bank of the Rhine. Nevertheless, in Gaul itself the bishops and the monks could not always go along with Charles. Rarely, in fact, has there been seen a greater lover of the Church or a greater despoiler of its goods. Charles plundered the bishoprics and the abbeys to enrich and reward his warriors. A number of episcopal sees remained vacant because their temporal possessions were taken over by his liege men.

Such was the origin of the misfortunes of St. Abel. He came from Scotia. St. Boniface, who had organized the Germanic Church, was then attempting to reform the Frankish Church. Knowing the merits of Abel who had distinguished himself in the conversion of the northern countries, he brought about in 743 his election to the episcopal see of Rheims. This see had been vacant ever since St. Rigobert had been driven out; and Milo, archbishop of Trier, who occupied it in order to handle its considerable revenues, was an interloper. Giving way to the insistence of St. Boniface, Charles Martel recognized Abel's election. But the latter could only maintain himself at Rheims for a few years, so great were the vexations caused him by Milo and the indulgence of the ruler for this rapacious man. Then Abel, whose very life was in danger, was forced to withdraw to the abbey of Lobbes in Hainaut where he died between 750 and 780.

DEDICATION OF THE CHURCH OF ST. MARY OF THE SNOW

THE Roman church of this name was consecrated by Pope Sixtus III about 435. According to a medieval legend, it was built by a patrician named John to whom the Blessed Virgin had appeared at night to tell him that snow would fall on the spot where she wished a sanctuary built in her honour. Although it was the month of August, John did, in fact, find snow on the Esquiline hill the following day.

St. Oswald

King of Northumbria, killed in the battle of Maserfield, August 5th, 642. He had spread the Christian religion and favoured the monastic life in his realm.

St. Nonna

Had three children: St. Gregory, who was bishop of Nazianzus; St. Caesarius, who was a physician; St. Gorgonia, who was mother of a family.

St. Emidius

Martyred at Ascoli in the Marches of Ancona about 304.

August 6th

ST. SIXTUS II (d. 258)

Sixtus II governed the Roman Church from 257 until 258. He was, says the author of the life of St. Cyprian, "a good and peace-loving pontiff." In default of other details concerning him we know the circumstances of his martyrdom.

Sixtus was arrested on August 6th, 258, at the cemetery of Praetextatus in virtue of the recent edict of Valerian prescribing death for the leaders of the Christians. He was sitting on his throne when soldiers appeared with orders for his arrest. They took him to the prefect who was holding continuous sessions for judging refractories, and the pontiff was condemned to be executed in the place where he had been arrested. As he was being taken back to the cemetery, the archdeacon Lawrence ran up to him. "Where are you going, father, without your son?" he said in tears. "Where are you going, priest, without your deacon?" "My son, I do not desert you," replied the pontiff. "Greater combats await you; but dry your tears for you shall follow me in three days." We know that in fact Lawrence was put to death three days later. As for Sixtus II, he continued on his way, went down to the crypt, sat for the last time on his throne, stretched out his neck for the executioner, and was beheaded.

BLESSED OCTAVIANUS (d. 1128)

Son of William II of Burgundy, called the Hard-Headed, Octavianus was born about 1060 at Quingey, today the chief town of the canton of Doubs.

Among his twelve brothers and sisters were Hugh III, who was archbishop of Besançon, and Callistus II, who was pope. Octavianus received his first schooling at Cluny where in 1078, to be exact, one of his relatives, Guy II, count of Mâcon, embraced the monastic life with thirty of his knights.

A knowledge of law was then necessary for those destined to high office, and nowhere was it better taught than at Bologna. At his father's command, Octavianus had to leave the abbey of Cluny for the University of Bologna; there he stayed as pupil, then as professor; but when William II died, his son, free to follow his vocation, entered the monastery of San Pietro in Cielo d'Oro, at Pavia. There he lived for thirty years in the practice of religious observances and the study of Holy Scripture. Sometimes he also gave his help to the bishop of the diocese. He had to pass the five last years of his own life on the episcopal throne of Savona. He had not sought this office, but once a bishop, he took all the measures demanded by the interests of his flock. Difficulties were created for him by his canons; to reform them, he temporarily removed their prebends. He constrained Roger II of Sicily to restore to Savona a galley which he had taken from the city. Above all he gave free rein to his love for the sick and the poor, spending his entire fortune for their sake and working several miracles.

Sts. JUSTUS and PASTOR

Martyrs in Castile (d. 304).

Blessed BERTHA (d. 1151)

Is buried at the abbey of Biburg which she founded.

The TRANSFIGURATION OF OUR LORD

From the 5th century on, the Nestorians celebrated a feast called the Metamorphosis of Christ, in memory of the happening related by the Gospels (Mark ix, Luke ix, Matt. xvii). Pope Callistus III extended it to the whole Church in 1457 to commemorate the victory of John Hunyady and John Capistran over the Turks.

August 7th

ST. CAJETAN (1480–1547)

BORN in Vicenza, Cajetan de Tiene was noted from his infancy for his piety and his great love of the poor. After having studied law at Padua and practised it for some time in his native town, he bought a post as apostolic secretary at the Roman court. He did not take orders till the age of thirty-six; an indult of Leo XI authorized him to receive them all in four days. In 1518, he returned to Vicenza where the death of the countess of Tiene, his mother, placed him in possession of a considerable fortune. The destitute and the sick were the only ones to profit from it, for he himself embraced voluntary poverty and spent his time in the hovels of the poor. At first his noble relatives and friends bore him a grudge for seeking the company of the unfortunate, but little by little he found among the nobility of Vicenza and of Verona and Venice helpers in his work of sweeping out the hospitals and caring for the incurable.

In 1523, when Luther was so angrily fulminating against ecclesiastical scandals, Cajetan was inspired to found an order of priests whose lives would recall that of the apostles and who would serve as models for all the clergy. He again took the road for Rome, and there found understanding and support in Giovanni Pietro Caraffa, Bonifacio da Colle, and Paulo Consiglieri. Caraffa was placed at the head of the new religious order, and as he was bishop of Theate or Chieti, it was called Theatine. The poverty of the monks was at first so great that, not content with possessing nothing, they abstained from begging, confining themselves to receiving voluntary gifts. They were obliged to care for the sick, aid those condemned to death, spread the use of the sacraments among the laity, and bring back the clergy to their duties by their example. In Cajetan's lifetime they were already established at Rome, Naples, and Venice.

It was at Naples that our saint died, stretched out upon ashes, after asking that his body be thrown into the common grave.

St. DONATUS (7th century)

Bishop of Besançon, he founded the monastery of St. Paul in that city and wrote a rule for the nuns of St. Mary's Abbey. This rule was inspired by that of St. Benedict, but it also prescribed numerous corporal corrections.

Another St. DONATUS

Also honoured today; considered by some to have been the second bishop of Arezzo.

Blessed JORDAN OF PADUA

Benedictine abbot of St. Justina in that town. He was much concerned with politics, leagued the Lombard towns together against Otto IV and Frederick II, was at one time imprisoned by Ezzelino, and died at almost ninety years of age at Venice in 1248.

August 8th

STS. CYRIACUS, LARGUS, SMARAGDUS, AND SISINNIUS

CYRIACUS, Sisinnius, Largus, and Smaragdus succoured the Christians employed in the building of the palace and the thermal baths which Maximianus destined for his father-in-law, Diocletian. Their charitable role having been discovered, they were imprisoned, then constrained to take part in the forced labour of their persecuted brethren. Sisinnius was then condemned to death for having given help to an old man named Saturninus. As for Cyriacus, called to the bedside of Artemia, Diocletian's daughter who was possessed of a demon, he delivered her and received in recognition from the emperor a house which later became the Church of St. Cyriacus. Artemia and the empress, her mother, were converted. It happened that the king of Persia's daughter likewise fell into the power of a demon, and appealed to the ministrations of the powerful exorcist. He left with Largus and Smaragdus, cured the princess, converted her as well as her father to Christianity, then helped by his companions, administered baptism to several thousand Persians. Finally they were all, on returning to Rome, put to death for the faith. This was the little hagiographical romance thought up in the 5th or 6th century to explain how the church, which at that time arose at Rome near Diocletian's baths, is called the cardinalate church of St. Cyriacus.

FOURTEEN HOLY HELPERS

THE devotion to the Holy Helpers or Auxiliaries started in Germany and from there spread to Italy, France, and other countries. It was in great vogue in France in the 14th century.

Fourteen saints are thus called, and their collective feast is celebrated today. The reader will find information about each of them on the day of his special feast. We will limit ourselves here to giving their names and indicating the powers which are attributed to them.

St. Blaise (February 3rd) is invoked for maladies of the throat; St. George (April 23rd) for skin diseases; St. Erasmus (June 2nd) for intestinal diseases; St. Guy or Vitus (June 15th) for nervous attacks and the dance bearing his name; St. Margaret (July 20th) cures ailments of the kidneys and comes to the help of those in childbirth; St. Christopher (July 25th) is protector against all kinds of accidents and notably sudden death; St. Barbara

(December 4th) also prevents sudden death and is, in addition, the patroness of mathematicians, artillerymen, and firemen; St. Acacius (May 8th) cures headaches; St. Cyriacus (August 8th) maladies of the eye; St. Pantaleon (July 27th) wasting diseases; St. Giles or Egidius (September 1st) is invoked in cases of diabolical possession; St. Eustachius (September 20th) is supposed to fight effectively against fires and to protect us from eternal fire; St. Catherine (November 25th) is the patroness of lawyers, philosophers, and scholars; St. Dionysius the Areopagite (October 9th) is invoked against headaches and attacks by the devil.

St. HUGOLINA (d. about 1300)

Lived for forty-seven years as a recluse near Vercelli, clothed in men's garments.

Blessed JUANA OF AZA

Mother of St. Dominic (d. about 1190).

August 9th

ST. JEAN-BAPTISTE-MARIE VIANNEY (1786–1859)

JEAN-MARIE is the first name which the holy pastor of Ars received at baptism on May 8th, 1786; twenty-one years later, when he was confirmed by Cardinal Fesch at Ecully, he chose St. John the Baptist as additional patron and signed himself from that time Jean-Marie-Baptiste or Jean-Baptiste-Marie Vianney.

His childhood was passed in a time of political upheaval and religious persecutions. At his parents' home at Dardilly, near Lyons, the crucifix and other Christian emblems had to be removed from the house. Little Vianney made his first Communion in secret at the neighbouring village of Ecully. There, lived a holy priest, Abbé Balley, who later helped him to follow his vocation. While waiting, Jean-Marie watched his parents' sheep and helped his brother work in the fields. Called up for military service, he became ill, and having become a delinquent conscript in spite of himself, was obliged, in order to escape Napoleon's police, to hide in the Cévennes. He had a thousand difficulties in becoming a priest; knowing nothing of philosophy and being unable to learn Latin, he was dismissed from the seminary at Lyons; three months later, in spite of much supplementary coaching from Father Balley, he again failed in the examinations for ordination. Finally the vicar-general came to interrogate him in French in the presbytery of Ecully; only then, in his thirtieth year, was he judged worthy to receive the priesthood and to become curate to Father Balley. The latter died in December 1817, bequeathing to him his instruments of penance; some weeks after, the Abbé Vianney was named pastor of Ars.

It took him but twenty-five years to transform this parish of two hundred and thirty inhabitants, from which the practice of religion had disappeared, into a fervent Christian community. He achieved this by the force of his zeal, patience, prayers, charity, and the revived penances of the Desert Fathers. Ars became celebrated throughout Europe; in a single year it was visited by more than a hundred thousand pilgrims. From all France and from abroad people flocked to throw themselves at the feet of the saintly pastor who clearly could read hearts. For thirty years he spent sixteen to twenty hours a day in the confessional. For thirty years, too, he was tormented by the demon.

His end was one of perfect serenity. On Saturday, July 31st, 1859, he received with tears in his eyes the Viaticum and extreme unction; and the following Thursday, August 4th, he drew his last breath with a smile.

St. AMOR

Honoured in Franche-Comté where, it is believed, he was one of the Theban legion.

St. SAMUEL OF EDESSA

A priest whose polemical writings in Syriac are considerable (5th century).

St. MAURILIUS (d. 1067)

Born at Champagne, he studied at Rheims and Liége, taught at Halberstadt, was a monk at Fécamp, a hermit in Italy, abbot of St. Mary's at Florence, and ended his days as archbishop of Rouen.

August 10th

ST. LAWRENCE (d. 258)

THE edict published by Valerian in 258 against the Christians was extremely rigorous; the most important of them were to be put to death and their goods confiscated. We have seen that one of the first victims of this persecution was Pope Sixtus II. In order to seize the possessions of the Church, the arrest of the archdeacon Lawrence was decided immediately thereafter. According to St. Ambrose it happened as follows:

Holder of the ecclesiastical purse, guardian of the account books and keys, Lawrence found himself, after the pope, the chief personage in the Christian community. The prefect of Rome, Cornelius Saecularis, sent for him and enjoined him to deliver up his treasure. Having foreseen confiscation, Lawrence had hastened to change the property he administered into cash, and all had been passed out as alms. And St. Ambrose, a century later, praises him for having acted in this way. "It is a breach of trust," he wrote, "for the riches of the Church to be put to one's own use; but it is an act of charity to use them in ransoming captives and succouring the poor."

Lawrence asked the prefect for time to get together and inventory his treasures. He came back the next day followed by a crowd of beggars. "Behold the treasures of the Church," he said, indicating them. Furious at having been tricked, the magistrate condemned the archdeacon to be roasted over a slow fire. He had him stretched on a gridiron, believing evidently that this long and frightful torture would make the sufferer reveal the whereabouts of the riches he was hiding. But Lawrence showed admirable courage. He even kept his good humour, if St. Ambrose is to be believed, for at a given time he began to mock his tormentor. "My flesh is well cooked on one side," he said to him, "turn the other, and eat." And, his eyes to heaven, he died praying for the city of Rome.

St. PHILOMENA

In 1802 the name of St. Philomena was given to an unknown martyr whose bones were found in the catacomb of Priscilla; near the tomb was a broken tablet with the inscription *Filumena, Pax Tecum.* Her renown became universal. She worked numerous miracles, and the Curé d'Ars, notably, attributed to her all that he accomplished.

St. AREY or AREGIUS

Appointed archbishop of Lyons in 603 by Queen Brunehaut, died about 620. His political activity has been strongly criticized.

St. HUGH OF MONTAIGU

Abbot of St. Germain of Auxerre, later bishop of that town (d. about 1136).

St. AUTOR

Was, it seems, bishop of Metz when, in 451, this city was taken by the Huns.

St. Blane

It is believed that he was a bishop in Scotland in the 6th century.

August 11th

ST. SUSANNA (d. end of the 3rd century)

Susanna was a young Roman woman who was put to death at the end of the 3rd century for having wished to remain a virgin. Her cult is very ancient, but the *Acts* of her martyrdom are a mass of anachronisms and inaccuracies.

They place on the scene the following: the Emperor Diocletian and his wife Serena; Caesar Galerius, son-in-law of Diocletian; Susanna, a young Roman patrician, daughter of Gabinius, herself related to Diocletian; Pope Caius, brother of Gabinius; Claudius, his wife, his sons, and his brother Maximus, who were also relatives of Diocletian; finally, Macedonius, an officer of the imperial guard.

The story begins at the moment when Caesar Galerius became a widower and thought of marrying a second time. Diocletian decided to make him marry Susanna and sent Claudius to ask her father. Having discussed the matter together, Gabinius and Caius resolved to let Susanna decide freely. Claudius then went to Susanna's; as soon as he opened his mouth, she declared that she wished to remain a virgin; she then sang the praises of her faith so warmly that Claudius went away converted. Having gone home he converted his wife and two sons and, entirely occupied with good works, thought no more about his mission. A month went by; Diocletian was informed about Claudius, let fall that he was ill, and charged Maximus to take his place. Susanna greeted Maximus in the same way as Claudius and with the same discourse, so that he in turn was converted.

These conversions determined Diocletian to burn Claudius alive with his wife, his sons, and his brother, and to put Susanna in prison. After spending fifty-five days there, she was taken to the house of the Empress Serena, who was to make her listen to reason, but Serena, who practised Christianity in secret, strengthened Susanna in her resolution.

It was at that moment that Caesar Galerius appeared and, on the advice of the emperor, decided to try his luck. He had no sooner entered Susanna's house than, seeing an angel with flaming eyes guarding her, he fled in terror. Exasperated, Diocletian then ordered Macedonius to go and behead Susanna in her home. After which, Serena was seen coming the following night to gather the remains of the martyr and to lay them to rest in the cemetery of Alexander.

St. GERARD OF GALLINARO (d. about 1103)

A noble of Auvergne, who went on the first crusade, fell from exhaustion at Gallinaro (Abruzzi), and died in the hospital there.

St. GERY

Was born at Carignan, received the tonsure at Trier, became bishop of Cambrai about 587, and died there some thirty years later.

St. TAURINUS

It is said that he was bishop of Evreux in the 4th century.

St. GILBERTA or AGILBERTA

Abbess of Jouarre in the 7th century.

August 12th
ST. CLARE (d. 1253)

A WOMAN is generally worth what the ideas of the man she admires are worth, and her capacity for sacrifice allows her to attain the heights of heroism when that man shows her the way. Such was St. Clare, who better than anyone else and almost as well as he himself, realized the ideal of St. Francis of Assisi.

Born in that town in 1193 or 1194, she belonged to the noble family of the Offreducci of Coccorano. Her father Faverone died young; her mother Ortolana, as well as her sisters, Agnes and Beatrice, entered the Order of Poor Ladies. This had been founded on the night of Palm Sunday, 1212, when Clare, who had fled from her mother's palace with her cousin Pacifica, joined Francis at the Portiuncula. After having cut off their hair, the Poverello clothed them in coarse brown wool and received their religious profession. The new-born community established itself at San Damiano and from there spread throughout the whole of Europe. Everywhere the Franciscans established themselves went also the daughters of Clare, practising penance, cultivating spiritual joy, and observing poverty as St. Francis wished them to do; that is, deprived of all revenues and depending solely on alms. Today there are still twelve thousand persons leading this kind of existence, which at that time was an innovation in the Church.

Clare loved music and well-composed sermons; she was humble, merciful, charming, optimistic, and chivalrous. She blessed the Creator for having made the world so beautiful; she got up at night to tuck in the bedclothes of her companions who were uncovered; every day from midday to nones, she meditated on the Passion and experienced mysterious tortures which filled her eyes with blood and tears. Learning in 1221 of the martyrdom of the Franciscans in Morocco, she would have gone to the Saracen country to shed her blood if she had not been prevented.

Francis always watched over his "little spiritual plant"; he even wished to console her after his death. The day when his body was being carried to the Church of St. George, the funeral cortège turned aside in order to pass San Damiano. The open bier was borne into the chapel of the recluses; thus Clare could see once more the face of her beloved father. She washed with tears the blessed remains and covered the sacred stigmata with kisses. When twenty-six years later, Clare in her turn was near death, she was heard to murmur: "Depart in peace, for the road thou hast followed is the good one." A sister asked her to whom she was speaking. "I am speaking to my departing soul," she replied, "and he who was its guide is not far away." Doubtless it was St. Francis who was coming to lead her to heaven. "Lord God," she said again, "be blessed for having created me." Then she gave up her spirit.

St. CECILIA

Abbess of Remiremont (7th century).

St. ANICETUS

Said to have been burned alive at Nicomedia under Diocletian.

St. HILARIA

It is believed that she was the mother of St. Afra and was martyred on the very tomb of her daughter at Augsburg in the 4th century.

August 13th
ST. RADEGUNDE (d. 587)

SHE was, some historians say, the most perfect woman of her time. A niece of the king of Thuringia, she had been brought back by Clotaire and Thierry, sons of Clovis, from their victorious expedition to this country. She was then, in 531, eight or nine years old. Clotaire, king of Soissons, finally obtained her as part of his booty, and while waiting to dispose of her, housed her in one of his villas. The worst was to be feared from this cruel and debauched prince who had nothing Christian about him except, in his better moments, a fear of hell.

In 540 he married her. In order to escape the gross being whom she regarded as the murderer of Berthar, her father, Radegunde had fled during the night, but she was overtaken and the marriage took place, followed by fifteen years of common life in which the young wife perfectly fulfilled all her duties.

Radegunde had a brother, taken prisoner like herself in 531, from whom she had never been separated. Clotaire had him assassinated; it is not known why. That day the queen, with his permission, took leave of the king and left the court. Having received the veil of deaconess from St. Medard, she withdrew to her villa of Saix in Poitou, then, as soon as the building was ready, to her abbey of Notre Dame of Poitiers. There she lived to an advanced age, practising penance and humility, reading the Fathers of the Church, taking pleasure in the poems composed by Venantius Fortunatus, her protégé. The saints and the great bishops of the time were her friends; the Frankish kings venerated her; and she frequently intervened to turn them from crime or urge peace upon them.

St. MAXIMUS THE CONFESSOR (d. 662)

He was one of the great spirits and admirable spiritual writers of the Greek Church. His orthodoxy caused him to have his tongue slit and his right hand cut off, and he died in exile.

St. VITALINA

Virgin of the Arve, buried at Artonne near Riom (10th century).

St. JOHN BERCHMANS

Was born at Diest (Belgium) in 1599; he became a Jesuit in 1616 and died at Rome in 1621, without having committed the least deliberate fault.

Sts. HIPPOLYTUS and CONCORDIA (d. 258)

It is said that the soldier Hippolytus had been posted as guard to the deacon Lawrence in prison; St. Lawrence converted him; in his turn Hippolytus converted his old nurse, Concordia; and both were then martyred.

August 14th

ST. ATHANASIA or ANASTASIA (d. about 860)

ATHANASIA passed her whole life on the island of Aegina, of which she was a native. She intended from childhood to embrace the religious life, but her parents prevented her and she was forced to accept an advantageous marriage which they proposed to her.

Her husband died in defending the island of Aegina when it was attacked by Moors from Spain. Uninterrupted wars having depopulated the country, the authorities took such measures against celibacy that Athanasia found herself obliged to marry a second time. Her new husband was as rich as the first and no less generous than she herself. Their house became the abundant storehouse of the unfortunate. Even the Manichaeans, says a contemporary chronicler, shared in their generosity. The affairs of the couple were so regu‍lated that, except for the hours consecrated to prayer, the husband stayed at home to receive the indigent who presented themselves, while his wife went about outside seeking the infirm and the poor who were too proud to come.

Both finally convinced themselves that God had called them to a yet more perfect state. He became a monk, leaving all their common possessions to his spouse. She first gathered in her home some companions and trained them in the religious life; then, helped by a priest named Matthias, she took them into the wilderness of Timia. And there, soon arose the great convent which Athanasia directed until her death.

Our saint had been in correspondence with the Empress Theodora, credited with putting an end to the quarrel of the images; like her, Theodora finished her life in a convent.

St. MARCELLUS

Bishop of Apamea, was roasted alive about 390.

St. EUSEBIUS

Built a church at Rome about the end of the 4th century.

Blessed EBERHARD

First abbot of Einsiedeln, died in 958.

August 15th

ST. ARNOUL (d. 1087)

SON of a Flemish nobleman of the Audenarde country, Arnoul de Palmèle first followed a career of arms, serving under various princes. About 1060 he became a monk at the abbey of St. Medard of Soissons, then governed by the Abbot Raynaud. In order to increase the austerities practised in common and to expiate the sins of speech committed by worldly people, he withdrew into a sort of tannery where he remained practically motionless and never broke silence.

We know of the laxity of ecclesiastical life at that period, when Gregory VII himself did not always succeed in suppressing the simony and incontinence of the clergy. Arnoul had been living for three years in his tannery when he was sought out and placed at the head of the abbey to repair the damage caused by Ponce, simoniac successor of the late Abbot Raynaud. Later, he was obliged in like manner to replace Bishop Ursio, who was bringing discredit to the episcopal see of Soissons. He tried for two years to reform the clergy of that church; meeting with no success, he resigned in 1082 and went to die at Oudenbourg in Flanders, in an abbey he had founded there.

Although written by a contemporary, the biography of Arnoul contains various charming details which appear to be a trifle legendary. Such was the miracle he wrought in favour of the ass on which he travelled. Ashamed to see their superior go about on such a poor mount, his monks cut the throat of the animal; but Arnoul cured it with a simple sign of the cross. The story is also told of how, having asked the monks who wanted him as their abbot to reflect for twenty-four hours, he took advantage of it to flee; but a wolf caught him and, holding the skirt of his habit with its teeth, brought him back to the monastery.

The ASSUMPTION OF THE BLESSED VIRGIN

The feast of the entry of the Blessed Virgin into heaven which has been celebrated in the East since before the 6th century, was introduced later into the West. However, at the end of the 13th century, the Roman Church had already placed it within certain limitations on the same level as Easter, Christmas, and Pentecost. In November 1950 the dogma of the assumption of the Blessed Virgin was definitely defined by the Church.

St. TARSICIUS (3rd century)

An inscription of Pope Damasus relates in these terms all that we know of this martyr: "St. Tarsicius went away bearing the mysteries of Christ, when a criminal had tried to profane them. He, for his part, preferred to allow himself to be murdered rather than to deliver the body of Christ to mad dogs."

St. STANISLAS KOSTKA (1550–1568)

A young Polish noble, entered the Jesuit order at Rome in 1567 and died there the following August 15th.

August 16th

ST. ROCH (d. 1327?)

ST. ROCH is invoked in all countries against contagious diseases of men and animals; in Italy, Germany, and France old-clothes dealers, cooks, carders of wool, and pavers of streets have taken him as patron; he is said to have preserved the Fathers of the Council of Constance from the plague so that they were able to continue their work; at Paris his feast was formerly a holy day of obligation, and there was a general hue and cry when, in the 17th century, the religious authorities decided to observe it with a little less solemnity.

Roch was born at Montpellier at the end of the 13th century, the only son of a high-ranking magistrate and of a mother named Liberia. Having lost his parents when about twenty, he distributed his goods to the poor and left for Rome, clad in the coarse habit of a pilgrim. Travelling more or less at hazard, he often stopped in the hospitals to dress the sores of the sick, and frequently restored them to health by making the sign of the cross. His solicitude went by preference to the plague-stricken; he cured a great number of them at Cesena, Acquapendente, Rome, and elsewhere.

"It is St. Roch and his dog," is a proverbial saying to designate two inseparable persons, and it is true that rarely is St. Roch represented without his dog as companion. This tradition comes from the fact that in the forest near Piacenza, attacked by the plague and dying of hunger, our saint was fed by a good dog which every day brought him a piece of bread stolen from his master's table. The latter was intrigued by the beast which stole with such measured regularity; he followed it into the forest, found the sick man, became his friend, and learned from him to better his life.

Roch was a little over thirty when he returned to his native country. His mortifications and sufferings had disfigured him. As Montpellier was then torn by civil war, he was taken for a spy and thrown into a foul dungeon. Like his divine Master on Calvary, Roch did not make the slightest complaint; he died miserably in his dungeon and his fellow citizens only recognized him after his death. Later, Dominicans and Franciscans claimed him as one of their tertiaries.

St. SIMPLICIANUS

Successor to St. Ambrose of Milan (d. 401).

St. FRAIMBAULT (d. about 542)

A former courtesan who led a hermit's life first at Ivry near Paris, then in a forest in Maine.

Blessed LAWRENCE LORICATUS

Led the life of a hermit near Subiaco. His surname came to him because he wore next to his skin a coat of mail lined inside with iron spikes (d. 1243).

Blessed BEATRIX DA SILVA (1424-1490)

She was so beautiful that she had to leave the Spanish court to escape her admirers. In 1484, she founded in honour of the Virgin Mary the order of the Conceptionists, who first followed the Cistercian rule, and in 1511 adopted that of St. Francis.

August 17th

STS. LIBERATUS, BONIFACE, RUSTICUS, SERVUS, ROGATUS, SEPTIMUS, AND MAXIMUS (d. 483)

FOR some fifty years the Vandals had been masters of Roman Africa when their king, Genseric, died, leaving the throne to his son Huneric. The latter's reign (477-488) was but a succession of crimes. Not content with putting to death the ministers and friends of his father, and even the wives and children of his own family, he unloosed against the orthodox Christians a persecution in which forty thousand persons are said to have perished. Professing Arianism like all the Vandals, he pursued the Catholic bishops and monks with special hatred.

The martyrs whose feasts are celebrated today, belonged to a monastery of the country of Capse in Byzacena. In 483 they were uprooted from their solitude and dragged off to Carthage. Their group consisted of an abbot,

Liberatus; a deacon, Boniface; two subdeacons, Rusticus and Servus; and three simple monks, Rogatus, Septimus, and Maximus.

They were called upon to deny the Catholic faith and to embrace Arianism. All refused and were thrown into prison. An order was given to the jailers to treat them harshly in order, if possible, to provoke their apostasy; but the jailers allowed themselves to be bribed and permitted the prisoners to receive spiritual and material aid. For the rest, nothing shook the constancy of any one of them. Maximus, the youngest, replied to those who wished to separate him from his companions: "No torment can ever make me abandon the father and well-beloved brothers who have taught me to serve God in the monastery." The executioners thought to kill them by placing them on a gridiron loaded with burning faggots. But the fire went out, and they had to be finished off with blows from oars.

St. HYACINTH (d. 1257)

Dominican missionary in Poland.

Blessed JEANNE DELANOUE (1666–1736)

Born and died at Saumur, foundress of the Sisters of St. Anne devoted to the service of the poor.

St. MAMAS

This miracle-worker of the Eastern Church was an illiterate shepherd; he was martyred at Caesarea in Cappadocia in 273 or 274.

St. ELIAS THE YOUNGER (d. about 903)

Born in Sicily, he was taken captive by the Saracens, lived as a hermit in Calabria, and died at Thessalonica.

August 18th

ST. HELENA (d. about 329)

HELENA was about twenty-seven when a Roman officer, passing through Bithynia to fight against Zenobia, queen of Palmyra, fell in love with her and married her. This soldier, who was always gentle and tolerant, was called Constantius Chlorus, and Helena was then but a poor innkeeper's daughter. In 284, they had a son whom they named Constantine.

Constantius Chlorus reached the highest ranks of the military hierarchy, and in 293 was called by Diocletian and Maximianus Herculius to share with them the government of the Empire. Political expediency constrained him to separate from his first wife and to marry the daughter-in-law of Maximianus Herculius.

We do not know what happened to the repudiated wife until the accession to the throne of her son Constantine. Become the sole master of the Empire, the latter called his mother to him and converted her to the religion which he himself had just adopted. From that time on Helena frequented the Christian assemblies, led a holy life, took advantage of her freedom to draw on the imperial treasure to build churches and to succour the poor.

She left Rome in 326 to make a pilgrimage to Palestine. By order of the emperor, excavations were made on the supposed site of the Holy Sepulchre. It seems to have been in the course of the following year that the Holy Cross was found. The empress, then over eighty years of age, venerated the relics of the Saviour and built various monuments to commemorate their recovery; two especially, the basilica of Bethlehem and that of the Mount of Olives, were greatly admired by her contemporaries.

St. MILO

Led the eremitic life in Normandy and died about 740.

St. AGAPITUS

Martyr of the primitive Church, was buried at Palestrina.

St. RUSTICUS

Bishop of Cahors, assassinated in 630.

Blessed LEONARD

Abbot of Cava, was one of the advocates of Frederick II at the Council of Lyons (d. 1255).

Blessed AIMO TAPARELLI

Dominican and inquisitor for northern Italy (d. 1495).

August 19th

ST. JOHN EUDES (1601–1680)

SOLE survivor of a family wiped out by the plague, Isaac Eudes was not able, because of his poverty, to realize his desire to be a priest. He became a little village surgeon, who cultivated the soil and recited his breviary every day. His wife, Marthe Corbin, was no less pious than he. At Ri, in Normandy, where they settled, there were born to them seven children, of whom two became famous in different ways: Francis, surnamed Seigneur de Mézeray, author of a monumental *History of France*, and John, canonized by the Church.

The latter was an exemplary child and a brilliant student at the Jesuit college at Caen. He had need of heroism, it is said, to resist his parents, who pressed upon him an advantageous marriage. Entering the Oratory of Paris in 1624, he had as his masters Fathers de Bérulle and de Condren, whose spirituality impressed him deeply. He was to remain an Oratorian until 1642 and was chiefly occupied with preaching missions in the towns and villages of Normandy. This was a ministry to which he gave his whole life. He travelled throughout Brittany, Perche, Beauce, the Ile-de-France, Picardy, Brie, Champagne, and Burgundy, teaching the great truths of the faith, fulminating against sin, making a host of conversions. In the pulpit he showed himself an incomparable orator and in the confessional a compassionate father.

There came the moment when, upon the most judicious advice and at the counsel of Marie des Vallées, John Eudes resolved to leave the Oratory and to found an institute combining the work of parochial missions with that of the reform of the clergy. It was the Society of Jesus and Mary, later called the Eudists; between 1643 and 1670 it established seminaries at Caen, Lisieux, Evreux, Rouen, Rennes, and Coutances. Father Eudes also founded, in 1644, the Sisters of Our Lady of Charity of the Refuge, devoted to the rescue of fallen women.

Through these two institutions, as well as by the spoken and written word, he spread devotion to the Sacred Heart in France; moreover the popes have called him the "author, father, doctor, apostle, promoter, and propagator of the liturgical devotion to the Hearts of Jesus and Mary."

Blessed BURCHARD
Archbishop of Vienne in Dauphiny (d. 1025).

St. SEBALDUS
Son of a Danish king, worked with St. Willibald and St. Boniface in the evangelization of Germany, and died a hermit in the Nuremberg country about 760.

St. LOUIS OF ANJOU or OF TOULOUSE (1274–1297)
Son of the king of Naples, Charles the Lame, great-nephew of St. Louis of France, nephew of St. Elizabeth of Hungary, he passed many months in captivity at Barcelona, became a friar minor, and, shortly before his death, bishop of Toulouse.

August 20th

ST. BERNARD OF CLAIRVAUX (1090–1153)

IMMENSE was the influence wielded by St. Bernard on the spirituality of the West. This influence appears in such later writings as *The Imitation of Christ*, which follows his doctrine and sometimes his very words.

He was born of a noble family at Fontaines-les-Dijon in 1090. After a virtuous youth, he became at twenty-two a monk of the abbey of Cîteaux, taking with him four of his brothers, twenty-five of his friends, and his uncle Gaudry. His father, Tescelin, and his youngest brother, Nicard, joined them a few years later.

Bernard then governed the monastery of Clairvaux, which he had founded in 1115 and which soon was to number as many as seven hundred monks. Clairvaux spread in its turn and gave birth, even in the lifetime of its founder, to one hundred and sixty daughter houses. The religious activities of Bernard were by no means limited to houses of the Cistercian reform; they extended to the clergy, the order of the Templars, and even to the Benedictines of Cluny who, however, would never consent to his wish to banish works of art from their churches.

His activity was extended everywhere. It fell to him to remind the kings of France, Louis the Fat and Louis the Young, of their duties; he made the celebrated Abelard and Gilbert de la Porrée retract or suffer condemnation when their errors or theological subtleties threatened to imperil dogma. He thrice crossed the Alps to put an end to the schism of the anti-Pope Anacletus II; preached at Vézelay; crossed the Rhineland; wrote on many subjects; moved all of Europe to organize the second crusade, the failure of which was so painful to him. With the object of reforming the Roman Curia which was attacked by Arnold of Brescia, he composed the *De Consideratione*, intended for Pope Eugene III, a former monk of Clairvaux and his disciple.

There have come down to us from St. Bernard some ten other spiritual treatises, more than three hundred sermons, and more than five hundred letters. A host of writings have been attributed to him, such as the *Memorare*, the *Ave Maris Stella*, and the *Salve Regina*, which are not his.

St. SAMUEL

Prophet of the Old Testament and supreme judge of Israel (11th century B.C.).

Sts. CHRISTOPHER and LEOVIGILD

Andalusian monks, martyred at Cordova in 852.

St. PHILIBERT

Born in Gascony and son of a high official of King Dagobert, he first lived at the court, where he became friends with St. Wandrille and St. Ouen; then, in 636, he retired to the monastery of Rebais. In 654 he left Rebais to found the abbey of Jumièges. In 676 he was thrown into prison by St. Ouen, who was influenced by Ebroin. The assassination of this mayor of the palace (683) marked Philibert's return to favour and his reconciliation with St. Ouen. He founded still another abbey, at Noirmoutier, and died there in 685.

St. AMATOR or AMADOUR

Attempts have been made to identify this mysterious personage, whose body was found in 1166 under the threshold of the church of Rocamadour (Lot), with Zaccheus, the publican of the Gospel.

August 21st

ST. JANE FRANCES DE CHANTAL (1572-1641)

JANE FRANCES FRÉMYOT, baroness de Chantal, was thirty-eight years of age and had been a widow for ten years when she founded the Order of the Visitation. Her eight years of conjugal life at Bourbilly had been happy ones. "The couple," we are told, "offered a model of the most saintly marriage imaginable, and loved each other with extraordinary tenderness." Her husband having died from a hunting accident, Madame de Chantal went to live at Monthelon, near Autun, with her father-in-law, a crotchety old man who, backed up by a peevish housekeeper, made her suffer greatly. She remained patient, amiable, and self-forgetful, preoccupied only with the careful upbringing of her children and helping the unfortunate. She nursed the most revolting maladies with her own hands; she granted the most inopportune requests of beggars. "My God," she said, "I beg without ceasing at the door of your mercy; would I myself want to be sent away the second or third time?" Resolved to give herself entirely to God, she refused all suitors who presented themselves, and entered the Franciscan third order.

In 1604 the baroness de Chantal had met St. Francis de Sales at the house of her father, Bénigne Frémyot, president of the Burgundian parliament, at Dijon. It was the beginning of one of the most beautiful and holy friendships ever known. In 1607 they decided to found an institute "where no harshness could deter the weak and infirm from attempting to perfect themselves in divine love." This was the Visitation; Madame de Chantal established its first house at Annecy three years later. Of the four children who remained to her, the eldest of the daughters was married; the other two accompanied her to the convent to finish their education; as for her son, aged fifteen, who was to become the father of Madame de Sévigné, when the time came to say good-bye he lay before the door and his mother had to step over his body.

The long religious life of Madame de Chantal was filled with work, suffering, and consolations. She died at Moulins, December 13th, 1641. At that date eighty-six houses of her order existed in France. St. Francis de Sales had never abandoned his spiritual daughter; she outlived him nineteen years; her body reposes next to his in the chapel of the Visitation at Annecy.

St. PRIVATUS

One of the first bishops of Mende, put to death by the Alamanni in 266.

Blessed HOMBELINA

Sister of St. Bernard, died a nun at Jully-les-Nonnains (1092–1141).

St. BALDWIN

Cistercian abbot of San Pastore, near Rieti, died in 1140.

St. ALBERIC

Bishop of Cologne, evangelized Dutch Limburg and died about 784.

August 22nd

ST. HIPPOLYTUS (d. about 235)

BORN about 170, Hippolytus was one of the most learned persons of his epoch. He was already a priest and enjoyed great prestige when, about 212, Origen heard him preach at Rome. He composed scriptural and dogmatic works, chronicles and poems; he refuted heretics, attacked pagans, and his rigid attitude led him to write against the heads of the Roman Church, censuring their conduct and doctrines. In 217 he separated himself from the communion of Pope Callistus and became anti-pope. He remained so under Callistus' successors, St. Urban and St. Pontian, but became reconciled with the latter when he was deported to Sardinia in 235, and died like him of sufferings endured in exile. His martyrdom caused his schism to be forgotten and he is honoured as a saint.

The greater part of Hippolytus' works have been lost. There remain to us a *Treatise on the Antichrist*, a *Commentary on Daniel*, another on the Song of Songs, a *Refutation of Heresies* or *Philosophumena*, and a most valuable canonical treatise entitled *Apostolic Tradition*.

ST. SYMPHORIAN (2nd or 3rd century)

THE exact date of the death of this martyr is unknown; doubtless he must be placed under Marcus Aurelius or Septimius Severus.

Here and there among the people, the Christians were at that time the object of ridiculous slanders and the most childish vexations. They were driven from the markets and the public baths; they were refused the hire of lodgings, to say nothing of being often put to death under pretence of having disturbed the public peace.

Such was the lot of Symphorian who, during the feasts celebrated by the town of Autun in honour of Cybele, aroused popular fury by mocking the alleged mother of the gods. Taken before the Roman magistrate, he only made his case worse by roundly mocking the divinities of the Empire and proclaiming his fidelity to Christ. He was condemned to be beheaded. As he was going through the town gate on his way to execution, he saw his mother, who from the top of the walls said farewell to him and exhorted him not to flinch in the face of death.

St. Sigfrid

Abbot of Wearmouth, died a consumptive in 690.

August 23rd

ST. SIDONIUS APOLLINARIS (d. between 479 and 486)

BORN about 430, Caius Sollius Sidonius Apollinaris was a Gallo-Roman, native of that Auvergne country which, in the 1st century, was the last to surrender to Caesar and, in the 5th, the last to open its frontiers to the barbarians.

The Roman Empire was then on the brink of its downfall; the emperors followed one another rapidly on the throne. In the twenty years or so of his public career, Sidonius had dealings with the eight last of them: Avitus, Majorian, Libius Severus, Anthemius, Olybrius, Glycerius, Julius Nepos, and Romulus Augustulus. He himself filled the highest posts; he was senator, patrician, ambassador, and pretorian prefect. He was governor of the province of Arvernia when, in 472, he accepted, although married, the bishopric of Clermont. He had married the daughter of the Emperor Avitus; from that time on, he treated his wife as a sister, handed his hereditary duties over to his son, and ceded the government of the province to his brother-in-law. Three years later the Empire had succumbed and Arvernia was in the power of the Goths, awaiting the conquest by Clovis which was soon to come.

Ever since he had been a Roman official, Sidonius had been in contact with the Goths; he had even played tennis with King Theodoric II. Although the latter's successor, Euric II, was an Arian, he at first treated the bishop of Clermont with honour; then religious reasons put them in conflict, and Sidonius was forced into exile. He took refuge in Narbonnais Gaul, where he was able to continue watching over his people, and from whence the king was not long in recalling him.

Historians vie with one another in describing the importance of the role played by Sidonius in his time. They tell of how he fed four thousand Burgundian refugees in his diocese. They also note the worthiness and austerity of his life after he became a bishop and record a thousand incidents of his goodness. He gave so freely to the poor that, if he had nothing else available, he gave them his furniture and silver plate; his wife would go to buy them back; this allowed him soon to begin all over again.

Such of the literary work of Sidonius as has come down to us, comprises twenty-four poems and nine books of letters.

The IMMACULATE HEART OF MARY
This feast was instituted by Pius XII in 1944.

St. FLAVIAN
Bishop of Autun (5th or 6th century).

Blessed RICHILDE
Lived as a recluse with the Benedictines at Hohenwart (Bavaria) and died in 1100.

St. PHILIP BENIZI (1233-1285)
Born at Florence, he studied at Paris and Padua, became a doctor, entered the Servite order as lay brother, received the priesthood in 1259, was named general of his order in 1267, had to hide in 1269 in order to avoid being named as pope. Through his influence a young blackguard who insulted him became a monk later known as St. Peregrine Lazios; and two streetwalkers who approached him became his two first recruits to the order of cloistered Servite nuns.

August 24th

ST. BARTHOLOMEW (1st century)

IN THE list of apostles given in the Synoptic Gospels and the Acts, the name of Bartholomew is always joined with that of Philip; from this it has been concluded that the two were old friends. But apart from his title of "apostle," no other details about St. Bartholomew are given us in these passages of the Scripture.

St. John does not mention him in listing, albeit incompletely, the apostolic college. Twice, however, he speaks of a friend of Philip called Nathanael, who was "of the disciples" of the Saviour.

Had Bartholomew two names? Is he the same person as Nathanael? In this case the following passage from the fourth Gospel tells us the circum-stances in which he became a member of the apostolic college:

We are at the banks of the Jordan where on seeing Jesus St. John the Baptist cries: "Look, this is the Lamb of God; look, this is he who takes away the sin of the world." Three of his own disciples, John, Andrew, and Simon, leave him to join Our Lord from then on. "He was to remove into Galilee next day; and now he found Philip; to him Jesus said, Follow me ... And Philip found Nathanael, and told him, We have discovered who it was Moses wrote of in his law, and the prophets too; it is Jesus the son of Joseph, from Nazareth. When Nathanael asked him, Can anything that is good come from Nazareth? Philip said, Come and see. Jesus saw Nathanael coming towards him, and said of him, Here comes one who belongs to the true Israel; there is no falsehood in him. How dost thou know me? Nathanael asked; and Jesus answered him, I saw thee when thou wast under the fig-tree, before Philip called thee. Then Nathanael answered him, Thou, Master, art the Son of God, thou art the King of Israel. Jesus answered, What, believe because I told thee that I saw thee under the fig-tree? Thou shalt see greater things than that. And he said to him, Believe me when I tell you this; you will see heaven opening, and the angels of God going up and coming down upon the Son of Man" (John i, 29-51).

St. John again mentions Nathanael in the passage where he shows the risen Jesus appearing on the shore of the Lake of Tiberias, eating a repast of bread and fish with His disciples (John xxi, 1-15).

Towards the end of the 4th century, Rufinus affirms that Bartholomew had preached the Gospel "in nearer India," but this is a late and vague indication; and we have no other on the life which St. Bartholomew led after the dispersal of the apostolic college.

St. OUEN (d. 683)

Bishop of Rouen, played an important political role among the Merovingians.

Blessed EMILIF DE VIALAR (1797–1856)

Born at Gaillac (Tarn), founded the Sisters of St. Joseph of the Apparition.

St. MARIA-MICHAELA (1809–1865)

Born at Madrid, founded the Servants of the Blessed Sacrament and of Charity.

August 25th
ST. LOUIS (1215–1270)

HAVING lost his father, Louis VIII, in 1226, St. Louis was consecrated king of France at eleven under the name of Louis IX. Until 1234, when he came of age and married Margaret of Provence, his mother, Blanche of Castile, exercised the regency. His wife gave him six sons and five daughters. The first part of his reign was marked by the revolt of certain vassals aided by the English; he vanquished them one after another in 1242 at Taillebourg and at Saintes.

Having fallen ill and promised if he recovered to go on a crusade, St. Louis embarked at Aigues-Mortes in 1246, landed in Egypt, took Damietta, fought heroically at Mansurah, then fell into the hands of the infidels. He gave Damietta as ransom, visited the holy places and repaired the shrines in Syria which were still in Christian hands. He returned to France in 1254. Meanwhile his mother, Blanche, regent for the second time, had died after repressing the revolt of the Pastoureaux; this was only an alleged crusade of shepherds and drovers who under pretext of going to deliver the king in Palestine were committing crimes and robberies in France.

St. Louis spent the next sixteen years profitably in assuring the external and internal peace of his kingdom. He suppressed private wars and judicial disputes, destroyed the remaining Vaudois and Albigenses, promulgated admirable laws, revived commerce, himself on occasion sat in justice, founded the Hospital of the *Quinze-Vingts* for the blind, built the Sainte Chapelle, began the building of the Sorbonne, showed himself so good, pious, wise, and disinterested that in the eyes of all he was considered as a saint in his own lifetime. Pope Gregory IX and Frederick II chose him as arbiter, and Henry III of England and his barons did the same. The two principal treaties he signed were that of Corbeil in 1258, and that of

Abbeville in the following year; the first ceded Catalonia, Rousillon, and Cerdagne to the king of Aragon in exchange for Languedoc; the second turned over to the English king, Limousin, Agenais, Périgord, and Quercy in exchange for Normandy, Maine, Anjou, Touraine, and Poitou.

The holy king died in 1270, in sight of Tunis where he was again fighting the infidels; his son, Philip the Bold, brought his remains back to France and they were interred at St. Denis. History has given the names of the seventh and eighth crusades to St. Louis' African expeditions.

St. GENESIUS OF ARLES

It seems that at the beginning of the 4th century this former clerk or notary shed his blood for the faith at Arles. His cult has spread widely.

St. GENESIUS OF ROME

He was a comedian, who was converted, says the legend, while playing before Diocletian, and he endured a painful martyrdom on the spot. But the existence of this personage is not historically proved.

St. PATRICIA (period uncertain)

It is believed that this pious virgin, native of Constantinople, died at Naples on a pilgrimage to the apostles' tombs.

St. AREDIUS or YRIEIX (d. 591)

This Limousin noble, a friend of Thierry I, king of Austrasia, of St. Radegunde and St. Fortunatus, became a priest, founded a monastery in his native land, and made innumerable pilgrimages.

Blessed THIERRY I (d. about 1088)

Born in the country of Thuin, was the friend of Godfrey de Bouillon. He is the most famous of the abbots of St. Hubert (Belgian Ardennes).

Blessed THOMAS À KEMPIS

Born at Kempen (Rhineland) in 1379 or 1380, had the family name of Hemerken. He was a monk with the Brothers of the Common Life at Deventer, and is supposed to have written the *Imitation of Christ*.

August 26th
ST. ZEPHYRINUS (d. 217)

POPE ZEPHYRINUS occupied the see of Rome from 199 to 217. He had much to suffer, being the object of attack by his own sons, not to mention the fact that in his time persecution of the Church broke out anew. It was towards the year 200 that Septimius Severus ordered the prosecution of all converts to Christianity and of those who were making proselytes. It was doubtless the application of this edict that disrupted the celebrated school of Alexandria. Clement, its chief, and Origen, its most illustrious professor, had to flee to escape death. The persecution made numerous martyrs and only ceased in 211.

The Church was also troubled at this moment by the Montanists, who, claiming prophetical powers, announced the imminent end of the world and professed an impractical rigorism. Constrained to condemn them, Zephyrinus had the sorrow of seeing the great Tertullian leave the Roman communion.

Another renowned writer, the priest Hippolytus, at this time embarked on the way leading to schism. He reproached Zephyrinus with failing in his duty in not settling divers doctrinal disputes. By his discourses and his writings, he carried on an implacable war with him and succeeded in arraying against him a considerable part of the Christian community.

Is it perhaps because of all the sufferings endured during his pontificate that Zephyrinus deserved to be honoured as a martyr, for there is nothing to show that he shed his blood for the faith.

St. Victor

A martyr of the primitive Church who was crucified at Caesarea in Mauretania (date uncertain).

St. Pelagia

Mother of St. Aredius, died in 584.

St. Jeanne-Elisabeth Bichier des Ages

Founded in the diocese of Poitiers (France) the Daughters of the Cross, devoted to the care of the poor and the instruction of country children (1773-1838).

August 27th
ST. CAESARIUS OF ARLES (d. 543)

BORN of a rich family at Chalon-sur-Saône about 470, Caesarius took minor orders at the age of eighteen; two years later he betook himself to Lérins and there led the religious life for five years; he was ordained priest at Arles about 499 and thereafter directed a monastery situated on an island of the Rhône; about 503 he became bishop of Arles and remained so until his death. Such is the biographical data which we possess about this personage whose influence was preponderant in the religious life of France in his day.

The church of Arles enjoyed at that time an unrivalled position. Its head supervised the ecclesiastical affairs of France and Spain; his right was recognized to convoke councils and to write under seal to the pope. To the prestige attached to his duties Caesarius united a greater one, which came from his own worth. Although they were Arians, he had succeeded in winning the favour of the Visigoth and Ostrogoth kings on whom his see depended. Thereafter it was possible to combat the semi-Pelagianism which reigned more or less everywhere throughout southern France. He convoked and presided over numerous ecclesiastical assemblies and in 529 succeeded in having the Council of Orange approve twenty-five articles defining the true doctrine of grace and original sin. As in his other works, Caesarius was inspired in that document by St. Augustine.

There have further been preserved of the writings of the bishop of Arles some minor works, letters, about a hundred and fifty sermons, and a rule which was used in convents in Gaul for almost two centuries, that is, till the day when that of St. Benedict supplanted it.

St. POEMEN or PASTOR

One of the great monks of Scete, one of the masters, as shown by the *Maxims* he has left, of Christian asceticism and mysticism (4th or 5th century).

St. LIZIER

Born in Spain, was bishop of Couserans in Ariège (d. about 540).

St. JOSEPH CALASANCTIUS (1556–1648)

A native of Aragon, he came to Rome where, moved at seeing so many of the poor given to vice, he founded for them the congregation of Clerks Regular of the Pious Schools or Piarists. Innocent X suppressed this foundation in 1646, but some twenty years later Clement IX re-established it.

August 28th

ST. AUGUSTINE (354–430)

AURELIUS AUGUSTINUS was born at Tagaste in Numidia on November 13th, 354. His father, Patricius, a pagan of moderate means, was baptized on his deathbed; his mother was St. Monica, of whom we have spoken on May 4th. She had her son inscribed among the catechumens and instructed him in the elements of Christianity. But Augustine lost his faith in the course of the studies he pursued from 365 to 369 at Madaurus, and from 370 to 374 at Carthage. From the age of sixteen he was given to sensuality, and about 372 formed a liaison with the woman who for a dozen years he regarded as his wife, and by whom he had a son named Adeodatus.

From 375 to 383 Augustine taught rhetoric at Carthage, and from 383 to 385 at Milan. There he broke with the Manichaeans, who for nine years had considered him as one of themselves. He found his faith again in 386 and was baptized with Adeodatus by St. Ambrose at the end of Lent of the following year.

In the autumn of 387 Augustine was at Ostia, ready to return to Africa with his mother, but she died unexpectedly; he stayed at Rome for a year and only went back to Tagaste at the end of 388. He at once distributed his goods to the poor and founded a monastery in one of his former estates. Moreover, until his death he himself led the monastic life.

Augustine became a priest of the church of Hippo at the beginning of 391, and he was at first charged with the preaching ministry. In 395, Bishop Valerius took him as coadjutor and the following year Augustine replaced him. He died on August 28th, 430, while the Vandals were besieging his episcopal city, in the midst of the fall of the Roman Empire.

St. Augustine is generally held to be the greatest doctor of Christianity. Of his ninety-six works the greater part are held as authoritative by all the Christian churches; certain, like the *Confessions* and the *City of God*, are known to all educated people. Some of his writings are refutations of Manichaeism, Donatism, Pelagianism, and other heresies of his time; others deal with spirituality, philosophy, history, exegesis, and morals. He preached innumerable sermons, of which more than four hundred have come down to us. We also have extant two hundred and seventeen of his letters.

St. HERMES

One of the great Roman martyrs of the 2nd century.

St. JULIAN OF BRIOUDE or of AUVERGNE

Native of Vienne in Dauphiny, belonged to the imperial army and was martyred at Brioude in the 3rd century. There are at least eighty French townships which bear his name.

St. MOSES (d. end of 4th century)

Of Ethiopian origin, he was first a brigand chief, later became head of a monastery in the desert of Scete.

St. VIVIANUS

Bishop of Saintes (5th century).

Blessed GOBERT

Followed Frederick II to the crusade, then became a monk at Villers (Walloon Brabant).

The Blessed WILLIAM DEAN, WILLIAM GUNTER, ROBERT MORTON, HUGH MORE, THOMAS HOLFORD, JAMES CLAXTON, and THOMAS FELTON

Martyred in London in 1588.

August 29th

STS. SABINA AND SERAPHIA (1st centuries)

SABINA and Seraphia died for the faith at Vindena in Umbria under the Emperor Hadrian. The latter followed as far as the Christians were con‑ cerned the prescription outlined by his predecessor in his letter to Pliny the Younger. By their refusal to honour the state gods, said Trajan, the Christians were lacking in their duty as citizens and troubled the order of Rome. They were not to be sought out; that would cause an upheaval not in the least demanded by the situation; but if they were denounced and proved guilty, they should be punished unless they made amends by sacrificing to the gods —in that case they should be forgiven.

It was in the application of these measures that Sabina and Seraphia were arrested. As often happened, the virgin Seraphia found herself delivered to two young libertines, but God preserved her by striking them down with a sudden illness. This divine intervention then caused her to be accused of witchcraft, *superstitio malefica*; it was a more serious offence; and she was finally beheaded.

Sabina was a matron who gathered the remains of Seraphia and buried them in the mausoleum where she herself expected to be laid to rest. This pious act was imputed to her as a crime and she in her turn suffered martyrdom.

The *Acts* from which we draw this data are unfortunately of the 6th century and are full of discrepancies. And so one can only take from them the names of the two saints, the fact of their martyrdom, and the locality where it took place.

The BEHEADING OF ST. JOHN THE BAPTIST

The Church established this feast to commemorate in a particular way the martyrdom of St. John the Precursor, beheaded by Herod.

St. CANDIDA or ADAVISA

Roman martyr (period unknown).

St. MEDERICUS

Lived as a monk at Autun, then as a hermit in the Ile-de-France. He was formerly very popular in Paris and was reputed to cure intestinal ills (d. about 700).

August 30th

ST. ROSE OF LIMA (1586–1617)

ROSE was an angelic creature whose existence was passed in familiarity with heaven. Our Lord, the Blessed Virgin, and her guardian angel appeared to her and spoke to her; she was also visited by St. Catherine of Siena and, like her, belonged to the Dominican third order.

She was born at Lima to Gaspard de Flores and Maria d'Oliva, impoverished nobles whose ancestors had come from Spain to Peru. She had been called Isabella at baptism; but her mother, on account of her red cheeks, gave her the name of Rose; the little girl added to it that of the Blessed Virgin, and she was called in this way "Rose of the Blessed Virgin."

To all appearances her life flowed simply; she devoted herself to caring for the house, and she did needlework to help her parents. She hated to be conspicuous: her fasts had made her pale and thin, and, some sanctimonious people of Lima having singled her out for marks of veneration, she obtained from God the restoration of her healthy appearance so that she could fast without its being obvious. She could not, however, prevent attention from being drawn to her on the day when the Dutch fleet came to cruise off Lima; fearing that the heretical sailors would profane holy places, she ran to station herself before the tabernacle of the nearby church, as though to defend it at the peril of her life. As it turned out, the enemy ships withdrew without attacking Lima. Another time she was put into the limelight by the Inquisition and had to give account of her visions to certain stern theologians, who, in the end, recognized her sincerity and orthodoxy.

Her love for Christ's suffering drove her to inflict on herself the harshest penances. In addition, God permitted her to be subject to continual illnesses and to be persecuted for fifteen years by the devil. The well is still shown at

Lima where she kept the key of the iron belt which she wore next her skin; she reckoned that nobody would look for it there, and that she would be free to suffer as she wished. The tree is also shown where a bird came to sing while she was sewing; it sang, she said, to the glory of God; she answered it as best she could; and their dialogue often continued for hours.

St. FIACRE (d. 670)

Of Irish or Scottish origin, he came to live in the forest of Breuil, in the diocese of Meaux, dividing his time between prayer, the work of his hands, and the care of the poor. He is the patron of hosiers and gardeners. He gave his name to carriages put into service in 1640 for the transport of Parisians, the terminus of which was located at the Hôtel St. Fiacre.

St. PAMMACHIUS (d. 410)

Roman senator, son-in-law of St. Paula and friend of St. Jerome.

Blessed JUVENAL ANCINA (1545-1604)

Oratorian, bishop of Saluzzo, friend of St. Francis de Sales, poisoned by an evil wretch.

August 31st

ST. RAYMOND NONNATUS (d. 1240)

HE first saw the day at Potel in the diocese of Urgel, about the year 1200, and was baptized under the name of Raymond. Nonnatus (*non natus*) is a surname which was given to him because his mother had to undergo a Caesarean operation, and he was not born normally. As to his father, he was, some say, a shepherd; but others hold that he was a member of the Cardona family, one of the most famous in Spain.

As soon as he was free to follow his vocation, he entered the Mercedarian order recently founded by Peter Nolasco. After his ordination as priest in 1222, he devoted himself until 1231 to the redemption of captives. He freed one hundred and fifty of them at Valencia in 1226, two hundred and fifty at Algiers in 1229, and two hundred and twenty-eight at Tunis the following year. It was in this town that he had occasion to fulfil the special vow by which the Mercedarians obligated themselves to surrender their persons and their lives, if necessary, for the ransom of Christian prisoners of the infidels. Not possessing the whole sum demanded by the slave merchants at Tunis, Raymond gave himself up as prisoner. His captivity was very hard. After eight months of cruel treatment some Mercedarians arrived from Spain, bringing with them the necessary ransom.

The last ten years of his life were spent partly at Rome, where he was procurator of his order, partly in different countries, where he was taken by his duties of preaching the crusade. It was thus that he went to France in 1235, charged by Gregory IX to urge St. Louis to depart for the Holy Land. This expedition, as is known, only took place about ten years later. In the meantime Raymond died at the castle of Cardona on August 26th, 1240, some months after he had been raised to the cardinalate. He had just concluded a new mission in Spain when he was overtaken by sickness as he was returning to Rome.

St. ARISTIDES (2nd century)

Athenian philosopher converted to Christianity.

St. AMATUS

It is agreed that he was bishop of Nusco and died a nonagenarian, but it is disputed whether he lived in the 11th or 12th century.

St. PAULINUS

Bishop of Trier. The Emperor Constantius had him deposed for his opposition to Arianism, and he was sent to die in Phrygia (d. 358).

THE SAINTS OF SEPTEMBER
September 1st
ST. LUPUS (d. 623)

RANKISH IN origin and of noble birth, St Lupus was born near Orléans and was baptized with the name of Wolf. St. Austremius, bishop of Orléans and St. Aunarius, bishop of Auxerre, his materna uncles, inculcated in him the priestly virtues and he succeeded St. Artemius as archbishop of Sens in 609 His biographers tell us he was humble, disciplined eloquent, a lover of music, and a great friend to the poor.

It seems, however, that it is to his misfortunes more than to his evangelica virtues that St. Lupus owes his great popularity. A liturgical prayer ask God to "preserve us, through his intercession, from the calumny of which he was a victim during his life." Lupus had to suffer especially from slanders because he showed kindness to Volusia, a relative of his predecessor, St. Artemius. Thierry II, king of Burgundy, having asked him for an explana tion on this subject, he replied that, although she was a woman, Volusia was none the less of his flock, and he could not in conscience abandon her.

When Thierry II died in 613, Clotaire II, king of Soissons, seized

Burgundy in spite of the claims of Sigebert, legitimate heir of the dead man As the archbishop of Sens showed no haste in paying court to the despoiler new calumnies were circulated about him which caused Clotaire II to remove him from his see and to give it to the ambitious monk Monegisil. St. Lupus was then exiled to Ansenne, in the present department of the Somme. He evangelized this district which had remained to a great extent pagan, even converting his jailer, Duke Boso, governor of the country.

Meanwhile the church of Sens was mourning the absence of its true pastor. When Monegisil was murdered in a riot, the people of Sens sent to Clotaire II to ask that Lupus be restored to them. The king granted their request and punished the prelate's detractors. Lupus was buried at Sens, "under the gutter" of St. Columba's basilica, as he, in his humility, had requested.

St. GILES or EGIDIUS (7th century)

First he lived as a hermit at the mouth of the Rhône, then on the banks of the Gard; later he founded the monastery called after him.

St. AUGUSTUS (5th century)

Was driven out of Africa by the Vandals, landed in Campania, and there exercised his apostolic ministry.

St. NIVARD (d. about 673)

Brother-in-law of Childeric II, king of Austrasia, was bishop of Rheims for some twenty years.

September 2nd
ST. JUSTUS (d. 390)

APPARENTLY of Gallo-Roman origin, Justus was a deacon of the church at Vienne when, about 374, the church of Lyons chose him as its bishop. In 361 he presided at the Council of Aquileia, where two bishops who favoured Arianism were deposed. There he met St. Ambrose with whom he became friends. Two letters of the latter are extant, from which it is evident that his friend asked him not to write him any more news, but to comment upon the Scriptures, as all else was a pure waste of time.

Delicate and even scrupulous in conscience, Justus gave up his first see after a murder which he was powerless to prevent. A madman had run amok in the streets of Lyons, striking passers-by with his sword, and mortally wounding several. Pursued and about to be apprehended, he took refuge in a church. The bishop rushed in and was able to get the man away from those who were about to kill him, but shortly after, the mob fell upon the madman and tortured him to death.

The gentle bishop may have previously cherished thoughts of retirement. In any case, he fled the following night in the direction of Marseilles and there embarked for Egypt. Just as the ship was weighing anchor, one of his clerics, Viator, joined him. Having reached the region of Scete, both entered a monastery and, without revealing their identity, for eight or nine years lived the penitent life of the Desert Fathers. However, a pilgrim from Lyons who had ventured into this region recognized them, and they also received a visit from the priest Antiochus, who had come from Lyons in order to see his old bishop once more.

Justus and Viator died a few years apart. Later the Christians of Lyons travelled to Egypt to fetch their relics, which they brought back to their own land. For a long time the cult of St. Justus was popular in France.

St. ELEAZAR

The third son of Aaron, was, with Moses and Josue, a leader of Jewish theocracy; and he was the founder, with his brother Ithamar, of the priestly class in Israel. The lists which mention St. Lazarus today are in error; they apparently confuse St. Eleazar with St. Lazarus.

St. COMUS OF CRETE

Lived a solitary life on the island of Candia (d. about 706).

St. STEPHEN OF HUNGARY (977–1038)

Son of Geza, duke of Hungary, he embraced Christianity and at baptism took the name of the first martyr. Called to the throne at the age of twenty, he made the conversion of his subjects his principal care, dedicated his country to the Blessed Virgin, and earned from the pope the title of "Apostolic King."

September 3rd

ST. REMACULUS (d. about 664)

OF Aquitanian origin, Remaculus lived during part of his youth at Bourges, which had been made a centre of Christian life and sanctity by the bishops St. Austregisilus (613–624) and St. Sulpitius (624–644).

At that time "the good king Dagobert" ruled over the whole of Gaul. Actually, he was very profligate, but at least he excelled in choosing admirable advisers. To enumerate his counsellors is to name the worthiest men of the time: Blessed Pepin of Landen, mayor of the palace; Sts. Arnulf, Cunibert, and Desiderius, respectively bishops of Metz, Cologne, and Cahors; and finally the great St. Eligius who was to die bishop of Noyon.

It was the latter who discovered Remaculus and placed him at the head of an abbey he had just founded at Solignac, near Limoges. Remaculus showed such wisdom in this assignment that he was again called upon when, in 652, St. Amandus had to be replaced in the see of Maestricht. This diocese was composed of miserable Christians who had even been known to massacre their shepherd. After a three years' sojourn among them, St. Amandus had left them, shaking the dust from his feet. Remaculus persuaded King Sigebert, Dagobert's son, that the best way to win these savages would be to develop monastic life in the region. With Sigebert's aid, Remaculus founded the abbeys of Malmédy and Stavelot, whose fame was lasting and widespread. According to certain etymologists, Malmédy or *Malmundarium* means "place which has been purified from evil spirits," and Stavelot or *Stabuletum*, a "stable" where wild animals formerly took shelter.

Among the disciples of St. Remaculus, mention must be made of St. Trond, founder of the monastery and town of the same name; St. Babolen, abbot of Malmédy; and St. Theodard and St. Lambert, both bishops of Maestricht, who were assassinated. As for our saint, he ruled his church for a dozen years, then he resigned and went to finish his days at Stavelot.

St. Antoninus (date unknown)

Some think that he was martyred at Apamea, in Syria. For many of the people of Languedoc, he was a solitary from Pamiers, who shed his blood for the faith at NobleVal, which later became SaintAntonin (Rouergue). Actually there existed as early as the 8th century a monastery in the neighbourhood of Foix which bore the name of St. Antoninus. His feast is also celebrated on September 2nd.

Sts. Euphemia, Dorothea, Thecla, and Erasmus

Honoured at Venice and Ravenna as martyrs of the 1st century.

St. Mansuetus

Is said to have been bishop of Toul and is considered to have been the apostle of Lorraine (4th century).

September 4th
ST. ROSALIA (d. 1160)

ST. ROSALIA is the patroness of Palermo, and the citizens of that place annually celebrate two feasts in her honour. One of these was raised to the rank of a holy day of obligation by Pius XI in 1927. It is celebrated by a procession of unequalled magnificence, heralded by cannon fire. The saint's shrine, atop a gigantic carriage filled with musicians, is drawn through the town by forty mules, accompanied by prayers, hymns, and acclamations. The top of the carriage is level with the roofs of the houses; fireworks are set off everywhere; the musicians blow ceaselessly on their trumpets; and for the five days during which this celebration lasts, enthusiasm mounts to an increasingly high pitch.

The saint of Palermo thus honoured, seems to have delivered her country from the plague in 1625 and, since then, to have brought about innumerable cures. Her legend states that she was born around 1130 at the court of Roger II, king of Sicily, of a father called Sinibald, who was descended from Charlemagne. As her beauty constituted a danger to her soul, the Virgin appeared to her to urge her to leave the world. Rosalia was just fourteen. She took her crucifix, her discipline, and a few books and left her father's castle by night. Two angels, one armed like a knight, the other disguised as a pilgrim, were waiting to escort her to the summit of Mount Quisquita. There they left her at the entrance of a grotto hidden among the trees, buried under the snow. The young girl remained hidden there several months, after which the angels came to warn her that she was sought by her parents and had better flee elsewhere. They led her to the top of Mount Pellegrino. There, it is said, Rosalia, devoting herself to penances and miraculously nourished by the Host, passed the last sixteen years of her life. She died at the age of thirty; her body, long sought in vain, was found in the 17th century encased in a sheath of rock crystal; and it is the recovery of this relic which is commemorated by the procession mentioned above.

St. CANDIDA

Naples honours today two saintly women of this name; one is said to have been converted by St. Peter when he was passing through the city on his way to Rome; the other, also a Neapolitan, died in 586 after having converted her husband and her son.

St. MARINUS (4th century)

A former stonemason, he went to live as a hermit on the present site of San Marino.

St. MOSES (12th century B.C.)

Son of Amram and Jochabed, he was born in Egypt and lived there at the court of the Pharaohs for forty years. Then God ordered him to deliver the Jewish people and to lead them to the Promised Land. Having received the tables of the Law from Jehovah on Mount Sinai, Moses became the lawgiver of the Hebrews. He married Sephora and by her had two sons, Gersam and Eliezer. He died, say the Scriptures, at the age of one hundred and twenty.

September 5th

ST. BERTIN (d. about 700)

THE name of the abbey of Luxeuil recurs constantly in the history of the saints of France in Merovingian times. Almost all of them were, in fact, its monks, and almost all the abbeys of the time followed the rule of St. Columbanus of which Luxeuil was the model. This was, as is well known, extremely severe, including frequent confession, innumerable genuflexions and signs of the cross, immersions in freezing water, exhausting fasts, corporal chastisements, and other practices borrowed from Irish monasticism.

It was at Luxeuil that St. Bertin, as well as Mommelinus and Ebertram, the companions of his apostolate, received their religious formation. It is said that all three were natives of the country around Constance. About 639 they joined their compatriot and fellow monk, St. Omer, bishop of Thérouanne, who had been evangelizing Morinia for the past two years. In this almost wholly idolatrous district they founded, not far from Thérouanne on the banks of the Aa, on a hill surrounded by marshes, a monastery of which the first abbot was Mommelinus. Eight years later they established another in the island of Sithiu; dedicated first to St. Peter, it later bore the name of St. Bertin and gave birth to the town of Saint-Omer. Our saint ruled it for nearly sixty years, left his mark upon it, and made it famous.

From the abbey of St. Bertin came twenty-two holy personages whom the Church has placed on her altars, not to speak of a host of prelates who did honour to their country and were worthy of their calling. Like the Irish monks and their imitators of the Franche Comté, Bertin practised terrifying austerities. After having travelled much and trained disciples who in their turn founded monasteries, Bertin died in the midst of his monks, having, it is said, passed his hundredth year. As for his childhood friends, one, St. Mommelinus, had succeeded St. Eligius as bishop of Noyon; the other, Ebertram, had become abbot of the monastery of St. Quentin in Vermandois.

St. LAWRENCE JUSTINIAN (1380-1455)

A Venetian nobleman, he became patriarch of Venice after having been general of the canons regular of St. George of Alga. He was a model for the prelates of his time, and left several pious treatises.

St. AMAN or AIGNAN

Is said to have occupied the episcopal see of Besançon in about 366.

St. URBAN (d. 370)

He presided over the delegation sent by the Catholics to the Emperor Valens in Nicomedia to complain of the persecutions of the Arians of Constantinople against them. Valens received the delegates rudely and ordered the prefect Modestus to dispose of them. The latter arranged to set fire to the boat by which they were returning, and all perished in the fire or in the sea.

September 6th

ST. MAGNUS or MAGNOALDUS (7th century)

THE Jesuit Fathers who published the *Acta Sanctorum* devoted no less than eleven thousand six hundred lines to St. Magnus. They covered his origins, voyages, virtues, miracles; the division and dispersal of his relics; even the miracles he accomplished with his staff.

Innumerable examples are given of the popularity enjoyed by St. Magnus during his life, and of the results of his intercession in heaven. The Italians of the middle ages had such faith in his healing powers that they joined his name to those of the Fourteen Holy Helpers.

However, credence cannot be given to all these documents, for they bristle with contradictions and all are of a much later date than the saint's life. Nor do they contain picturesque or pretty legends which deserve to be recorded. To be on the safe side, let us confine ourselves to saying that Magnus, the presumed founder of the monastery of Füssen, in Bavaria, doubtless lived in the 7th century, exercised his ministry in Italy, Switzerland, and Bavaria, and acquired imperishable fame in these countries.

St. Eve

Patroness of Dreux, is honoured in that city as a martyr. Her body is venerated in the Church of St. Stephen.

Sts. DONATIAN, MANSUETUS, GERMANUS, PRAESIDUS, FUSCULUS, and LAETUS

They were victims of the persecution which the Arian King Huneric unleashed against the Catholics of Africa, in 483 or 484.

Sts. FAUSTUS and MACARIUS, and ten other Christians

Beheaded at Alexandria during the persecution of Decius about 250.

St. ZACHARIAS

Son of Barachias, one of the twelve minor prophets of the Old Testament. He died 520 B.C.

September 7th

ST. REGINA (d. about 251)

IF we are to believe her *Acts*, Regina was martyred at Alesia on the very spot where, two centuries earlier, Vercingetorix fought so valiantly against Caesar. The *Acts* say that Olybrius, prefect of Gaul, on his arrival before the town in 251, saw a fifteen-year-old shepherdess and immediately wished to make her his wife. This was Regina who, baptized by her wet nurse and driven away from her paternal home, found herself at that time reduced to tending sheep. Olybrius sent for her and learned that she was of noble race and a Christian. Bidden to deny her faith, the young girl refused and was thrown into prison. There she remained, chained to the wall by a chain with thirty-seven links, while Olybrius was summoned to the frontiers to repulse a barbarian attack. On his return he found Regina more determined than ever to keep her vow of virginity and not to sacrifice to idols. In vain, to move her, he had recourse to the whip, to red-hot plates, to burning pincers, and to iron combs. The virgin's constancy exhausted her torturers; she did not cease to praise God and defy Olybrius in the midst of her torments; finally it was found necessary to silence her by cutting her throat.

ST. CLODOALD or CLOUD (d. 560)

WHEN he died, Clodomir, son of Clovis and king of Orléans, left three children, Theobald, Gontaire, and Clodoald. The first two were killed in

533 by their uncles, Childebert, king of Paris, and Clotaire, king of Soissons, who seized the estates of the dead king of Orléans. Only Clodoald escaped, and it is he whom today the Church honours as St. Clodoald or Cloud. To show that he had renounced the world and given himself to the service of God, he cut his hair. For some time he lived a hermit's life in the environs of Paris, under the direction of St. Severinus; then he went to Provence, where he remained for some years. It is said that to escape the veneration of which he became the object, he decided to leave that country and return to the region of Paris, where he was consecrated priest by Bishop Eusebius. Having nothing more to fear from him, his two uncles gave him a small estate on the banks of the Seine, two miles from Paris; there he made his last retreat and built a church; and there it is that the town of Saint-Cloud arose.

St. GRATUS

Bishop of Aosta in Piedmont (d. about 470).

St. MADELBERTE

Daughter of St. Vincent Madelgaire and St. Wandru; succeeded her sister, St. Aldetrude, as abbess of the convent of Maubeuge, which their aunt, St. Aldegundis, had founded (beginning of the 7th century).

September 8th

BLESSED SERAPHINA SFORZA (1434-1478)

LIKE Bramante and Raphael, Seraphina was a native of Urbino and, like them, lived at the time of the Renaissance. Her father was Guido, count of Montefeltro, and her mother, Cattarina Colonna, was the niece of Pope Martin V. Having lost her parents when young, the child was brought to Rome to be raised in the Colonna palace. She lived there until she was given in marriage in 1448 to Alexander Sforza, duke of Pesaro. This dreadful widower at first treated her with deference. In any case he had such an opinion of her that when he went off to war in 1456, he left the government of the duchy in her hands. Everyone agreed that she took good care of his affairs during her husband's absence. However, when he came back from the battlefield, he fell in love with a doctor's wife called Pacifica, and life became a long calvary for his legitimate wife.

There were no menial tasks, no humiliations which he did not heap upon her. He beat her in public, taunting her with her slight build and her ugliness; he seized her by the hair in front of the servants; once he tried to strangle and several times to poison her. Finally, he shut her up in the convent of the Poor Clares at Pesaro. Armed soldiers were stationed at the convent to prevent aid from being brought to the prisoner. He presented himself with judges at the grating in order to drag from his irreproachable spouse the admission of pretended infidelities. Seraphina kept silence, why, one does not know.

Twenty months later, she voluntarily donned the Franciscan habit. Thenceforward for eighteen years her life was that of an exemplary daughter of St. Francis, modestly accomplishing her humble tasks and guiding her sisters with kindness as abbess of the community. Her biographer notes that she remained half paralysed on one side as a result of attempts her husband had made to poison her.

The NATIVITY OF THE BLESSED VIRGIN

It has been documentarily established that this feast was celebrated at Rome during the last years of the 7th century.

St. ACHILLES

Was one of a group of confessors who died for the faith at Alexandria in Egypt during the first centuries of the Christian era.

St. BELINA (12th century)

A martyr of purity, she was savagely murdered by a noble of Lendreville (diocese of Troyes).

September 9th

ST. OMER (d. about 670)

BORN at the end of the 6th century at Goldenthal, near Lake Constance, Omer lost his mother, Domitila, when he was of an age to choose a career. With his father, Friulf, he entered the monastery of Luxeuil which had recently been founded by St. Columbanus, and at that time was ruled by St. Eustace. Although the life led there was of the most extreme severity, this abbey then numbered more than five hundred monks. Often the Merovingian kings chose bishops from their ranks. Omer was designated by Dagobert I to occupy the episcopal see of Thérouanne in the Morins country, which had been vacant for nearly one hundred years. Converted at the end of the 3rd century, the people of Morins had for the most part returned to idolatrous practices. To St. Omer is due the credit of having re-Christianized them, a task in which he was aided by St. Bertin, St. Mommelinus, and the venerable Ebertram, all of them like himself monks of Luxeuil. Among the monasteries founded by him, mention should be made of Mount Sithiu, whose direction he confided to St. Bertin. About 648 Omer gave shelter to a young fugitive who was in danger of being forced into marriage. Later she became St. Austreberta; at the same time, he ordained the future St. Wandrille; and it is known that he assisted at the translation of the remains of St. Vaast, bishop of Arras, and of St. Lambert, bishop of Maestricht.

Although advanced in holiness, Omer sometimes felt the prick of the flesh. He remedied it by prayers and austerities, in particular by rolling himself among brambles and thorns. Towards the end of his life he became blind, and replied to those who commiserated with him: "Leave the heavenly Father to manage things; does He not know as well as I what is good for me?"

After thirty years as bishop, he died at Wacrans-sur-Aa; assisted by St. Bertin, the monks of Mount Sithiu carried his body off to their abbey; and gradually the town of Saint-Omer grew up around his tomb.

St. PETER CLAVER

Catalan Jesuit, born about 1582, spent the last forty-four years of his life in America, devoting himself especially to the negroes (d. 1654).

St. BETTELIN

English penitent of the 8th century, honoured at Stafford.

St. OSMANA (7th century)

Escaping from either Ireland or England, where she was to be married against her will, she came to Brittany and lived in virginity and penitence in the neighbourhood of Saint-Brieuc.

Blessed AESOP

A child honoured at Saint-Germain d'Auxerre (date unknown).

September 10th

ST. PULCHERIA (d. 453)

"To you is due the suppression of scandals raised by the spirit of evil; thanks to you the whole earth is at present united in a same confession of the truth."

In these words Pope St. Leo praised the Empress Pulcheria who was a worthy granddaughter of Theodosius the Great. She had been baptized at Constantinople by St. John Chrysostom, and while still a child had taken a vow of virginity, together with her two younger sisters. Her father Arcadius being dead, she was proclaimed "Augusta" at fifteen and given the guardianship of her brother Theodosius II, two years younger than she; and in 414 she assumed the responsibilities of power. Rarely has such wisdom been accompanied by such precocity. Under her government the Eastern Empire enjoyed great tranquillity.

When Theodosius II was twenty, Pulcheria made him marry Athenais, daughter of a pagan philosopher of Athens, who was as beautiful as she was learned. She was given the name of Eudocia at baptism and at first put up with Pulcheria's ascendancy over her husband. Later she took umbrage, persecuted her sisterinlaw, and forced her to retire to the country. There Pulcheria remained for three years, until 450, when St. Leo begged her to come to the defence of the Church, besieged by heresy. The patriarch Eutyches, condemned by the Council of Ephesus in 431, had recovered the emperor's favour, and under his leadership heresy triumphed over the archiepiscopal see of Constantinople. It was enough for Pulcheria to appear at court to disabuse her deceived brother, and to obtain from the Council of Chalcedon a condemnation of Eutychianism and all its tenets.

The death of Theodosius, and Eudocia's retirement at this time, left Pulcheria sole mistress of the Empire, now threatened by Attila.

Pulcheria thought to stabilize her authority by marrying General Marcian, eight years her junior. She could be happy in this marriage for Marcian respected her vow of continence, pursued the followers of Nestorius and Eutyches, and forced Attila to withdraw from the frontiers.

St. NICHOLAS OF TOLENTINO

Born of poor parents at Sant' Angelo about 1246, joined the hermits of St. Augustine at Tolentino, became a priest, and died there in 1308.

St. AUBERT

Bishop of Avranches, celebrated for having built the church of MontSaintMichel. He himself dedicated it on October 12th, 709.

St. THEODARD (d. 669)

Successor to St. Remaculus as head of the monastery of StavelotMalmédy, he also succeeded him as bishop of Maestricht. He was assassinated in Alsace, returning from a visit to the Austrasian court.

Sts. SOSTHENES and VICTOR (d. 307)

They were converted after having martyred St. Euphemia of Chalcedon, and were themselves burned alive in that city.

September 11th
STS. HYACINTH AND PROTUS (d. about 257)

THESE two martyrs were burned alive during the persecution of Valerian in which St. Eugenia also perished. They were slaves, and it is said that it was due to them that this noble young woman embraced the faith. Such of their relics as were saved from the flames were wrapped in a cloth of gold and placed in the cemetery of St. Hermes, on the ancient Salarian Way. In the 4th century, as the funeral chamber where they lay had become inaccessible, Pope Damasus had it cleared, placed a light there, and built a staircase giving access to it. These labours are recalled by inscriptions in verse. Four or five centuries later, searches in the devastated catacombs made possible the recovery of the holy bodies of many confessors. The remains of St. Protus were then transported to Rome. Those of St. Hyacinth were not touched because it was feared that a whole wall would collapse if the masonry niche which held them were opened. Father Marchi discovered this niche intact in 1845. The marble slab which sealed it bore the inscription: "DP.III IDUS SEPTEMBR. YACINTHUS MARTYR"; and inside, mixed with ashes and gold thread, appeared a part of the charred bones of St. Hyacinth from which arose a subtle perfume of roses.

BLESSED JEAN-GABRIEL PERBOYRE (1802-1840)

THE sufferings of this martyr equal anything that is related in the ancient Passions. Son of a labourer, Pierre Perboyre, and of his devout wife, Marie Rigal, Jean-Gabriel was born at Mongesty (Lot) on January 6th, 1802. He had two brothers and two sisters who, like him, entered the spiritual family of St. Vincent de Paul. He became a Lazarist at Montauban in 1820, and a priest in Paris in 1825. For ten years he filled various confidential posts in his congregation and then, in 1835, embarked at Le Havre for China. After eighteen months spent in Honan, he went in 1839 to exercise his zeal in the mountains of Hu-pe. For a long time Jean-Gabriel had prayed each morning that he might shed his blood for the faith. His prayer was granted, and his martyrdom lasted a whole year. Betrayed by a young Christian and arrested in a forest on September 16th, 1839, he was taken to Kou-Tching, then to Siang-Yang-Fou, then to Ou-Tchang-Fou, where he was crucified on September 11th, 1840. A mandarin had offered him freedom if he would profane the cross of Our Saviour. Everywhere his executioners could torture him as their fancy devised; they loaded him with chains, mashed his feet in a vice, beat him with bamboos, disfigured him with blows from thongs and made him drink dog's blood. Even while he was dying, his limbs stretched out on a cross, they still kicked him in the stomach.

St. ADELPHUS

Abbot of Remiremont, died at Luxeuil around 670.

St. EMILIAN (420-520)

Led the solitary life for forty years before becoming bishop of Vercelli.

St. VÉRAN

Former monk of Lérins, became bishop of Vence (d. 480).

September 12th

BLESSED MARIA VICTORIA FORNARI (1562-1617)

OF Genoese origin, Victoria Fornari was married at seventeen to one of her noble compatriots named Angelo Strata. They spent eight happy years together; then Angelo died, leaving his wife with five small children and a sixth on the way. She almost despaired. Later she related how, as she was kneeling in a state of collapse before the statue of the Virgin Mary, the latter had stretched out her arms and said: "Victoria, my daughter, do not fear; it is I who will henceforth take care of your home."

Sixteen years passed during which Victoria raised her family and redoubled her prayers and her good works. She took in the abandoned sick, prepared Turkish slaves for baptism, and led fallen girls back to virtue. When all her children had entered the religious life, she herself realized a long-planned project to endow her native town with a convent consecrated to the honour of the Annunciation of the Blessed Virgin. On March 13th, 1604, Clement VIII approved the new foundations for which Father Zanoni, a Jesuit, had drawn up the statutes; and on the August 5th following, Victoria and her companions received the religious habit—white tunic, blue scapular, belt and cape—in which they were to lead the contemplative life.

They were called the Celestial Annunciades to distinguish them from the Franciscan Annunciades, founded by Jeanne de Valois, discarded wife of Louis XII.

For six years, Mother Maria Victoria carried out the duties of abbess and superior of the community; then she became once more a simple nun, and was often humiliated by the new abbess. Five convents of the Celestial Annunciades still exist today, two in France and three in Italy.

Sts. LEONTIUS and VALERIAN and four other Christians of Alexandria (Egypt)

Thrown into the sea about the year 300, for having confessed their faith.

St. BONNA (7th century)

Virgin honoured at Treviso.

St. GUY OF ANDERLECHT (d. 1012)

He was a poor boy born near Brussels who, when he grew up, for a long time performed the duties of beadle in the church of Laeken. After having unsuccessfully tried commerce, he left for Jerusalem and returned by way of Rome where he met the vicar of Anderlecht who, at the head of a devout group, was himself on his way to the Holy Land. Guy offered to serve as guide to his compatriots. All, excepting he, died of the plague on their way back. Sick and exhausted, he returned to his own land after an absence of seven years, was harboured by another priest of Anderlecht, and soon gave up the ghost.

September 13th

ST. AMATUS (d. about 627)

GENERALLY St. Amatus is represented with a crow. This commemorates an incident that took place while he was still at the abbey of St. Maurice at Agaunum, in Switzerland. His superior had authorized him to live in a cave; twice a week a monk called Berin placed a jug of water and a loaf of barley bread at its entrance. Then one day a crow upset the jug and flew off with the bread, obliging the solitary to make a lengthy fast. Amatus then began to cultivate a tiny field of barley and to draw water from a nearby spring.

He had been living in this manner for three years, when Agaunum received a visit from Eustace, abbot of Luxeuil, who had been to see St.

Columbanus at Bobbio. It is known how severe was the rule at Luxeuil; on some winter nights up to seventy-five psalms were recited at matins. Attracted by the picture the traveller drew of the austerity of Luxeuil, Amatus left the valley of the Rhône and followed Eustace. Very occasionally, thereafter, he left the monastery to evangelize the idolatrous populations of the Austrasian regions. At Metz he converted a former count palatine from the court of Theodebert II, named Romaric. On March 29th, we mentioned here the revolt of the monk Agrestius, severely and promptly repressed by St. Eustace. For what honourable reasons no one knows, St. Romaric and St. Amatus for a while took sides with Agrestius. Later they left Luxeuil, and with St. Eustace's approval founded at Habend, on a property of the former palatine, a dual monastery for men and women, later given the name of Remiremont (*Romarici mons*). Amatus, who was its first abbot, established the custom of the perpetual office for the nuns. Divided into seven choirs like the angels, the nuns succeeded each other, day and night, in chanting the psalter, so that the divine praises were never interrupted. As for Amatus, he usually lived at the bottom of a crevice, in a grotto where his food was let down to him at the end of a rope; he only mounted on Saturdays and Sundays to assist at the offices and preach to the two communities.

Today is celebrated the feast of another St. AMATUS.

Having been abbot of Agaunum, he became bishop of Sion (Switzerland), and died, exiled by Ebroin, at the abbey of Saint-Pierre-du-Breuil (today in the diocese of Arras) in 690.

St. MAURILIUS

A native of Milan and a disciple of St. Ambrose, came to Touraine to become the disciple of St. Martin and ended his life as bishop of Angers in 437.

September 14th

ST. MATERNUS (4th century)

HIS cult is particularly popular in Trier, Cologne, Alsace, and generally in the countries bordering the Moselle, the Meuse, and the Lower Rhine. Maternus is supposed to have been the great apostle of these countries, who first brought the Gospel to them. Unfortunately, little is known of his history and his apostolate.

All that is certain is that at the beginning of the 4th century, there was a wise bishop of Cologne called Maternus. He enjoyed the confidence of the Emperor Constantine and took an active part at the Council of Rome, 313, as well as at that of Arles in the following year. Apart from this, everything that is related is pure legend and indicates mainly the desire on the part of the churches of Gaul and of Rhenania to lay claim to antiquity, by making their foundations appear to go back to the time of the apostles themselves.

Maternus, it was even claimed, was none other than the risen son of the widow of Naim. About the year 50, St. Peter gave him Eucharius and Valerius as companions, and our missionaries set off by way of the Alps for Germany. They had just reached Alsace, when, wasted by a fever, Maternus fell seriously ill and died. Eucharius and Valerius returned to Rome to advise St. Peter of this misfortune. This latter consoled them and said: "Take my pastoral staff; you shall lay it on the dead body and, in the name of the Lord, you will order him to return to life." They did so, and the son of the widow of Naim for the second time rose again.

St. Maternus is credited with a host of further miracles. Special mention should be made of that by which, one Easter day, he was able to celebrate Mass at the same time at Trier, Tongres, and Cologne; and of the one which indicated the place where he wished to rest after his death. As the three cities were disputing his relics, his bier was placed on the Rhine and it floated upstream to Trier, where it stopped.

The EXALTATION OF THE HOLY CROSS

It appears to have been between 325 and 347 that Our Lord's cross was discovered. A basilica was dedicated on the site of the Holy Sepulchre, and the ceremony commemorated today was first held there, the bishop showing the wood of our salvation to the people for veneration. This ceremony drew crowds from all over the world.

St. ODILARD

Bishop of Nantes, was a contemporary of Charlemagne, and like him, died in 814.

September 15th
BLESSED ROLAND (d. 1586)

ONE day, hunting with falcons in the forest of Borgone, Marchesa Antonia Pallavicini found an old man lying like a corpse among the leaves. This was a hermit, called Roland de' Medici, who, abandoned and alone, was awaiting death. Twenty-six years earlier this mysterious person had arrived in that part of the world, from where no one knew, dressed in black. When his robe had fallen to pieces, he replaced it with a goatskin. In summer he lived on grasses and fruits; in winter he begged for enough to keep him from starvation. Never had he been heard to say a word; several times he had been seen to stand for five or six hours, motionless on one leg, his arms held high, his eyes fixed on the sun.

The marchesa gave up hunting for the rest of that day; she offered to carry the dying man to her castle of Borgone; he refused by a sign. She told him that at least he should not die without confession, adding that she would put at his disposal her director, Father Dominic, a Carmelite, professor of Holy Scripture. Roland indicated that he would go the next night to the nearby church to receive the last sacraments. He dragged himself there, and Father Dominic questioned him for two hours.

A contemporary chronicler has preserved in detail the declaration made by the hermit as he lay on the straw on the pavement of the church. He stated that he had kept silence and fled from the company of men to avoid sin, and that his ecstasies and the apparent eccentricities of his conduct were due to the consolations showered upon him by God. He received the last sacraments, agreed to swallow the warm broth which the marchesa had given Father Dominic for him, and lived another four weeks. After which St. Michael appeared to him, surrounded by angels, to lead him to heaven.

St. Nicomedes

Various martyrologies say he was a priest and shed his blood for the faith at Rome, under Domitian.

St. Albinus

Was bishop of Lyons at the end of the 4th century; resigned and ended his days as a hermit.

Blessed Aichardus

Disciple of St. Bernard, founded the abbey of Hemmerode in the diocese of Trier in 1139, and later was novice master at Clairvaux (d. about 1170).

St. Aper

Born near Trier, became bishop of Toul (d. end of the 5th or beginning of the 6th century).

St. Catherine of Genoa (d. 1510)

Daughter of Giacomo Fieschi, viceroy of Naples. Against her will she married Guiliano Adorno, a spendthrift and a profligate, whose death, however, was edifying. She had lost her fervour while married but spent the thirty-six years of her widowhood in doing penance and in caring for the poor, enjoying the most sublime graces. She left a treatise on *Purgatory* and one on the *Pure Love of God*. Her feast is also celebrated on March 22nd.

September 16th

ST. CYPRIAN (d. 258)

St. Cyprian is one of the great figures of the first Christian centuries. Bishop of Carthage from 249 to 258, he was born, it is thought, into the upper middle class of that city in about the year 210; and before his conversion, he taught rhetoric. He was baptized about 245, and thereafter led a holy life which, he wrote, gave him peace and happiness. His writings and his correspondence concern dogma, morals, asceticism, and ecclesiastical discipline. Because of his virtue and prestige, he became the leader of the Christians of Africa, gathering around him a hundred or so of the prelates of that land. The story of his martyrdom is one of noble grandeur.

The proconsul Galerius Maximus said to him: "You are Thascius Cyprianus?"

"I am."

"You made yourself leader of these sacrilegious men?"

"Yes."

"The most holy emperors have ordered that you sacrifice."

"I will not do it."

"Reflect."

"Do what you have been commanded to do, for there is no reason for reflection in such a case."

Having taken the advice of his counsel, Galerius regretfully pronounced this sentence: "You have made yourself the enemy of the gods of Rome and of its holy laws; also, as our holy emperors have not been able to bring you back to the practice of their cult, your blood will be the sanction of their laws." Then he read the following decree: "We order Thascius Cyprianus to be put to death by the sword."

Cyprianus replied: *"Deo gratias."*

Having arrived at the place of execution, he took off his coat, knelt down and prayed with his face to the earth. Then he took off his dalmatic tunic, gave it to the deacons, and, dressed in a linen shirt, awaited the executioner. When he arrived, the bishop ordered him to be given twenty-five gold pieces. During these preparations, the faithful spread sheets and towels around the martyr. Cyprian himself bound his own eyes. Being unable to bind his own hands, the priest Julian and a subdeacon rendered him this service. And it was thus that Cyprian received death.

St. EDITH

Natural daughter of Edgar, king of England, was brought up in the monastery of Wilton, where her mother, St. Wulfrid, had retired. She took the veil there in her turn and died aged twenty-three, on September 17th, 984.

St. CORNELIUS

Became pope in 251 and died the next year in exile. The sufferings he endured during his brief pontificate earned for him the title of martyr. His name is mentioned in the canon of the Mass.

St. LUDMILLA

Of Bavarian and pagan origin, married Borziwoi, duke of Bohemia, and with him was converted to Christianity. Her son Wratislaus having died in 916, she took over the power and exercised it until 927 when, urged on by Wratislaus' widow, two pagan princes strangled her in her bed.

September 17th

ST. LAMBERT (d. about 705)

ST. LAMBERT was victim of the bloody warfare waged by the descendants of Clovis with their mayors of the palace. Born of rich and noble parents at Maestricht, he had been elected to the episcopal see of that city on St. Theodard's death, through the favour of Childeric II, king of Austrasia. Childeric having been assassinated in 673, Dagobert II seized his estates, and forced Lambert to retire to the monastery of Stavelot. There he lived for seven years, humble and obedient as any novice.

The assassination of Dagobert II and of Ebroin placed the power in the hands of Pepin of Heristal, who drove the usurping bishops away and restored the sees to their legitimate pastors. Lambert returned to Maestricht and was able for some thirty years thereafter to evangelize the vast regions included in his diocese.

It is noted that he overthrew many idols in Taxandria, and that he often took counsel with the apostle of Frisia, his friend St. Willibrord. He died a violent death in the village of Leodium, for reasons which have not yet been made clear. For a long time it was thought that he had been assassinated at the orders of Alpaide, the concubine of Pepin of Heristal and mother of Charles Martel, from whom he wished to separate this prince, but he probably was the victim of a private feud. In any event, he is considered a martyr. His remains were first venerated at Maestricht; then St. Hubert, his successor, brought them to the actual place of his death, where soon rose the town of Liége.

The STIGMATA OF ST. FRANCIS

The miracle which gave birth to this feast is that of the stigmatization of St. Francis of Assisi. It took place on Mount Alvernia where, on September 17th, 1224, the Poverello received on his body the exterior and lasting marks of the passion of the Saviour.

St. COLUMBA (d. 853)

She was a nun at Cordova; during a persecution, she deliberately left her convent to declare her faith before the cadi's tribunal, and she was beheaded.

St. NARCISSUS (d. about 260)

According to the *Acts* of St. Lawrence, was beheaded for having given shelter to persecuted Christians.

St. HILDEGARD (d. 1179)

Is one of the great Rhenish mystics. Abbess of the convent of Diesenberg, then of that of Mount St. Rupert, near Bingen, she was in touch with the most important people of her time and left letters and three volumes of *Revelations*.

September 18th
ST. SOPHIA (date unknown)

OFTEN in the primitive Church the Christians substituted some pious pseudonym for their true name. Some of these pseudonyms were Greek: *Sophia* (wisdom), *Pistis* (faith), *Agapè* (love). Others were Latin: *Renatus* (reborn), *Redemptus* (redeemed), *Renovatus* (renewed). All had a mystic meaning and carried a lesson. So it was apparently with the saint who is commemorated today. Nothing is known of her except her baptismal name. And as it was found on a tomb in a cemetery reserved to martyrs, it was concluded that she had given her blood for the faith.

ST. RICHARDIS or RICHILDA (d. about 896)

THE life of this empress was tragically linked to some great events in history. Daughter of Erchingen, powerful lord of the Nordgrau, in 862 she married Charles the Fat, third son of Louis the German. No one would have thought that this sickly, irresolute, possibly abnormal, and in any case little gifted prince would ever have succeeded to Charlemagne, his great grand father, but that is what happened. Death having unexpectedly carried off his father, uncle, and two brothers, Charles the Fat became king of Italy, emperor of France and Germany, not to count the fact that Pope John III had crowned him emperor in St. Peter's at Rome in February 881. It was his duty to defend the papacy against the Saracens, France against the Normans, and to keep the peace in Europe. Unfortunately, he failed in practically everything. A letter is preserved which John III wrote to the empress in 881; he cries anew for help, already sees himself prisoner of the unbelievers, dragged by them into captivity and perhaps massacred. He was, in fact, killed by blows from a hammer the following year in the Lateran. Five years later, Charles the Fat was solemnly deposed at the Diet of Tribur; the Carolingian Empire fell into ruins, and a dozen little kings divided the pieces. The emperor only survived his fall a few weeks; he died on January 13th, 888, at Neidingen on the Danube.

Richardis was then no longer at his side. A short time before, accused of adultery, she had expected to be repudiated. At the Diet of Kirckheim where she appeared to hear her sentence, Charles affirmed that he had not consummated his marriage with the empress, and she appealed to the judgment of God that she had remained a virgin. It is not known if the ordeal by fire took place, but it is known that, after having pardoned her unfortunate husband, Richardis retired immediately to the abbey of Andlau and died there. In 1049, Pope St. Leo IX came there to venerate her remains and on that occasion raised her to the altars.

St. STEPHANA

A virgin martyr honoured at Scala, near Amalfi (date unknown).

St. JOSEPH OF CUPERTINO (1603–1663)

Born at Cupertino, near Brindisi, he became a conventual friar minor
and passed most of his life at Assisi. He is one of the most extraordinary
ecstatics who ever lived.

September 19th

ST. JANUARIUS (d. 305)

ST. JANUARIUS was martyred during the persecution of Diocletian, which
was particularly severe in Campania. He was then bishop of Benevento
and about thirty years old. He was arrested just as he was about to visit the
deacon Sossius in prison. Arraigned before the tribunal presided over by the
governor Timothy, and ordered to sacrifice to the gods of the Empire,
Januarius confessed his faith and had his head cut off not far from the great
amphitheatre of Pozzuoli. His head and his body, first buried at the place
of execution, were transported to Naples when, only a few years later,
Constantine gave religious liberty to the Church. To it were added two
phials in which a Christian woman had gathered some of his blood, and
all were placed in a subterranean chamber over which the present cathedral
was built.

Among the fifty or so patrons adopted by the Neapolitans, there is no
doubt that Januarius occupies first place. They give him credit for delivering
them from the plague in 1497, and add that if Vesuvius did not destroy their
city in one or other of the eruptions of 1631, 1698, 1767, and 1779, as it
destroyed Herculaneum and Pompeii in A.D. 79, it was St. Januarius'
doing.

The ritual liquification of his blood is known all over the world. It takes
place generally three times a year, on September 19th, on December 16th,
and on the first Sunday in May. The first of these dates is that of his feast;
the second recalls the eruption of Vesuvius in 1631; and the third commemorates the translation of his relics mentioned earlier. The miracle consists in that his blood, contained in a sealed phial, passes from a state more
or less solid to a state more or less liquid, and in that it manifestly augments
in volume. Scientists have never explained this phenomenon. Polemicists
have found no other explanation than the fraudulent intervention of the
clergy. But Montesquieu, who was present at two liquefactions in 1728,
wrote in his *Voyages*: "I can declare that the miracle of St. Januarius is not a
trick; the priests are in good faith."

St. Desiderius

Lector of St. Januarius, as Sossius was his deacon, was like them decapitated.

St. Miletus

Thought to have been bishop of Trier in the 5th century.

St. Lucy of Scotland (d. 1090)

Daughter, it is said, of a king of Scotland, she left the licentious court of her father to come to Lorraine, near Sampigny, to guard the sheep of a certain Thiébaut. He died and left her his fortune, and Lucy used it to build a church and a hermitage on a mountain which still bears her name. Sterile wives invoke her to become mothers. Anne of Austria came as a pilgrim to her tomb the year before Louis XIV was born.

St. Marie-Emilie de Rodat (1787–1852)

Founded in France the congregation of Sisters of the Holy Family, one branch of which is contemplative and another devoted to the care of the sick and to education.

September 20th

ST. EUSTACHIUS (date uncertain)

The *Acts* of St. Eustachius will please the collectors of marvellous stories. One may read that he was first called Placidus and his wife, Theopista. He possessed an immense fortune and commanded the emperor's armies. She was most beautiful and gave abundant alms. Both served the false gods with fervour and brought their sons up in luxury and virtue. Placidus was converted while deer hunting; a young stag with a cross between its antlers, suddenly turned to him and made a long speech which transformed his soul. A few hours earlier, in her room, Theopista is said to have been favoured with an apparition which revealed to her also the Christian verities. Next day, therefore, the whole family betook itself to the priest John to receive baptism, and, on this occasion, Placidus changed his name to Eustachius.

The stag reappeared to him to warn of persecutions which the devil was preparing for him. Soon, indeed, all his servants died of the plague; an epidemic carried off all his cattle; brigands stripped his house, and he barely escaped by fleeing with his family to the sea. A boat took them to Egypt. As Eustachius had no money to pay the fare, the captain detained his wife as surety, but sudden death prevented him from abusing her. As for the two children, they were carried off, one by a lion, the other by a wolf; luckily, shepherds came running up in time to save and adopt them.

Fifteen years had elapsed after this family dispersal when the barbarians invaded the Empire. The besieged emperor had a search made for the old commander-in-chief of his armies, who was found working on a farm; and Eustachius threw the enemy back from the frontiers.

It would take too long to relate how his sons, now become soldiers, shared in his triumph, and how Theopista was recognized by them in an inn where she was serving; all the family was reunited in time to take part in the victory celebrations. These were to be preceded by sacrifices to the idols. Eustachius, his wife, and sons refusing to participate, they were shut up in a bronze bull, roasted over a slow fire for three days, and perished together without their bodies being consumed.

Sts. PRIVATUS and DIONYSIUS

The Roman martyrology relates that they died for the faith in Phrygia.

St. VINCENT MADELGAIRE or MAUGER (d. about 687)

Husband of St. Wandru (*see April 9th*); took the name of Vincent and founded a monastery at Soignies (Belgium).

Blessed YVES MAYEUC (1462–1551)

Breton Dominican, confessor of Anne of Brittany and bishop of Rennes.

Blessed FRANCIS DE POSADAS (1644–1713)

A Dominican of Cordovan origin, preached successfully in southern Spain and twice refused to be made bishop.

September 21st

ST. MATTHEW (1st century)

As was customary among the Jews, Matthew, son of Alphaeus, had two names; he was also called Levi. He was a publican or collector of taxes at Capharnaum, not far from the frontier separating the lands of Herod Antipas from those of his brother Philip. His profession was one of the least honourable; everyone considered all tax collectors and their masters to be more or less robbers, and the Pharisees treated them as public sinners. It was as direct a

challenge to public opinion for the Saviour to associate Matthew the publican with His apostolate as it was later for Him to visit Zaccheus, another
member of this despised profession.

The Gospel tells that, after having healed a paralytic, "As he passed further
on his way, Jesus saw a man called Matthew sitting at work in the customs-
house, and said to him, Follow me; and Matthew rose from his place and
followed him. And afterwards, when he was sitting at table in the house,
many publicans and sinners were to be found sitting down with him and
his disciples. The Pharisees saw this, and asked his disciples, How comes
it that your master eats with publicans and sinners? Jesus heard it, and said,
It is not those that are in health that have need of the physician, it is those
who are sick. Go home and find out what the words mean. It is mercy that
wins favour with me, not sacrifice. I have come to call sinners, not the just"
(Matt. ix, 9-13).

From that moment, Matthew withdraws into the apostolic college and no
longer calls attention to himself. With the other apostles, he witnessed the
ascension and was in the upper room on the day of Pentecost. Transformed
by the Holy Ghost, he, like his colleagues, became a herald of the Christian
message; then, having spread it for a long time by word of mouth—for
perhaps some twenty years—he wrote it down. He did this in Aramaic, in
the language which had supplanted Hebrew and which Jesus spoke. This
Aramaic version addressed to the Palestinian Jews has not been preserved;
we possess only its translation into Greek made towards the end of the 1st
century; it is this, placed first among our Sacred Scriptures, which we call
"The Gospel according to St. Matthew." The writers of Christian antiquity
are not in agreement as to which country was the scene of the apostolate of
the first of the evangelists, nor as to the date of his death.

St. Iphigenia

She is said to have been an Ethiopian, and she was dedicated to God
by St. Matthew.

Blessed Bernardina

Nothing is known of her except that she is honoured in Spain as a
Franciscan tertiary.

September 22nd

STS. MAURICE, EXUPERIUS, CANDIDUS, AND OTHER MARTYRS OF THE THEBAN LEGION (d. 286)

MAURICE, Exuperius, and Candidus were officers in the army which was ordered, in 286, to put down the insurrection of the Bagaudae. (Bagaud comes from the Celtic word *bagad*, and means "multitude.") These were a host of peasants, shepherds, and slaves, who in certain parts of Gaul had revolted against their masters and threatened Roman domination.

Maximianus Herculius was ordered by Diocletian to put an end to this uprising. Having crossed the Alps, he paused in Switzerland to rest his troops. His advance guard camped at Agaunum, fifteen miles from the Lake of Geneva. It was to this advance guard that Maurice and his com٬ panions belonged; they formed a wholly Christian detachment, drawn, it is said, from the Egyptian armies which habitually guarded the southern frontiers of the Thebaid—hence the name "Theban legion," which they later acquired.

Before they began the campaign against the Bagaudae, Maximianus Herculius ordered all his troops to offer sacrifice to the gods and to take the oath. The Theban legion refused to participate in a ceremony it considered sacrilegious and superfluous. The commanding general decimated the legion. This punishment having had no effect on the remaining mutineers, Maximianus decimated it a second time. And as the survivors did not show themselves any more reasonable, he had every last man of them killed.

This is the traditional way of telling the story of the Theban legion. But it is necessary to mention that certain writers tell a different story. Certainly, they say, there were Christians martyred at Agaunum between 286 and 304, but they add that there is nothing to prove they were so numerous, and it is not even known that they were soldiers.

St. Lô (d. about 568)

Belonged to a noble family from Briovère, which has since become the town of Saint Lô. He was appointed bishop of Coutances, about 528, and was present at the three councils held at Orléans between 536 and 541.

St. SALABERGA (d. about 665)

Sister of St. Bodo, bishop of Toul, and the second wife of St. Blandinus, was blind from birth and cured by St. Eustace of Luxeuil. Of her five children two were raised to the Church's altars: Blessed Baudoin and

St. Austruda. Salaberga founded the monastery of St. Peter at Poulangey and also that of St. John the Baptist at Laon, in which she died at the head of three hundred nuns.

St. SILVANUS

Patron of the town of Levroux, in Berry.

September 23rd

ST. LINUS (d. about 79)

IN the last years of Nero's reign, the Christians were accused of being, as Tacitus puts it, "the bitter enemies of the human race"; and a violent perse-cution arose against them, in which St. Peter and St. Paul were notable among those who perished. It lasted four years and ended in 68. It was at about that date that St. Linus entered upon the succession of St. Peter. If he was not, as some say, a former slave, at least it is generally agreed that he was of very humble extraction. St. Epiphanius reports that he ruled the Church of Rome for twelve years. His pontificate then coincided with the coming of the Flavians, under whom the Christians were first left in peace. For more than twenty years, in fact, it was possible for them freely to practise the religion which at that time found adherents even in the highest ranks of Roman society. Also, if it is true as one tradition has it, that St. Linus died a martyr, his was a very exceptional case for that time.

ST. THECLA (1st century)

THERE was no more famous name in Christian antiquity; to say of a woman that she was another Thecla was to attribute to her the highest virtues of her sex. St. Jerome expresses himself in this way in order to praise St. Melania, and St. Gregory of Nyssa to exalt the holiness of Macrina, his own sister.

The information found on the subject of St. Thecla in the Fathers is taken from the *Acts of Paul and Thecla*, an apocryphal document of the 2nd century which was much quoted by heretics, but which St. Augustine complained had been interpolated and falsified.

Converted by St. Paul, Thecla lived for a certain time at Iconium. She endured a thousand tribulations to remain true to her faith and to the vow of virginity which she had pronounced; she ended her days peacefully at

Seleucia, where her tomb was venerated as early as the 4th century. And this is all that is known for certain of this illustrious virgin who was honoured no less in the Greek than in the Roman Church, who is mentioned in the canon of the Mass, extolled by St. Epiphanius, St. John Chrysostom, St. Methodius of Olympus, and St. Ambrose, and who is invoked in the liturgy at the bedside of the dying in the following prayer: "Lord, who delivered the blessed Thecla, virgin and martyr, from three cruel torments, we beseech Thee also in Thy goodness to deliver this soul, and to grant him the enjoyment of the celestial blessings with Thee. Amen."

The three torments mentioned here are the stake, lions, and serpents to which, according to the *Acts of Paul*, Thecla was condemned and which did her no harm.

St. HERESWITHA (d. about 690)

Niece of St. Edwin, king of Northumbria, and sister of St. Hilda, was first married to St. Ethelbert, then to Anna, king of East Anglia. With the consent of the latter she left the world, came to France about 646, and with her daughter Ethelburga and her granddaughter Ercongata, she took the veil at Chelles, where St. Bathilde, another queen, was soon to enter.

September 24th
OUR LADY OF MERCY

WE know that by 621 the Visigoths had finally made themselves masters of Spain. In 710, the Arabs came in their turn, drove them into the mountains of Asturias, and conquered almost the whole Peninsula. It took no less than six centuries to get them out. During this endless period of wars, innumerable Christians were taken captive into Africa. Those who accepted Islam were treated as free men; the others were sold as slaves to the Saracens. In this case, ransom had to be paid to obtain their deliverance, and many families could not do this.

It was in order to free these unfortunate people in danger of apostasy that St. Peter Nolasco founded, in 1218, the Order of Our Lady of Mercy for the redemption of captives. He had been encouraged by an apparition of the Blessed Virgin herself. Peter told his vision to Raymond of Penafort, his confessor, and to King James of Aragon who helped him realize his project. To the three customary religious vows, the Mercedarians added another—to deliver themselves up as hostages if they had no other means to accomplish their mission. This order, thanks to their heroism and to the generosity of Christians, was fruitful in results and continued until the Moorish piracy was ended.

"It is in order to give to God and to the Virgin Mother," says the Roman breviary, "worthy thanks for the benefit of such an institution, that the feast of Our Lady of Ransom was established." As we have already seen on July 16th, the name Mercedes comes from this particular title of the Virgin.

St. ANDOCHIUS (2nd century)

A priest honoured for his martyrdom at Saulieu (Côte d'Or), with St. THYRSUS, deacon, and St. FELIX. Later, it was said that all three had been sent by St. Polycarp to convert Gaul.

St. RUSTICUS (d. middle of the 5th century)

Was pastor of a parish in Auvergne before succeeding St. Venerandus as bishop of Clermont.

St. PAPHNUTIUS (4th century)

An Egyptian anchorite, he left his desert when he learned that the Christians were being persecuted and asked to share their fate. He was tied to a palm-tree and left there to die.

St. GERMER (d. about 638)

After having been an ornament at the court of Dagobert I, he retired with his wife's consent to the monastery of Pentale. Later he lived in a grotto, then founded on his estate of Flay an abbey which later bore his name.

September 25th

ST. FIRMINUS

A RICH and distinguished senator lived at Pampeluna. His wife, Eugenia, was as famous for her beauty as for her virtues. As they were both on their way to the temple of Jupiter, they met a Christian priest called Honestus, who was railing against the gods. Interrupting his speech, they asked the preacher with what he proposed to replace the religion at which he mocked. Honestus then put before them the proofs of Christianity and called upon the authority of his master Saturninus, one of the seventy disciples of the Saviour. St. Saturninus, who was later to found the church of Toulouse, was at that time evangelizing Spain. A week had barely passed when he arrived at

Pampeluna, and put the last touches to the conversion of the senator and his wife.

Now these two had a son called Firminus. They confided him to Honestus, who trained him piously and made him his acolyte, and when he had grown old, with his last strength led him to Toulouse, to have him consecrated bishop. Later, Firminus evangelized Aquitaine, Agenais, and the country of the Arverni; then turning northward, he settled at Amiens where he was martyred.

Thus the story of St. Firminus is commonly told, but it all seems to be legendary, and it is better to be content with saying that Firminus was without doubt the first bishop of Amiens, and that he has always been held in great veneration.

Sts. PAUL and TATTA and their children

Martyred at Damascus (date unknown).

Sts. AURELIA and NEOMESIA

Pope Leo IX authorized their cult in the 11th century; they are still honoured at Anagni. They were, it is said, holy women who had come on a pilgrimage to Rome and who, molested by the Saracens near Capua, fled to Macerata where they died.

St. LUPUS OF LYONS

Led the eremitic life on the island of Sainte-Barbe near Lyons; became bishop of this city; suffered from troubles which followed the death of King Sigismund; was present at the third Council of Orléans, and died in 542.

St. AUNARIUS (d. 605)

A native of Orléans, he spent his youth at the court of Guntram, king of Burgundy; became a disciple of Syagrius, bishop of Autun; then was himself made bishop of Auxerre about 570.

September 26th

STS. JUSTINA AND CYPRIAN (d. 304)

THE story of Justina and Cyprian has long been well known; it was accepted by Prudentius and St. Gregory of Nazianzus, and the Empress Eudocia herself put it into verse in the 5th century. It is very probable if it is stripped of its trappings of legend and reduced to the following facts:

In the first years of Diocletian's reign, there lived at Antioch a famous magician named Cyprian. He had studied philosophy at Athens, the occult sciences in Phrygia, the secrets of divination in Chaldea, and the art of casting spells in Egypt. When he had learned everything that men or demons were capable of teaching him, he settled down to doing all sorts of evil, committing almost as many sins as he wished. Nothing and no one seemed able to resist him, until the day when a young Christian of Damascus called Justina, whom he tried to seduce, resisted his wiles. Understanding then that all his evil knowledge was powerless against divine grace, Cyprian burned his magic books, embraced Christianity, and lived ascetically. After long years of penance he became priest and even bishop. As a result of the edict of persecution of 304, Cyprian was arrested at Antioch, and Justina was taken at Damascus. Both appeared before the delegate of the East, who condemned them to the torture of a boiling cauldron; both came out safe and sound. Their judge then sent them to Nicomedia, where Diocletian condemned them to capital punishment. According to the custom of the time, the bodies of these two martyrs were left without burial, but some Christian sailors gathered them up and transported them to Italy.

St. VIGILIUS

Bishop of Brescia in Lombardy (6th century).

Sts. ISAAC JOGUES (1607-1646), JEAN DE LALANDE (d. 1646) and RENÉ GOUPIL (1607-1642)

These French Jesuits were tortured and massacred by the Iroquois, the two first in 1646, the third in 1642. A native of Orléans, Father Jogues arrived at Quebec in 1630; he escaped the massacre of 1642 in which his brother-helper René Goupil perished; after remaining a captive for some time in the hands of his torturers, he was ransomed and returned to France; but at the beginning of 1646, he re-embarked for America and several months later, with the oblate Jean de Lalande, he was killed by the Mohawks on the site of the present town of Auriesville (New York State).

September 27th

STS. COSMAS AND DAMIAN (d. about 300)

THEIR cult is one of the most ancient and has spread everywhere; daily still their names are mentioned in the canon of the Mass. They were two brothers, who had come from Arabia to practise medicine in Syria. They treated sickness of the soul as well as that of the body, converting sinners, delivering the possessed. Their patients were numerous, as they treated everyone free, following the Gospel saying, "Give as you have received the gift, freely without payment" (Matt. x, 8). However, a matron named Palladia managed to make them quarrel on this subject. Having been cured by them of a grave chronic illness, she offered them some money which they refused. Next day, taking Damian aside, she begged him to accept the honorarium in the name of Christ. At the mention of this blessed name, Damian consented; Cosmas, learning this, declared he would no longer collaborate with him. However, their misunderstanding did not last.

Meanwhile, the fame of the conversions they effected came to the ears of Lysias, who had been ordered to hunt out the Christians. He summoned the two brothers to appear, reproached them with emptying the temples of the idols, tried to force them to sacrifice to the gods. When they refused, they were subjected to various tortures and were finally beheaded. Their bodies were later transported to Cyr, in Syria. Three centuries later, the Emperor Justinian, when gravely ill, prayed to St. Cosmas and St. Damian to be cured. Having obtained his request, he enlarged and fortified the town of Cyr, repaired their church in Constantinople, and even raised a new one to them; all this increased the devotion of the Christian people to the two martyrs.

St. HILTRUDE (d. end of the 8th century)

Daughter of a Poitevin noble established in Hainaut, she resolved when very young to remain a virgin. As a suitor was being presented to her, she fled from the paternal roof and only returned the day she learned that this suitor had married her sister. Soon after, she took the veil at the hands of the bishop of Cambrai, and began to live in a cell attached to the church of Liessies the recluse's life in which she persevered until her death.

St. ELZÉAR (1285-1325)

Born at Robians (Provence) and son of Hermengild of Sabran who had been made count of Ariano, in the kingdom of Naples, Elzéar married, at the age of fourteen, Delphine of Glandèves, who was sixteen. By mutual agreement, the young couple agreed to observe continence. They loved each other dearly, were very happy, were rivals as to which would better observe the rules of the Franciscan third order, of which they were members. After his father's death, Elzéar had to divide his time between his Provençal estate and his lordship in Italy. He made himself loved by his subjects and admired by his enemies for his courage and loyalty in war.

He died in France, where his king, Robert of Naples, had sent him to ask the hand of the daughter of the count of Valois for the prince of Calabria. Pope Urban II canonized Elzéar of Sabran in 1369, while his wife, Countess Delphine, was still alive.

September 28th

ST. WENCESLAUS (d. 929)

WENCESLAUS was only thirteen at the death of his father, Wratislaus, duke of Bohemia. While he awaited his majority, his mother, Drahomira, was regent. Christianity, recently introduced into the country by St. Cyril and St. Methodius, had not yet become deeply rooted, and many of his vassals were still pagan. The court itself was divided between the two religions. Ludmilla, mother of the late duke, professed Christianity; Drahomira, his widow, held to the ancient beliefs. Wenceslaus received the lessons of the former, whilst Boleslaus, his brother, was influenced by the latter. Drahomira took advantage of her regency to persecute the Christians, to have her mother-in-law strangled, and to force Wenceslaus to participate in idolatrous ceremonies. However, the future sovereign secretly practised his faith and received the sacraments at night.

As soon as he came into his power at the age of eighteen, he made his authority felt. He built churches, recalled the exiled priests, opened the frontiers to missionaries from Swabia and Bavaria, and recognized the suzerainty of the Empire in preference to seeing his country destroyed by the Germans. His morals were pure, his heart magnanimous; he himself prepared, with wheat from his fields and grapes from his vines, the Eucharistic bread and wine. Such was his horror of bloodshed that he challenged the duke of Kourim to single combat in order to bring to an end a struggle which was dragging on endlessly between them, and in which thousands of innocent people were losing their lives.

By his fair dealings Wenceslaus had become reconciled with his mother, Drahomira, and Boleslaus, his brother. But the latter, helped by friends of the former regent, sought to supplant him. On September 27th, 929, Wenceslaus invited Boleslaus to join with him at Boleslava in the celebration of the feast of Sts. Cosmas and Damian, to whom the chapel of the castle was dedicated; next morning, as Wenceslaus was on his way to Mass, his brother had him assassinated. Wenceslaus was then about twenty-two years old.

St. Thiemo (d. 1101)

Born into the Bavarian high nobility and became a monk; returned to the world where he was mixed up in some scandal; was converted and elected in 1079 as abbot of St. Peter at Salzburg, becoming bishop of that town in 1088. Some years later he went with the duke of Bavaria on a crusade and, captured by the Turks, was put to death on refusing to apostasize.

St. Chariton

Spread monastic life in Palestine at the end of the 4th century.

Blessed Bernardine of Feltre

A Franciscan preacher, evangelized Italy for twenty-five years, reformed many convents of Poor Clares and founded *monti di pietà* or pawnshops to protect the people against usurers.

September 29th
ST. MICHAEL THE ARCHANGEL

St. Michael is, with St. Gabriel and St. Raphael, one of the three archangels mentioned in Holy Scripture. There he appears as prince of the celestial hierarchy, protecting the chosen people and achieving the downfall of the infernal powers. The primitive Church considered him also the defender of Christians and their consolation in trials. Still today the liturgical prayers show him charged with the guidance of souls here below, to protect them from the devil's snares and to lead them to the light eternal: *signifer Sanctus Michael repraesentet eas in lucem sanctam.*

From the earliest Christian times St. Michael was the object of a cult. In Phrygia, near Hierapolis, he took the place of the god of the thermal waters; here and there in Gaul he turned Mercury out of the high places; in Germany he sometimes was substituted for Wotan on the banks of the Rhine. A church dedicated to him was built near Constantinople as early as the 4th century.

On May 8th, 492, the archangel appeared on the summit of Mount Gargano, and the cave where he had appeared became the most frequented place of pilgrimage in southern Italy. The Lombards chose him as their patron, struck coins in his image, and consecrated to him their most beautiful temples. A hundred years later, when the plague was raging at Rome, Pope Gregory the Great saw him in a vision sheathing his flaming sword to signify that he would put an end to the scourge. A cryptiform church was built about 608 on Hadrian's mausoleum in gratitude to the archangel for this good office.

Doubtless still more famous than the Roman and Apulian sanctuaries is the one dedicated on a Norman hill in 709, called Mont Saint Michel. The archangel, it was said, had appeared to St. Aubert, bishop of Avranches, expressing his wish to be honoured by the Gauls. From that moment, devotion to St. Michael took on a new impetus; it travelled to the east with the Celtic monks, who carried it as far as the Bavarian Alps, from whence it spread throughout the West.

St. CYRIACUS (d. 556)

Abandoned the world at eighteen to retire to a desert in Palestine. He was almost ninety when, in 536, he left the seclusion of St. Sabbas to defend the true faith at the Council of Constantinople against the Eutychians; then he retired to his solitude and died at the age of one hundred and seven.

St. FULGENTIUS

Is honoured at Atino, near Monte Cassino, as a former bishop of that town.

Blessed CHARLES OF BLOIS

Son of Louis de Chatillon and nephew, through his mother, of King Philip of Valois, he became duke of Brittany in 1341 and fought for twenty three years to defend his rights. Conquered and taken prisoner in 1347, he was deported to England and imprisoned for nine years in the Tower of London. He took up arms on his release from captivity, and was killed at the battle of Auray in 1364.

September 30th

ST. JEROME (d. 419)

ST. JEROME'S great claim to glory is the Vulgate, or the Latin version of the Scriptures, which the Roman Church still uses today. He undertook it at the order of Pope Damasus and took thirty years to finish it. For the Psalms and the New Testament, Jerome was generally content to revise the ancient Latin translation in use in Rome at his time; the other scriptural texts he translated from the original.

Born about 347 at Strido, in Dalmatia, of a rich and Christian family, he was young when he reached Rome and followed an excellent course of classical studies. Until he received baptism in 365, his behaviour at times left something to be desired. He began to study theology at Trier; then having resolved to become a monk, he settled at Aquileia, where he lived some years in the company of Rufinus and other young clerics. From 374 to 382 we may follow Jerome to the desert of Chalcis in Syria, where he practised terrible austerities; to Antioch, where he received holy orders; to Constantinople, where he studied under Gregory of Nazianzus and worked with Gregory of Nyssa.

Returning to Rome in 382, he remained there only three years, undertaking the duties of secretary to Pope Damasus and directing a group of patrician ladies, among whom were Marcella, Paula, and Eustochium. Calumny fastened upon his relations with them: "The infamy of a false crime has been imputed to me," he wrote to them, "but it is not the judgments of men which open or shut the gates of heaven." Nevertheless, he bid the West farewell for ever, travelled in Palestine and Egypt, then went to settle in the monastery that Paula had built for him at Bethlehem. There it was that he passed his last years in study and in piety. He wrote enormously; his works take up no less than six thousand columns of Migne's *Patrology*; among them are translations of Origen, exegetic works, histories and polemic writings, several biographies, and a very extensive correspondence. As Benedict XV wrote in 1920: "The Church venerates in Jerome the greatest doctor given her by heaven for the interpretation of the Holy Scriptures."

St. Ambert

Abbot, later suffragan bishop of Moissac in Quercy (d. about 680).

St. Léry

Honoured at Mein-en-Gails, near Saint-Malo. It is thought that he exercised his sacerdotal activity in that region in the 7th century.

St. Conrad (d. 1227)

Son of the count of Seyne, Conrad was successively canon of St. Lambert at Liége, monk and abbot of Villers in Brabant, legate of the Holy See, and cardinal bishop of Porto. At the conclave which followed the death of Honorius III, his colleagues wished to elect him pope, but he prevented them. Then, feeling his death was near, he said: "Why did I not stay in my abbey of Villers, taking my turn at washing the dishes, like my brothers!" At the Synod of Cologne a parish priest had complained that the Dominicans came to preach in his parish and to collect alms there. "How many parishioners have you?" asked Conrad, who was presiding. "Nine thousand," replied the priest. "And you, who must give account before the tribunal of God for the salvation of everyone of them," added Conrad, "you find it a bad thing that holy monks come to help you save them?" And he took all benefices away from the grasping parish priest.

THE SAINTS OF OCTOBER
October 1st
ST. REMIGIUS (d. 533)

 EMIGIUS was born about the year 438, the son of Emilius, count of Laon, and of a pious mother honoured as St. Celina. This noble youth, half French, half Roman, admired by the rhetoricians of his day for a collection of eloquent discourses, was made bishop by the people of Rheims at the age, it is said, of twenty-two.

Fifteen years later the Roman Empire had succumbed in the West. The Germanic tribes were in occupation of Gaul: the Visigoths were south of the Loire; in the Rhône and Saône basins were the Burgundians; to the north, from the Channel to the Rhine, the Franks. Among these last, the Sicambri of Tournai had Clovis at their head, and his authority was soon felt as far as the Loire.

This pagan was not unaware of the prestige enjoyed by the bishops. Yielding to their counsels, he had, in 493, married the Catholic Clotilda. Three years later, at grips with the Alamanni, masters of Alsace, who were threatening to invade Gaul, his troops began to retreat. Clovis then made a

vow. "God of Clotilda," he said, "if you give me the victory, I will believe
in you and receive baptism." He kept his word, and, on Christmas Day of
496, he was baptized at Rheims with three thousand of his warriors. Pouring
the holy water on him, St. Remigius said to him: "Proud Sicambrian, bow
your head; adore what you have burned and burn what you have adored."

Victorious at Tolbiac, Clovis beat the Burgundians at Dijon in 500, and
the Visigoths at Vouillé near Poitiers in 507. These victories gave him
dominion from the Rhine to the Pyrenees, and they had another important
result: the Burgundians and the Visigoths were all more or less Arians; their
defeat was the defeat of Arianism in Gaul, and all the territories ruled by
St. Remigius' spiritual son then came under obedience to the Roman
Church.

The bishop of Rheims long survived these happenings. Blind and aged
almost a hundred, he died after an episcopate of seventy-seven years.

St. BAVO or ALLOWIN (d. 654)

A Brabançon noble who had had a wild youth, and, having become
a widower, was converted after hearing St. Amandus of Maestricht
preach. He became a monk at St. Peter of Ghent and ended his life as a
recluse.

Sts. JULIA, VERISSIMA, and MAXIMA

Three sisters martyred at Lisbon at the beginning of the 4th century.

St. PIAT

This saint, whose body was found in the 7th century by St. Eligius,
had come from Benevento; he evangelized the district of Tournai
(Belgium), and was martyred about 286.

October 2nd
ST. LEODEGAR (d. 679)

BORN about 616, St. Leodegar was raised at the court of Clotaire II. His
mother, named Sigrada, had two brothers of whom one, Athabric, was duke
of Alsace, and the other, Didon or Desiderius, was bishop of Poitiers. At the
age of ten, Leodegar left the court and was entrusted to his uncle Didon,
who, about 638, appointed him his archdeacon.

Queen Bathilde, who recognized Leodegar's virtue and ability, had him
elected to the episcopal see of Autun in 663. After she became a widow and
regent of the kingdom, she appointed him to be her privy counsellor. From

that time on, Leodegar was involved in politics and no longer enjoyed any peace.

His loyalty to Bathilde and his love of the public welfare made him side against Ebroin, chamberlain of the palace; but the latter quickly ousted him and he was sent back to his episcopal city. His retreat was the forerunner of his sovereign's, who had to retire in 666 to the monastery of Chelles. The events that followed placed on the throne Childeric II, second son of Bathilde; and Leodegar, who had been among his supporters, became his prime minister. It was Ebroin's turn to fall into disgrace, to have his head shaved and be confined in the abbey of Luxeuil. However, Childeric could not long endure a minister who reproached him with his drunkenness and debauches; and on the night of Easter, 675, he almost killed him with his own hands in the basilica of Autun. Having changed his mind, he exiled him to Luxeuil, where Ebroin still was.

The death of the king ended the imprisonment of the two adversaries, and their rival politics proceeded afresh. The bishop supported Thierry III, youngest son of Queen Bathilde, while Ebroin favoured a certain Clovis who would have given him all the power. On August 26th, 676, he came to lay siege to Autun where Leodegar was cut off with a small army. Reduced to extremity, the bishop gave himself up to spare the horror of a massacre of his troops. Ebroin caused his eyes to be plucked out and the sockets burned with hot irons; some weeks later he ordered his lips cut off and his tongue slit; then he kept him prisoner in the monastery of Fécamp and after two years had him beheaded there.

THE GUARDIAN ANGELS

In the 16th century the Spanish Christians began to celebrate a feast of the Guardian Angels, which until then had been celebrated at the same time as the feast of St. Michael; in 1679 Pope Clement X extended this feast to the universal Church and fixed the celebration on October 2nd.

St. THEOPHILUS (8th century)

A monk of Constantinople, he was beaten, imprisoned and died in exile, for having opposed the Iconoclasts.

Sts. CYRIL, PRIMUS, and SECUNDUS

Died for the faith at Antioch in Syria (period uncertain).

St. ELEUTHERIUS (d. 303)

He was accused of having set fire to the palace of Diocletian at Nicomedia and, for this, was condemned to death with some other Christians, alleged to be his accomplices.

St. THOMAS OF HEREFORD (1219–1282)

Eldest son of a celebrated warrior named William of Chanteloup, he became bishop of Hereford, after having been chancellor of England, and died in Tuscany while returning from a journey to Rome.

October 3rd

ST. THERESA OF THE CHILD JESUS
(1873–1897)

OF a merchant family, St. Thérèse de l'Enfant Jesus was born at Alençon on January 2nd, 1873. Louis Martin and Zélie Guérin, her parents, had in their youth wished to embrace the religious state. Of their nine children, only five daughters survived, all of whom became nuns.

Theresa, the youngest, showed astonishing spiritual precocity. At two, she had the instinct of prayer; at three she was making sacrifices; at five she was able to profit by sermons. She lost her mother when four and a half, and two years later had a prophetic vision of the illness of which her father was to die. From October 1881 to December 1885, Theresa was brought up by the Benedictines of Lisieux; from March to May 1883 she suffered from a strange malady, characterized by violent crises, extended delirium, and prolonged fainting spells.

Her entry into the convent of the Carmelites of Lisieux took place on April 9th, 1888. Before pronouncing her vows she declared she "was come to Carmel to save souls and to pray for priests." After having worked in the laundry, the refectory, at the turning-box, and in the sacristy, she was made, in February 1893, assistant to the novice mistress. Out of obedience she adorned the chapel of her convent with paintings, and occasionally composed a few verses.

Nothing then appeared extraordinary in this life which was known later to have been filled with suffering and heroism. The young nun followed what Fénelon had once called the "way of childhood." "I prefer," she wrote, "the monotony of obscure sacrifice to all ecstasies. To pick up a pin for love can convert a soul." More even than scorn, she sought oblivion. In December 1894 she began her autobiography, entitled *The Story of a Soul*, which has spread the world over.

On April 3rd, 1896, Theresa began to cough blood. From that time on, enduring a true spiritual martyrdom, she seemed deprived of the light of faith and the sweetness of hope and speedily declined. On September 30th,

1897, at five o'clock in the afternoon, her last agony began. Shortly after seven she was heard to murmur: "I would not suffer less." Then she added: "I love Thee, my God," and drew her last breath. A short time before, she had written: "I want to spend my heaven doing good on earth."

St. GERARD (d. 957)

Native of the county of Namur, he became a monk at the abbey of St. Denis near Paris; founded the monastery of Brogne (Belgium), reformed various religious communities in Flanders, Lorraine, and Champagne, and finally returned to die at Brogne.

Sts. EWALD (d. 695)

There were two brothers of this name ordained priests in England, their native country, who, following St. Willibrord's example, went to Saxony to preach the Gospel and were almost immediately massacred.

St. CYPRIAN

First a monk of St. Victor at Marseilles, then bishop of Toulon; he was the disciple, friend, and later the biographer of St. Caesarius of Arles (6th century).

October 4th

ST. FRANCIS OF ASSISI (d. 1226)

BORN at Assisi in 1181 or 1182, the son of a rich cloth merchant, Francis Bernardone spent a very flighty youth, taking part in street battles and military adventures. After long months of captivity in the jails of Perugia, divine grace transformed him.

The Gospels, understood literally, became his rule of life, and his only thought was the imitation of Our Lord in all things. Having wedded Lady Poverty, as he expressed it, he was to be seen barefoot, in rough clothes, begging at the gates and preaching purity of heart and peace to all.

A few disciples joined him in 1209. They formed the nucleus of the order of Friars Minor. In 1212, Clare of Assisi placed herself under his guidance and brought into being the order of Sisters of the Poor. The third order was established some ten years later, for people in the world who wished to live the religious life without forsaking their calling.

The *Poverello* made three attempts to visit the Saracens; only one, in 1219, succeeded. Apart from these journeys and some pilgrimages to Rome, he rarely left Umbria.

Francis loved God with an infinite love and all creatures for love of Him. He composed sublime songs to the glory of his brother the Sun, lived on intimate terms with the wolves and the birds, worked with his hands, swept out churches, cared for lepers, and sent food to brigands with his affectionate greetings.

From 1221, displaced by reformers, he resigned the direction of his order; in September 1224 he received the stigmata on Mount Alvernia; on October 3rd, 1226, he lay down naked on the bare earth at the Portiuncula and, singing, received the visit of his sister, Death.

The religious and artistic influence of the *Poverello* was immense and it endures to this day. No other figure has been the subject of so much contemporary literature; he is the saint best beloved of heretics and of sinners. It seems that this is due to his chivalrous character, his absence of book knowledge, his poetic gifts, his charm and, to quote Benedict XV, "because he is the most perfect image of Christ that ever was."

St. AUREA

Was abbess of the convent of St. Martial in Paris which St. Eligius had founded in 633. She died there on October 4th, 666, of the plague which carried off one hundred and sixty of her nuns with her.

St. CALLISTENA (4th century) and St. ADAUCTUS (d. 312)

Said to have been a native of Ephesus, Adauctus, a Roman army general, had a daughter named Callistena who was coveted by the Emperor Maximinus. He found her a place of refuge in Lower Mesopotamia, and was put to death at the order of her cheated suitor. Callistena, however, reappeared at Ephesus on Maximinus' death and there piously ended her days.

St. MAINFROY

Said to have been a choir bishop; he is honoured at Moissac in Quercy.

October 5th

ST. PLACIDUS (d. about 540)

THE story of St. Placidus is still very obscure, and some incidents borrowed from the acts of other martyrs may possibly have become confused with it. It is believed that he was born in Rome about 515. His father, Tertullus, prefect of the city, confided him while still young to St. Benedict who lived

THE SAINTS OF OCTOBER

at that time at Subiaco. Four centuries earlier, Nero had arranged artificial lakes in these deep gorges above which a marvellous villa, called *Sublaqueum*, had been built. This villa gave its name to the first Benedictine foundation, and in one of these lakes Placidus almost drowned at the age of fifteen.

We have related elsewhere, how St. Benedict left Subiaco to go with a few disciples to settle at Monte Cassino. Placidus received a visit there from his father, Tertullus, on which occasion that wealthy man presented him with some great estates in Sicily. When St. Benedict deemed the time ripe, Placidus, accompanied by two other monks, embarked for Sicily to establish the Benedictine order there. Not far from the port of Messina, with the help of his father's farmers and workmen, he built in four years a monastery and church dedicated to St. John the Baptist.

The feast of dedication and their material interests drew his brothers, Eutychius and Victorinus, with his sister Flavia, to the island. They were staying at the monastery when some Moorish corsairs forced their way into the harbour and overran the surrounding coast. One night these pillagers burst into the abbey at the time when the monks were returning to their cells after matins. Placidus was walking in front, accompanied by his brothers and sister; then came two deacons, followed by the thirty monks who made up the new community.

After having inflicted a cruel beating on them all, the barbarians tried to suffocate them with smoke in an attempt to make them apostasize. Placidus, encouraging his companions in torture, had his lips cut off, his jaw broken with a stone, and his tongue plucked out. Then he was beheaded with all the others.

Blessed AYMARD

Succeeded St. Odo as abbot of Cluny. Having become blind, he abdicated in 942, in favour of St. Mayeul (d. 965).

Sts. CONSTANT and ALEXANDER

Are believed to have been martyred at Constance (unknown period).

Sts. FLAVIA and FIRMATUS

Are honoured at Auxerre as a brother and sister who died together for the faith.

Blessed JOHN OF PENNA (1201-1271)

Born at Penna, in the diocese of Fermo, he became a Franciscan, left Italy to spread his order in Provence and Languedoc, and twenty-five years later returned to his country.

October 6th

ST. BRUNO (d. 1101)

BORN at Cologne of noble parents, about 1035, Bruno always led a very virtuous life. Having begun his studies in his native city, he continued them at Rheims, learned all that was then known, and became one of the best philosophers and theologians of his time. He is said also to have been a good poet. Teaching at Rheims he had among his pupils the future Urban II, instigator of the first crusade.

As chancellor of the diocese, Bruno appeared in 1077 at the Council of Soissons to prosecute a charge of simony against Manasses I, his bishop. The latter was found guilty, but, awaiting deposition, took his revenge on his accuser, despoiling him of his possessions. Bruno had for a long time been thinking of leaving the world; his misfortune caused him to carry out this project.

In 1084 Bruno settled in the mountains of Dauphiny and founded the Carthusian order. Six years later Urban II made him come to Rome to have the benefit of his counsel. But Bruno was unhappy at the papal court, and the pope, after having in vain offered him the archbishopric of Reggio, permitted him to retire into Calabria, in the diocese of Squillace. There a new charterhouse was founded in 1090, and the saint governed it until his death. "I live in a wilderness among the mountains," he wrote to a friend at Rheims. "The air is soft here, the pastures verdant, we have flowers and fruit, and we are far from men. But how can I describe this perpetual feast where we already taste the fruits of paradise? We live among ourselves, and in the midst of battles which we fight for God, we enjoy a peace that the world knows not and the joy of the Holy Spirit."

St. MARY FRANCES OF THE FIVE WOUNDS (1715–1791)

Before becoming a Franciscan tertiary of the Alcantarine rule, she was imprisoned by her father, who wished to force her to marry.

St. MODESTA (d. about 680)

Niece of Blessed Ita and cousin of St. Gertrude of Nivelles, she founded the monastery of Horren, at Trier, in the buildings of an ancient public granary (*horreum*).

Sts. EMILIUS and MARCELLUS

Martyrs venerated at Capua (period uncertain).

October 7th

ST. SERGIUS (d. between 286 and 305)

CALLED on to apostasize, Sergius, a Roman army officer, stood firm in the faith and was beheaded at Rasapa in Syria. In 431 a magnificent church was built upon his tomb, and two centuries later the Emperor Justinian I changed the name of Rasapa to Sergiopolis.

ST. ARTHOLD (1101-1206)

ARTHOLD was born at the castle of Sothonod in Bugey. His parents raised him piously and his mother early taught him to love the sick and poor. At sixteen he became a page at the court of Amadeus III of Savoy. The courtiers were astonished that he never lied, flattered none, and asked no favours of the ruler. "I have God and I need nothing besides," he replied.

At the age of nineteen he left the court to enter the charterhouse at Portes. Believing his decision to be premature, his parents came to beg him to remain in the world a little longer, but he reminded them of what he had learned from them: that above all else one must love and serve God. And they went away consoled.

Although he treated his body harshly and set himself to the meanest tasks, he was perfectly happy. When he became a priest, his happiness was still greater. It is said that it was enough to see him celebrate Mass to be forced, as it were, to believe in the Real Presence. Contrary to many others, he supported Pope Clement III whom Frederick Barbarossa maintained in Rome.

Arthold lived at Portes until 1152, when Humbert, bishop of Geneva, asked him to found a charterhouse in Valmontey. Amadeus III, who had already endowed the foundations of Hautecombe and Tamié, assisted this project, and Arthold built the priory of Arvières on a plateau of the Colombier. This was still standing at the time of the French Revolution.

The holy man was in his eighty-eighth year when the church of Belley named him as bishop. He hid in a cave but was discovered after three days and forcibly dragged to his consecration as bishop. Nevertheless, two years later the pope allowed him to go back to Arvières, and he died there at the age of a hundred and five, on his knees in the dust, after intoning a psalm of thanksgiving.

St. Augustus (d. about 560)

He was a poor man, unable to use his hands and feet, who regained his health after having had an oratory built to St. Martin. Later he was abbot of St. Symphorian at Bourges.

St. Justina

Her martyrdom is placed by some under Nero, by others under Diocletian; she is venerated at Venice and at Padua, where splendid churches have been built in her honour.

St. Pallais

He became bishop of Saintes about 573; was present at various councils; received several letters from Pope St. Gregory the Great and also relics of St. Peter and St. Paul which the pope sent him to place in his cathedral.

October 8th

ST. BRIDGET (d. 1373)

BRIDGET was born about 1302 at Finsta Castle near Uppsala. When she was fourteen she married Ulf of Nericia, a prince of the blood, by whom she had eight children. Some of them lived rather wickedly; others embraced the religious life; Catherine, the saint's daughter and wonted companion, merited canonization.

Bridget at one time was governess to the young wife of Magnus, king of Sweden. When she saw that she could do this flighty person no good, she left the court and went on a pilgrimage with her husband. In 1341 they visited Cologne, Tarascon, Sainte-Baume, and St. James in Galicia. At Arras, on their return journey, Prince Ulf first had attacks of the malady from which he was to die three years later. Before he died he placed on his wife's finger a gold ring which he asked her to keep as a token of their mutual and undying love.

Widowed, Bridget pursued afresh her taste for penance and contemplation. To worldly people who mocked her way of life she replied: "It was not on your account that I began, and your mockeries will not prevent my continuing." God favoured her with great graces, and the *Revelations* which she has left on the passion of the Saviour are very well known. Before leaving Sweden to settle in Rome, she had founded a congregation of nuns at Vadstena, of which her daughter, Catherine, became superior. It spread as far as Spain and later to Mexico.

From 1350 to 1364, St. Bridget and St. Catherine lived together in Rome; from 1364 to 1367 they made a pilgrimage to Assisi, Monte Gargano, Bari, Benevento, and Naples; in 1371 they made a journey to the Holy Land.

Bridget was many times inspired to recall kings and clergy to their duties. Popes Clement VI, Urban V, and Gregory XI venerated her and had recourse to her counsel. Constantly she pressed them to leave Avignon in order to return to Rome.

Her last years were full of trials and temptations; but finally her heart regained the sense of God's presence, and she died in ecstasy. First interred in Rome in the church of the Poor Clares of Viminal, her body afterwards was returned to Sweden and placed in the convent of Vadstena.

St. NESTOR

According to the Roman martyrology, died for the faith at Thessalonica.

Sts. LAURENTIUS and PALATIA (d. 302)

Laurentius, a slave, converted his mistress, Palatia, and both died for the faith at Fermo, under Diocletian.

St. THAIS (4th century)

Thais was trading her charms in Egypt when Paphnutius left his retreat to go to her aid. Having reached her house, he asked to speak to her where they were not observed. "If it is men you fear," said the courtesan, "they will not see us here; but if it is God, you well know that he is everywhere." Paphnutius enlarged upon this thought and spoke to her of her last end and, since he was a saint, converted her by God's grace. She made a bonfire of her finery and jewels; then the hermit led her to a convent in the desert. There he immured her in a cell after telling her: "Your lips are too soiled to dare yet to pronounce God's name. Say only this prayer: 'Thou who hast created me, have mercy upon me.'" Thais passed three years in her cell, praying and weeping ceaselessly, and at length found peace. After which, judging in consultation with Paul the Simple that her seclusion had lasted long enough, Paphnutius gave her back her freedom. The penitent then joined the nuns of the convent, but two weeks later she died.

October 9th

ST. DIONYSIUS OR DENIS THE AREOPAGITE
(1st century)

WHEN St. Paul arrived in Athens about the year 50, the city had fallen under the power of the Romans and lost all political importance, but still retained its rhetoricians and philosophers. According to the Acts, the Athenians devoted themselves largely to the fabrication and repetition of rumours. And, as there were still artists among them, their streets and squares abounded in statues of their idols. It was of Athens that Petronius wrote: "Our land is so full of divinities that it is easier to meet a god there than a man." Lest any be forgotten, the Athenians had raised on the Hamaxitos Way an altar "to the unknown god."

The Epicurean and Stoic philosophers whom the apostle met, took him to the assembly of the Areopagus in order to have him explain his doctrine to them.

"So Paul stood up in full view of the Areopagus, and said, Men of Athens, wherever I look I find you scrupulously religious. Why, in examining your monuments as I passed by them, I found among others an altar which bore the inscription, To the unknown God. And it is this unknown object of your devotion that I am revealing to you. The God who made the world and all that is in it, that God who is Lord of heaven and earth, does not dwell in temples that our hands have made. . . . Now, he calls upon all men, everywhere, to repent, because he has fixed a day when he will pronounce just judgment on the whole world. And the man whom he has appointed for that end he has accredited to all of us, by raising him up from the dead" (Acts xvii, 22–31).

Hearing the resurrection of the dead mentioned, certain members of the Areopagus laughed at the speaker; others arranged to meet him later, and Paul withdrew. Among the Areopagites one, at least, was converted; he was called Dionysius, and became bishop of Athens, dying, it is said, a martyr.

From the 6th century onwards, Dionysius was supposed to have been the author of certain writings such as *The Celestial Hierarchy* and *The Divine Names*, composed four centuries after his death; and from the 9th century on, he was deliberately confused with his namesake who had evangelized the Paris district and had been martyred there about the middle of the 3rd century.

St. LOUIS BERTRAND (1526-1581)

Dominican, native of Valencia, a great wonder-worker who evangelized the peoples of South America from 1562 to 1569, then returned to the Spanish Peninsula and preached there until his death.

St. JOHN LEONARDI

Founder of the clerks regular of the Mother of God; was first a pharmacy helper in Lucca; his apostolic zeal was exercised principally in Tuscany (d. 1609).

St. GHISLAIN

Founder of the monastery which gave rise to the Belgian town of the same name (d. 681).

October 10th

STS. DANIEL, HUGOLINUS, SAMUEL, NICHOLAS, LEO, AGNELLUS, AND DONULUS (d. 1227)

THIS was the time when the Saracens were holding Spain, Africa, and the Near East, and when Christianity, sometimes in defence, sometimes in attack, was fighting for its life. It was also the time when numerous of the first disciples of the *Poverello* were burning to imitate their seraphic father. St. Clare herself asked to go to Africa. The crusaders had sought in vain to prevail by shedding their enemies' blood; Francis, however, thought to win them to the Gospel by going to speak to them about Christ and by shedding his own blood. In 1220 he reached the Sultan, but the latter, far from harming him, loaded him with attentions and sent him away with fair words.

Daniel and his companions were the second group of martyrs in the first generation of Franciscans. Some months or years earlier, Otho, Berard, Peter, Adjutus, and Accursius had been put to death in Morocco. On learning this Francis had cried: "Now I can say I have five true friars minor!"

Now, accompanied by Nicholas, a native of Umbria, by Donulus, born in the diocese of Lucca, by Leo, Agnellus, Samuel, and Hugolinus, of whom we know but the names, Daniel, a minister of the province of Calabria, left Spain and landed at Ceuta. They are said to have followed the wishes of their spiritual father in carrying out the Gospel to the letter, seeking insults, not resisting those who wished to harm them, washing one another's feet. To the Christian merchants travelling in Africa they preached upon virtue and vice in the simplest terms. In the presence of the Moors they soon began to vituperate Mohammed, asserting that he was burning in the pit of hell and that all his followers would certainly join him there. Like certain Christians of the primitive Church, they sought martyrdom as the supreme testimony of their love for Christ and as the best means of spreading the true faith.

Their apostleship lasted but a few days. Imprisoned and challenged to acknowledge the law of the Koran, they vied in proclaiming their fidelity to the Gospel. Then they were led in chains to a public place and beheaded there amid the curses of the populace

St. PAULINUS

Was going on a pilgrimage to Jerusalem when, at Capua, the inhabitants of the town stopped him and compelled him to become their bishop (d. about 838).

St. CLAIR

Apostle of Brittany, whose relics are venerated at Nantes (3rd century).

St. TANCHA

Born about 620 at Saint-Ouen near Arcis-sur-Aube, this young girl was killed in resisting the assault of a knave.

St. FRANCIS BORGIA (1510–1572)

Son of the duke of Candia and husband of Eleanor of Castro, by whom he had eight children. He followed Charles V to the wars; lost his wife in 1546; resigned as viceroy of Catalonia; entered the Society of Jesus in 1550; was general of his order from 1565 until his death. The sight of the dead body of the Empress Isabella, whose face had once been so lovely and which became in a few days so horrible, was one of those things which disgusted him with the world.

October 11th

ST. ZENAIDA (1st century)

THIS saint is especially honoured in the East. According to a Greek text preserved at the Vatican, Zenaida was a cousin of St. Paul and had a sister named Philonilla, like herself a convert to Christianity. She was inspired by heaven to abandon her possessions, and taking leave of her sister, set off for the mountains which border the Cydnus, north of Tarsus, where she installed herself in a cave. There she spent much time praying for the conversion of the world and the overthrow of paganism. As she had previously studied and practised medicine, she continued to care for the sick who insisted on coming to her, and had especial power to cure children and those possessed of demons.

One day, three men of goodwill, Pappas, Pateras, and Philocyris, presented themselves at her cave. They came from afar, attracted by the renown of her holiness. They had learned, they told her, that she had found happiness in Christ's service, and they begged to enjoy from time to time the favour of her spiritual conversation. She granted this request for the love of God, and these three men began to live, near by, the life of contemplation after her example.

After several years they came to find Zenaida and said to her: "Why, instead of hiding in this wilderness the miracles and cures which God works at your prayers, do we not go and show them before men? Come with us, we will travel to the glory of God and for the world's salvation." Zenaida allowed herself to be persuaded and followed them. But it seemed that God was satisfied with her desire for apostleship, for, on the first day of the journey, she ran a thorn into her foot, and died on the stone where she had sat down to remove it.

St. Nicasius

Tradition says that he may have come from Rome in the 3rd century to convert the population of the Vexin. He is sometimes said to have been the first bishop of Rouen.

St. Emilius

Is honoured at Redon. Some say that he was a confessor who flourished in Brittany in the 9th century; others hold that he was the same person as St. Melanius, bishop of Rennes.

St. Placida

Virgin honoured at Verona (d. about 460).

Sts. Probus, Tarachus and Andronicus

Martyred at Tarsus in 304.

St. Gomer (d. 774)

Courageous soldier and relative of Pepin the Short, who thought to reward him by making him marry Gwin Marie; he suffered terribly from the frightful disposition of this incorrigible woman. He ended by leaving her and withdrawing to a solitary place which became after his death a place of pilgrimage, and the site of the town of Lierre (Belgium).

October 12th

ST. SERAPHIN (1540-1604)

HIS father was a poor mason of Montegranaro in the Marches of Ancona, as was his elder brother. He himself, while waiting to become old enough to learn their trade, earned his living by tending sheep in the neighbouring village. On the father's death, the younger son was called home; and his elder brother, for whom he served as mason's assistant, began to deride his piety, to humiliate and threaten him, and to harass him with blows.

Salvation for our wretched lad came from the word of a lady at whose house he was mixing mortar. She had spoken of the four last things. "But," observed Seraphin, "if one be thus in danger of eternal fire, why not live as a hermit in the forest?" Then the lady spoke to him about the Capuchins of Tolentino who often came to beg from her. Seraphin hastened to the monastery and asked to be admitted. They made him wait several years; and, even after his admission, he was not spared spite and petty persecution. Clumsy, illiterate, and in ill health, what could be expected of him?

Nevertheless, this simple lay brother soon surprised everyone by his virtues, his austerities, his ecstasies, and his miracles. He read men's consciences, explained obscure passages of Holy Writ to exegetes, understood straight away the original text of the mystical works of St. Bonaventure.

The most astonishing cure which he worked was that of Cardinal Bandini, who was infected with gangrene. The latter's death was only a question of days, when Seraphin was dragged by the governor of Ascoli to the cardinal's bedside; with the simple sign of the cross he gave him back his health. He himself, however, spent the greater part of his monastic life in interior desolation, often doubting his eternal salvation. He died at the monastery of Ascoli, and six years later Paul V permitted lamps to be lit at his tomb.

St. EUSTACHIUS (period unknown)

The Roman martyrology calls him priest and confessor; the Bollandists, an Egyptian martyr.

St. MAXIMILIAN

He was, it is said, elected bishop of Lorch in 256 and put to death for the faith under Numerian (d. 284).

St. WILFRID (634–709)

Born in Northumbria, Wilfrid studied at Lindisfarne and Canterbury. Accompanying St. Benedict Biscop to Rome, he tarried for a whole year at Lyons with St. Delphinus, who tried to make him marry his niece. Named bishop of York, he came to France to receive episcopal consecration and again remained for two years. It has been seen in St. Ceadda's life (March 2nd) that the latter filled the post in his absence, and later resigned in his favour. Wilfred was to suffer from the lack of obedience shown by his fellow citizens toward the apostolic see. The end of his life was almost exclusively devoted to the care of the monasteries he had founded.

October 13th

ST. EDWARD (d. 1066)

SON of King Ethelred II, Edward the Confessor was born at Islip near Oxford, about the year 1004.

For two centuries the Danes had been endeavouring to colonize England and had almost succeeded, when Ethelred conceived the idea of murdering their chiefs at a banquet. This massacre was the excuse for Suenon, king of Denmark, to annex Great Britain to his estates and to exile her rulers. His son and successor, Canute the Great, also ruled there from 1016 to 1042. Twenty years later, it was William of Normandy's turn to conquer the British Isles and there to implant his dynasty.

The reign of Edward runs exactly from Canute the Great's death to the coming of William the Conqueror. By his goodness and justice, this holy king won the hearts of his subjects; his wisdom baffled the foreigners' wiles; his love of peace was such that he would have preferred renunciation of the crown to shedding the blood of one single man; having no evil passions to satisfy, he was able to diminish taxes and even to suppress some of them. Forced for reasons of state to marry Princess Edith, the daughter of a former shepherd, he succeeded in making her share his taste for austerities, and he lived with her in continence.

St. Peter and St. John were his favourite patrons. During the thirty-five years of his exile in France he had vowed to visit the tombs of the apostles if God would give him back his throne and country. This vow had to be commuted by Pope Leo IX, and in compensation the king built a superb basilica at Westminster in honour of St. Peter. At the same time he restored and enlarged the neighbouring Benedictine abbey.

390 THE LIVES OF THE SAINTS

It is told that toward the end of his life Edward was accosted by a pilgrim who begged alms for the love of St. John. Having nothing else to give, the king gave him the golden ring which he wore on his finger. Soon after, an old man appeared to two Englishmen who had lost their way returning from the Holy Land. He showed them the right road, then gave them a ring, asking them to take it to the king. "I am John the Evangelist," he added, "and you may tell my servant Edward that in a few months I will come and fetch him to lead him to heaven."

St. Edward died January 5th, 1066, after having reigned twenty-three years, six months, and twenty days.

St. LUBENTIUS

Pastor of Cavern, near Trier (d. about 370).

St. REIMBAUT

Was abbot of St. Affre and reformed some Benedictine monasteries before occupying the episcopal see of Speyer (d. 1039).

St. THEOPHILUS

Was the fifth bishop of Antioch after St. Peter. He wrote many works of doctrine and apologetics which Eusebius and St. Jerome considered excellent, but which are almost all lost (d. end of the 2nd century).

October 14th

ST. CALLISTUS (d. 222)

CALLISTUS governed the Church of Rome during the schism of Hippolytus, from 217 to 222; he suffered greatly during his life and was fiercely attacked after his death, but historians have vindicated him.

At the time when he was the slave of a high official of the Emperor Commodus, he lost his master's money and that which some Christians had entrusted to him; becoming frightened, he took flight, was caught and shut up in a dungeon. Then his master realized that the best way of making up the loss was to free this honest and intelligent slave. Callistus was trying to obtain restitution from some Jews who had cheated him when these thieves accused him of being a Christian, and had him condemned as such to the Sardinian mines. He stayed there until the kindly Marcia, favourite of the emperor, obtained his liberation. Pope Victor took into his service this former slave, distinguished by his constancy in misfortune and his devotion to the Sardinian martyrs, and Callistus was named deacon of the Roman Church. Later he became secretary to Pope Zephyrinus and at his death he succeeded him.

His short pontificate was most difficult, being shaken by doctrinal controversies and disciplinary troubles. Callistus displayed the qualities of a wise, firm, and compassionate shepherd. He excommunicated Sabellius, chief of the "modalist" heretics, who denied the plurality of the Divine Persons; he also established the practice of absolution of all sins, including those which rigourists, such as Tertullian, considered irremissible.

St. FORTUNATUS OF TODI (d. 537)

Pope St. Gregory greatly esteemed this bishop of Todi and recognized his power to cast out demons. Moreover, it is known from other sources that he prevented Totila, king of the Ostrogoths, from sacking his episcopal city.

St. FORTUNATA

Suffered martyrdom at Caesarea in Palestine in 302.

St. DOMINIC LORICATUS (d. 1060)

He considered as simony the fact that his relatives had given a present to the bishop who had ordained him priest, and he refused from that time to exercise any sacerdotal office. Having led a hermit's life at Luceolo, then at Montefeltro, he entered Fonte-Avellano, at that time governed by St. Peter Damian, and became the latter's biographer. Except to take discipline, Dominic never put off the iron cuirass which he wore next to his skin.

St. BURCHARD or BURCKHARD

Came from England at the call of St. Boniface to take part in the work of converting Germany. For ten years he occupied the episcopal see of Würzburg; then, worn out, he retired to the monastery which he had founded near St. Kilian (d. 752).

October 15th
ST. TERESA OF AVILA (1515-1582)

ST. TERESA was born at Avila of a noble family, on March 28th, 1515. Her parents brought nine children into the world; her father, Alonzo Sanchez de Cepeda, had three by a first marriage. Teresa was in her twelfth year when she lost her mother. At the age of seven she ran away to join the Moors who, she thought, would consent to cut off her head. Cheated of martyrdom, for a time she imitated the anchorites by building hermitages in a garden. Then these holy aspirations were counteracted by what she later called her great sins, that is to say: reading novels, flirtations, and frivolous chatter.

At sixteen she was boarded at an Augustinian convent in her native town and remained there eighteen months. She then spent a few days at the house of an uncle whose pious conversation caused her to become a nun.

At the Carmel of Avila, where she took her vows in 1534, the nuns could receive visits in the parlour and even in their cells. For some twenty years Teresa tried to enjoy both the delights of prayer and the pleasures of secular conversation. Very unhappy, she finally understood that she owed God the gift of her whole self. From that time her life consisted in prayer, apparitions of Christ, sufferings, and ecstasies.

In 1562 Teresa set about the reform of the Carmelite order. At the cost of innumerable persecutions and difficulties, she established poor and austere convents at Avila, Toledo, Valladolid, Salamanca, Alba, and elsewhere. At Toledo she had only three ducats to begin her buildings. "Teresa and three ducats," she said, "are nothing; but God, Teresa, and three ducats are sufficient to make a success of everything." St. John of the Cross and Father Jerome Gratian helped her extend her reform to all branches of the Carmelite order.

St. Teresa is one of the most universally admired of women. Her intelligence and charm, her chivalrous spirit, her talent as a writer, and her experience of supernatural ways have won a privileged place for her among the saints of the Church. She died in ecstasy at the convent of Alba, her head supported by Mother Anne of St. Bartholomew, her eyes fixed on the crucifix, on the night of October 4th–5th, 1582.

St. AURELIA (11th century)

She was, it is said, a relative of Hugh Capet who, to escape marriage, fled to Alsace and hid there. She lived as a recluse in that country for fifty-two years, making herself known to none except Wolfgang, bishop of Ratisbon.

St. LEONARD OF VANDŒUVRE or OF CORBIGNY (d. about 565)

Vandœuvre is the name of the wilderness of Maine, where Leonard, who came from the Tongres country, founded a monastery. Corbigny, in the diocese of Autun, is the name of the village where his relics were honoured from 881 until the Wars of Religion.

St. ROGER

Bishop of Canna, in the kingdom of Naples (10th century).

October 16th

ST. BERTRAND OF COMMINGES (d. about 1123)

BORN at Isle-Jourdain, Bertrand was the son of Atton, lord of the Isle, and of Gervaise Taillefer, sister-in-law of Robert the Pious. He was brought up at Chaise-Dieu, for some time pursued a career of arms, then took holy orders and became archdeacon of the Toulouse cathedral. The wisdom and virtue which he displayed in these duties gained him the suffrage of the people and clergy when, about 1075, the church of Comminges had to choose a new bishop.

Perched on the peak where, a thousand years before, Pompey had sur-rounded the remnants of Sertorius' bands, the episcopal city of which Bertrand took possession was a heap of ruins. The Frankish invasion of 585 and the Saracen incursions wrought general destruction. It was to the new bishop's credit that he rebuilt everything. He restored prosperity to the districts where misery prevailed and built, on the slope of the Pyrenean range, those many and beautiful Romanesque churches which we still admire. For almost half a century he ruled his flock as an exemplary shepherd, requiring the virtues of their calling from his clerics, and travelling in person around his diocese to correct abuses and distribute benefactions. It is also noteworthy that with St. Ivo of Chartres he was one of the prelates who always refused to approve the adulterous marriage of Philip I with Bertrade de Montfort. This was all the more meritorious on their part because at the Council of Poitiers, in 1103, the populace invaded the hall where they were deliberating on this question and attempted to stone them to death.

St. GALL (d. about 646)

Disciple of St. Columbanus and like him an Irishman, he followed him to France, where together they founded the abbey of Luxeuil; then to Austrasia, when Columbanus had to take refuge to escape the anger of King Thierry. After the latter became ruler of that country, Columbanus moved on to Italy. Ill and unable to accompany his master, Gall concealed himself on the shores of Lake Constance until he was cured; then he resumed his apostolate and laid the foundations of the great abbey which was to add lustre to his name.

St. FLORENTINUS (4th century)

Certain lists of the bishops of Trier treat him as a martyr and list him as successor to St. Severinus.

St. MOMMELINUS (d. 685)

His story will be found combined with that of St. Omer on September 9th.

St. GERARD MAJELLA (1726–1755)

Born at Muro-Lucano, to the south of Naples, he first was a servant, then a tailor's apprentice. Becoming a lay brother in the newly formed congregation of the Redemptorists, his sanctity aroused so much admiration from the crowds and created such embarrassment for his superiors that he had to be moved from monastery to monastery. He died at Caposele, having worked so many miracles, writes one of his biographers, that several large volumes would be necessary to tell them.

October 17th

ST. HEDWIG (1174–1243)

DAUGHTER of Berthold III, duke of Karinthia, Hedwig had three sisters of whom the eldest, Agnes of Meran, was queen of France for five years, and the second, Gertrude, queen of Hungary, who gave birth to St. Elizabeth.

At the age of twelve Hedwig was married to Henry the Bearded, duke of Silesia, by whom she had six children; after this the couple took a vow of continence and applied themselves more than ever to the practice of virtue. From that time Hedwig fasted every day except Sundays and feast days, slept on the hard ground, and passed long hours in prayer.

For his part, the duke banished gold and silver from his home and reduced his scale of living in order to help the poor. Having decided to build a convent at Treibnitz, near Breslau, he employed the criminals of the duchy for the work, instead of leaving them idle in the prisons. It was this rich convent which became the appanage of Prince Blücher in 1815, after his victory at Waterloo.

Hedwig and her husband lived in perfect union. Only two disagreements are recorded in fifty-two years. The first was in 1233, when the Polish nobles dethroned Duke Ladislaus and offered his place to Henry the Bearded; against Hedwig's advice the duke of Silesia raised an army and added Poland to his realm.

About the same time he chose to make Conrad, his second son, his heir instead of Henry the Pious, his eldest son. The rivals waged war, and their mother, who supported the elder, suffered a great deal. These dissensions ended very soon, however, in the victory of Henry the Pious and Conrad's entry into a monastery.

After the death of her husband in 1238, Hedwig retired to the convent of Treibnitz. Three years later Henry the Pious was killed at the battle of Liegnitz by the Tartars. When the news reached her, Hedwig lifted her eyes to heaven and said: "My God, I have no other will but Yours. You have done with my son as You willed. I thank You for having given me this son who always loved me. Dear it was to me to see him alive; still more consoling is it to know that he is for ever in Your kingdom."

St. MARGARET MARY ALACOQUE (1645–1690)

Born at Leuthecourt in Charolais, she was from the age of ten favoured with graces in prayer. At twenty-six she became a Visitandine of Paray-le-Monial, and it was there she received from Our Lord a mission to spread devotion to the Sacred Heart

St. SOLINA

Is honoured at Chartres, Angoulême, and Poitiers as a virgin martyr of the 3rd century.

St. FLORENTINE (d. 526)

Bishop of Orange.

Blessed CONTARDO FERRINI

Son of a professor at the Polytechnical School of Milan, taught Roman law at Messina, Modena, and Pavia, dying in the latter town in 1902 at the age of forty-four; he belonged to the third order of St. Francis.

October 18th

ST. LUKE (1st century)

DISCIPLE, helper, and friend of St. Paul, "beloved Luke, the physician" (Col. iv, 14), is the only one of the evangelists who was not a Jew. A native of Antioch, he belonged to the Hellenic world; his mother tongue was Greek, and he used it with an elegant simplicity.

He never saw Our Lord in the flesh, but he may have been, before his conversion, one of those pagans who mixed with the Jews of the Dispersion, professing monotheism as they did, and with them frequenting the synagogue on the Sabbath day.

Did he embrace Christianity about the year 42, when Paul and Barnabas came to preach at Antioch; or was it even some years earlier when, after the stoning of St. Stephen, the Judo-Christians fled from Jerusalem to settle in the Syrian metropolis?

The fact is that about the year 50 he appeared at the side of St. Paul at Troas. He reached Macedonia with him and accompanied him as far as Philippi. It appears he remained there for some time, leaving the apostle to continue his journey alone. Paul found him there again on his return through Macedonia. Luke then accompanied him to Jerusalem from whence Paul, arrested in the Temple, was taken captive to Caesarea. He did not leave him at all between 57 and 59, the two years this captivity lasted.

When the apostle appealed to the tribunal of the Emperor Nero and was taken, escorted by soldiers, to Rome, Luke embarked in his company and was shipwrecked with him on the Maltese coast. Nothing is known of his last years, or when he died. It is only known that he never left his master during the latter's captivity in Rome which ended in martyrdom in 67.

St. Luke is the author of the Acts of the Apostles and of the third Gospel. He alone has preserved for us the parables of the lost sheep and the prodigal son, of the Pharisee and the publican, of Dives and Lazarus. He alone has recorded Jesus' words: "If great sins have been forgiven her, she has also greatly loved" (Luke viii, 47); the prayer of the Crucified for his executioners; and the promise to the good thief: "This day thou shalt be with me in Paradise" (Luke xxiii, 43). It is this which has made Dante call him "historian of the compassion of Christ."

St. MONO

One of the saints most venerated by the people of the Ardennes. He is said to have left his native Scotland to go to Rome when, passing through Belgium, he met St. John l'Agneau, bishop of Maestricht, with whom he formed a close friendship. His pilgrimage finished, Mono settled in the forest of the Ardennes as John l'Agneau had urged him to do, and he lived as a hermit in the woods of Freyr or Fridier, not far from the present town of Saint-Hubert. Some scoundrels assassinated him there about 630.

St. FABIAN OF SYLVAROLLE

Is honoured at Villers in Barrois (Meuse); he was formerly invoked against snakebite.

October 19th

ST. PETER OF ALCÁNTARA (1499-1562)

BORN at Alcántara of a noble family, Peter Garavito was educated at Salamanca and entered the Franciscans of Manxarretes at sixteen. He preached in Spain and Portugal for a score of years, fulfilled the duties of provincial and commissioner general of his order, and died at the monastery of Arenas in 1562. He is one of the great Spanish mystics of the 16th century, and one who carried austerity to a superhuman degree.

He declared to St. Teresa that he had lived three years in a monastery without lifting his eyes, only knowing his brethren by their voices; he always went barefoot without sandals; only ate every other day and, further, sprinkled his food with ashes; only slept for two hours a night, squatting or kneeling against the wall. Even in agony and consumed with fever, he refused a glass of water offered him, gasping: "Jesus was willing to thirst on the cross!" When they told him he was going to die, he murmured: "*Laetatus sum in his quae dicta sunt mihi.* I rejoice when they say unto me, I will go up into the house of the Lord." After his death, appearing to St. Teresa in glory, he said to her: "Blessed be that penance which has brought such a reward."

The celebrated Carmelite venerated him as her outstanding benefactor; it was he in fact who came to her rescue when all opposed or abandoned her. Having passed through the same mystical states, he alone understood and reassured her; and, in the face of all opposition, declared his conviction that God had destined her to reform Carmel.

Peter of Alcántara instituted a severe reform in his order known as the Alcantarine, from which arose a galaxy of saints. He wrote a *Treatise on Mental Prayer*, which St. Teresa, Louis of Granada, and St. Francis de Sales considered a masterpiece. Pope Gregory XV declared that he found in it "a shining light to lead souls to heaven and a doctrine prompted by the Holy Spirit"; and when he beatified its author in 1623 he accorded him the title of "doctor of mystical theology."

St. LAURA

Abbess of the convent of St. Mary of Culédor, was arrested by the Saracens and thrown into a cauldron of boiling pitch. Before becoming a nun she had been married.

St. Savinianus

Considered as the first bishop of Sens, and as having been martyred in that town in the 3rd century.

St. Aquilinius (d. about 690)

Had served in the militia under Clovis II before he became bishop of Evreux.

October 20th

ST. IRENE (7th century)

THIS saint, so venerated in Spain and even more in Portugal, has a romantic story which is told as follows:

Irene lived at Tomar in Estremadura in the reign of the nonagenarian King Chindaswinth. She was a young girl, nobly born, and her parents had had her brought up in a convent. To complete her education a monk from the abbey of Our Lady came to give her lessons at home; Irene only went out once a year, on the feast of St. Peter, to pray to the apostle in the church of his name. It was on the occasion of one of these outings that a nobleman named Britald saw her and fell madly in love with her. Having no hope of making her return his love, he fell into despair, wasted away, and was expected to die of consumption. Learning of this, Irene had herself taken to his bedside. She told him that she was no longer free, having taken a vow of virginity, encouraged him as much as possible, and left him, saying they would meet in Paradise. Britald convinced himself, as often happens, that Irene would have become his wife if she had not given herself to God, calmed himself, got well gradually, and for a time thought no more about the girl except to honour her in his heart.

At that time there were some bad monks in that country, and Irene's professor was one of them. Consumed with a wicked passion for her, he dared to speak to her of it and to incite her to evil. The girl had the strength to send him back to his monastery and to give up her lessons. The monk revenged himself by frightful slanders, notably by saying that Irene was soon to become a mother. When this rumour reached Britald's ears he became mad with jealousy, and hired an assassin to kill her who, he believed, had played him false. And thus it was that Irene was killed by the stroke of a sword and her body flung into the river. The Benedictines recovered her body on the banks of the Tagus, opposite the town of Scalabis, and its name was changed to St. Irene, or Santárem.

St. Caprasius

In order to escape persecution, he first hid in a cavern in the neighbour-hood of Agen, his native region. Learning of the courage with which St. Foy had faced torture, he changed his mind, went to the judges to declare himself a Christian, and was in his turn put to death for the faith (4th century).

St. John Cantius (d. 1473)

This Polish priest was at one time pastor of Ilkusi, but during the greater part of his life he was professor of theology at Cracow. In the course of a pilgrimage to Rome he had some dealings with a brigand who, having taken his possessions, asked him if he had anything else. "No," said John, forgetting some gold coins sewed into his cloak. When he remembered about them, he retraced his steps and went to tell the thief what he had forgotten; the latter, however, gave back everything.

St. Felician

Is honoured at Minden (Germany) as bishop and martyr (d. 3rd century).

October 21st

ST. HILARION (d. 372)

To Hilarion is due the credit, says St. Jerome, of introducing into Palestine and Syria the eremitic life as it was led in the Egyptian deserts.

He was born at Tabatha, not far from Gaza, had studied at Alexandria and, converted by a Christian philosopher, had received baptism at the age of fifteen. From a journey he made into the Thebaid where he had been able to see the work of St. Anthony of the Desert, he returned determined to follow the great anchorite's example. He gave his goods to the poor and went to settle on a marshy island seven miles from Majuma.

"It was only after twenty-two years," writes St. Jerome, "that his first miracles brought him imitators. From all parts monks came to him, desirous of living under his rule." For a long time he was their director, but finally so many came to him, without counting the sick, the inquisitive, and pilgrims of all kinds, that Hilarion said to himself one day: "I am receiving my reward here on earth; I must hide myself to pray and suffer if I wish to be found worthy of the divine mercy." They tried to prevent him. "I shall fast until you let me go," he said to the ten thousand persons who were keeping him there; and for seven days he refused all food. In the end they allowed him to go so as not to see him die of hunger.

Neither at Alexandria, nor in Greece, nor in Dalmatia, nor in Sicily, did Hilarion find the silence and oblivion he sought. Miracles followed him everywhere. Demoniacs cried out in fear at his approach. It was Hesychius, his disciple and companion, who found for him in the mountains of the island of Cyprus, a dozen miles from the coast, a craggy solitude where he could die in peace; he was then aged over eighty years.

St. Ursula and the Eleven Thousand Virgins of Cologne

Of the legends current on the subject, the most famous portrays Ursula fleeing from Great Britain with eleven thousand maidens to escape the outrages of the invading Saxons, and being massacred by the Huns with her companions at the instant of their landing at the mouth of the Rhine. What appears more probable is that eleven girls were massacred in the territory of Cologne at the end of the 3rd or the beginning of the 4th century. Their names, according to Dom H. Leclercq, could be the following: Ursula, Pinnosa, Martha, Saula, Brittica, Gregoria, Saturnina, Sabatia, Palladia, Sentia, and Saturia.

St. Wendelin (d. about 650)

Having been a hermit and shepherd in the Trier country, he became a Benedictine and was made abbot. The village of St. Wendel in Germany grew up around his tomb.

October 22nd

ST. SALOME (1st century)

Salome had married the Galilean fisherman Zebedee, and it is from their marriage that the apostles James the Greater and John the Evangelist were born.

With Mary Magdalen, Joanna, and several others, she was among those women who followed Our Lord, shared with Him their possessions, and served Him (Mark xv, 40-41; Luke viii, 2-3). She accompanied Him to Jerusalem when Jesus went there for His last Passover, followed Him to Calvary, and remained to the end at His agony (Matt. xxvii, 55-56). When the Sabbath was past, she bought spices to embalm Him, and on Sunday morning, having gone hastily with her friends to the sepulchre and found it empty, she was one of the first to know that Jesus was risen (Matt. xxvii, 56; Mark xvi, 1-8).

Various traditions tell that Salome then left Palestine, going with St. James on his travels, and retiring in the end either to Spain, to Italy, or to Provence. But rather than linger over these legends, nationalist in inspiration, it is much more worth while to meditate on the reply of universal significance which Our Lord addressed one day to this ambitious mother:

"Thereupon the mother of the sons of Zebedee brought them to him, falling on her knees to make a request of him. And when he asked her, What is thy will? she said to him, Here are my two sons; grant that in thy kingdom one may take his place on thy right and the other on thy left. But Jesus answered, You do not know what it is you ask. Have you strength to drink of the cup I am to drink of? They said, We have. And he told them, You shall indeed drink of my cup; but a place on my right hand or my left is not mine to give; it is for those for whom my Father has destined it. The ten others were angry with the two brethren when they heard it; but Jesus called them to him and said, You know that, among the Gentiles, those who bear rule lord it over them, and great men vaunt their power over them; with you it must be otherwise, and whoever has a mind to be first among you, must be your slave. So it is that the Son of Man did not come to have service done him; he came to serve others, and to give his life as a ransom for the lives of many" (Matt. xx, 20-28).

St. ALODIA and her sister St. NUNILONA

They were daughters of a Christian woman who had remarried a Moor of importance. So much did their stepfather importune them, that they were compelled to take refuge with their aunt at Huesca. They were found there when the persecution of Abd-er-Rahman II broke out, and from there they were brought to torture (d. 851).

St. ALEXANDER

Eastern bishop, was martyred with his jailer Heraclius, whom he had converted (period uncertain).

St. MELLON

Is said to have come from England to evangelize the country around Rouen (4th century).

St. FLORA

A virgin, whose body is venerated at Freiburg in Breisgau; is reputed to have been one of the companions of St. Ursula (5th century).

October 23rd

BLESSED MARIE CLOTILDE AND OTHER URSULINES OF VALENCIENNES (d. 1794)

FOR more than two centuries Valenciennes possessed an Ursuline convent. On September 30th, 1790, municipal officials came to make the inventory prescribed by law and to ask the thirty-two sisters present if they wished to re-enter the world. Following the example of their superior, Mother Marie Clotilde, they unanimously expressed their wish to remain nuns. In August 1792 they were deprived of the right of teaching and ordered to vacate their house. On September 17th, with the exception of five who were sick and their bursar, all were furnished with regular passports and reached Mons in carriages. This Belgian town was then in the power of Austria. The sisters stayed there until November of the following year at which time they returned to Valenciennes, which had just been seized by the Austrians. The latter gave the congregations the right to remain and to teach, and the Ursulines took advantage of it. It was then that three former nuns, deprived of shelter, joined them: two Brigittines and a Poor Clare.

However, the Austrian army evacuated Valenciennes in August 1794, and the victorious French, re-entering as liberators, immediately drove out those of their compatriots who were suspected of connections with the former régime. Numbered among the "fanatics, traitors, and emigrants," the Ursulines were confined to their convent. Two-thirds of them escaped their persecutors; eleven from choice or necessity remained in their hands. It was these who, in two groups, mounted the scaffold in the great marketplace on October 17th and 23rd, 1794. All died courageously, happy, they told their executioners, to have come back to Valenciennes "to teach the Catholic, apostolic, and Roman religion."

St. BONIZET or BENEDICT (4th century)

He is honoured at Quinçay (diocese of Poitiers) and at Aiseray (diocese of Luçon). He was, it is believed, a bishop of Palestine, whom the persecution of Julian the Apostate had brought into Poitou.

St. ODA

Widow of Boggo, duke of Aquitaine, passed her last days at Amay-sur-Meuse, Belgium, d. about 723.

St. Ignatius of Constantinople (797–887)

Son and grandson of emperors, he became a monk and then patriarch of Constantinople. He was supplanted by Photius, who completed the secession of the Greek Church and made his rival undergo harsh persecution.

St. Severinus

Two saints of this name are honoured today; one was fourth bishop of Bordeaux (5th century); the other was bishop of Cologne in the 4th century and distinguished himself by his zeal against Arianism.

October 24th

ST. RAPHAEL THE ARCHANGEL

St. Raphael is one of the three archangels mentioned by Holy Scripture and honoured by the Roman liturgy, the two others being St. Gabriel and St. Michael.

All we know of him is revealed by the Book of Tobias. Tobias was about to depart for Media in order to recover a sum of money lent by his father to Gabelus. Raphael appeared in the form of a beautiful youth in order to accompany him and, during the journey, was a constant source of benefaction to him.

On the banks of the Tigris he saved Tobias from a sea monster who was about to devour him. A little farther on he urged him to visit Raguel, whose demoniacal daughter brought death to all who married her. "He has a daughter called Sara, and neither chick nor child besides," said Raphael to Tobias. "Of all he possesses thou mayest be heir, if thou wilt claim his daughter's hand in marriage; thou hast but to ask him, and she is thine." As he hesitated, the angel added: "Heed me well . . . and thou shalt hear why the fiend has power to hurt some and not others. The fiend has power over such as go about their mating with all thought of God shut out of their hearts and minds, wholly intent on their lust, as if they were horse or mule, brutes without reason" (Tob. vii, 11–17).

The marriage was celebrated and the first three days were devoted to prayer. "The evil spirit fled; it was overtaken by the angel Raphael and in the waste lands of Upper Egypt, and there held prisoner" (Tob. viii, 3–4). Then, while the wedding feast continued, Raphael alone went to Gabelus, who discharged his debt. Returning to find Tobias, he led him and his wife home.

Before returning to heaven, he restored sight to Tobias' father. "Prayer fasting, and alms, said he, here is better treasure to lay up than any store of gold. . . . When thou, Tobias, wert praying, and with tears . . . I, all the while, was offering that prayer of thine to the Lord. Then, because thou hadst won his favour, needs must that trials should come, and test thy worth. And now, for thy healing, for the deliverance of thy son's wife Sara from the fiend's attack, he has chosen me for his messenger. Who am I? I am the angel Raphael, and my place is among those seven who stand in the presence of the Lord. . . . I was at your side, eating and drinking, but only in outward show; the food, the drink I live by, man's eyes cannot see. And now the time has come when I must go back to him who sent me; give thanks to God and tell the story of his great deeds" (Tob. xii, 8–21).

St. Antonio Maria Claret

Born at Sallent (Catalonia) in 1807. At first a tailor, he became a priest in 1835, and in 1850 archbishop of Cuba. He delivered, in the course of the six years during which he held the see, more than eleven thousand sermons; returning to Spain, he held the post of confessor to Queen Isabella II. Meanwhile he had founded at Vich the congregation of Missionary Sons of the Immaculate Heart of Mary, called Claretians. He died with the Cistercians of Fontfroide near Narbonne, in 1870.

St. Florentinus

Has for many centuries been invoked for mental ailments. He lived in the country around Toul in the 10th century and came, it is believed, from Ireland.

October 25th

STS. CRISPIN AND CRISPINIAN (d. 285)

ALTHOUGH in the last years of the 3rd century the Christians in Gaul were disturbed very little, there were some among them who were called upon to shed their blood for the faith. Among these were the brothers Crispin and Crispinian who, according to ancient tradition, suffered a frightful martyrdom at Soissons.

Born, it is said, of a noble Roman family, they had left their country to carry the Gospel to the peoples of Gaul, and, in order to exercise their apostleship without attracting attention, they learned the trade of shoemaker.

As they worked well and shod the poor free, their clientele was considerable, and numerous were the occasions they had to speak of Christ and to recruit the faithful for Him.

They displayed as much courage in their trial as the executioners showed ingenuity in torturing them. They were plunged into molten lead; their flesh was cut to ribbons; their nails were pulled out; and finally they were beheaded. Their cult spread through all countries; many churches were dedicated to them; shoemakers and leather merchants made them their heavenly protectors.

Among associations placed under their patronage the most celebrated is that founded in the 17th century by Henri Buche at Paris. A shoemaker himself, a great traveller and a very saintly man, "the good Henri," as he was called, wished to suppress the often criminal abuses to which the secret societies, called "shoemaker companions," gave rise. In 1645 he founded the "Society of Christian brother shoemakers of St. Crispin and St. Crispinian," a kind of religious body resembling the Lombardic third order, and its influence extended to Toulouse, Lyons, Grenoble, Soissons, and other great French towns.

St. CYRENE

Martyr in Cilicia (d. 302).

St. CHRYSANTHUS and his wife, St. DARIA

Roman martyrs (d. 283).

Blessed FRANCIS OF CALDEROLA (d. 1507)

Franciscan of the Ancona Marches, whose life was devoted to settling quarrels and to converting sinners.

Blessed LUDOVIC OF ARNSTEIN

Of the Premonstratensian order (d. 1185). Married to Buda de Bonneburg, this Rhenish count had made his castle a haunt of brigands and a place of debauchery. He was converted with his wife and became one of St. Norbert's best disciples.

St. TOUCHARD

Honoured at Amblis, in Berry (d. 463?).

October 26th

BLESSED BONNE D'ARMAGNAC (1439-1462)

OF a family famous for its chivalrous exploits and its treachery, Bonne had the celebrated constable of Armagnac as her grandfather and Jacques, duke of Nemours, who died on the scaffold, as her brother. Her birth was attri-buted to the prayers of St. Colette, who had enjoined her parents to bring up their daughter well and later to have her become a Poor Clare at the convent of Lézignan. Bonne wished at first to have nothing to do with these plans, made without her consent. Meanwhile "she tried in vain to imagine she could find peace among bodily delights and worldly glories." The grace of God, which "eyed her soul," touched her heart at twenty; asked in marriage by Charles, duke of Berry, younger brother of Louis XI, she heard a voice which said to her: "Bonnette, Bonnette, if you are not a nun as you should be, you will be well punished."

The princess' entry to the convent was accomplished with great pomp. "Having begged pardon of her father for all the vexations and annoyances she had caused him," and having sought the blessing of her mother, "who gave it to her weeping so much and uttering such piteous cries that all those present wept," Bonne made a last visit to the lazar house for women whom she tended. "She arrived at Lézignan from Carlat on Friday, March 24th, 1459. The principal people of the place went before her. Her escort was composed of a seneschal, seven gentleman, seven maidens, and six guards. She approached the convent, bareheaded, led by her seneschal who gave her his hand, and preceded by the six guards with muskets on their shoulders. Then followed the gentlemen, maidens, pages, and lackeys. The whole population stood in the doorways, admiring this moving sight."

The decision of his sister prejudiced the ambitious plans of Jacques of Nemours. He arrived at Lézignan from the court, and asked if her hair had already been cut off. "Would he like to seize me by the hair and take me back to Carlat?" said the new recluse, and with a few strokes of scissors she cut off her beautiful tresses.

Bonne lived for three years at the convent, practising all the austerities of the Colettine Clares, meditating day and night on the passion of Our Saviour. She was brave, a trifle derisive, generous, invariably joyful. Seeing her dying, her sister companions made many requests of her; she promised not to forget one of them, and in full serenity gave up her soul.

St. Magloire

Compatriot and disciple of St. Samson, he left England with him and accompanied him to Brittany. There he converted a great number of Bretons, founded several monasteries, and died on the island of Jersey (d. end of 6th century).

St. Evaristus

Governed the Church of Rome at the end of the 1st century or the beginning of the 2nd; it was in any case a time of persecutions and internal dissensions.

St. Rusticus (d. about 462)

Son of a holy bishop named Bonose, he had been a monk at Marseilles before being appointed, about 430, to occupy the bishopric of Narbonne.

October 27th

BLESSED ANTONIA (1407–1507)

ANTONIA GAINACI entered the convent of St. Catherine at Brescia, her native town, at a very early age; fear of hell, her biographer notes, made her decide to become a Dominican. But during her novitiate, she showed her resolution to suffer all in order to persevere in her vocation.

In 1447 she found herself charged with the reform of the Dominican convent of St. Catherine at Ferrara. She set about this so wisely that the nuns of this monastery soon returned to the regular observance and unanimously elected her prioress. Nevertheless, the moment came when some of them, finding her too severe, made a plot against Antonia and got the vicar-general of Ferrara on their side. He compelled her to resign her duties and to go back to the lowest rank. With good grace and perfect humility, she took her place below the lay sisters, until the day when all the sisters again found themselves unanimous in asking the vicar-general to give her back to them as prioress. It is believed that she remained there until her death, and it is known that she died in her hundredth year.

ST. FRUMENTIUS (4th century)

DESPITE its strangeness, the story Rufinus has left us of the establishment of Christianity in Ethiopia has turned out to be accurate. He reports that a

Tyrian philosopher named Merropius, and two of his pupils, Edesius and Frumentius, made a tour of Persia and Abyssinia to follow their studies. They had to put into an enemy port and the boat which was carrying them was pillaged and the whole crew massacred. Edesius and Frumentius, who at that time were not on board but under a tree studying, alone survived. Touched by their youth and their industry, the Ethiopians spared them and took them to Axum, the residence of their king, who, also delighted by their good bearing and intelligence, kept them in his service. Edesius became his cupbearer, and Frumentius one of his treasurers.

Our two Tyrians stayed at the court for fifteen years, gaining in influence and taking advantage of the royal favour to promote the establishment of Christian merchants in the country. After the death of the king, his son, Aeizanes, succeeded him; Edesius returned to Tyre, where he was ordained priest, and Frumentius, resigning his high administrative duties, went to St. Athanasius to persuade him to appoint a bishop of Abyssinia.

"Who more than yourself is filled with the Holy Spirit and better able to carry out those duties?" replied the Alexandrian patriarch. So he consecrated Frumentius bishop, and thus was founded, in the middle of the 4th century, the first Christian church in Ethiopia.

Sts. VINCENT, SABINA, and CHRYSTETA

Reputed to have been martyred at Avila under Diocletian.

St. FLORENTIUS

Has been considered to be a disciple of St. Desiderius, bishop of Langres, and to have been killed by the Vandals at Tille-Château, between Langres and Dijon (4th century?).

October 28th

STS. SIMON AND JUDE (1st century)

THE feasts of St. Simon and St. Jude are doubtless celebrated together because, in enumerating the apostles, the writers of the synoptic Gospels place them one after the other.

The first is surnamed by them "Quanana" or "the zealous," as much to distinguish him from Simon Peter as to mark the zeal which he put at God's service. The second was really called Judas, but we call him rather Jude, in order to distinguish him from his namesake, the traitor, Judas

Iscariot. This is also why St. Luke calls him "Judas, son of James," and why St. Mark designates him by his surname "Thaddeus" or "man with the strong chest."

At the Last Supper, Jude interrupted Jesus to ask Him a question which, however, received no reply. "Lord," said St. Jude, "how comes it that thou wilt only reveal thyself to us, and not to the world?" (John xiv, 22-23). "This question," writes Bossuet, "arose naturally from the talk which had preceded it because there we have seen that the Saviour had declared he would manifest himself by the Holy Spirit to his friends and not to the world. Here then is the great secret of divine predestination. St. Jude went at once to the great mystery: How is it? What have we done that we have merited more than others? Should we have believed, if you had not given us faith? Should we have chosen you, if you had not first chosen us?

" 'Why, Lord, why?' said St. Jude. Jesus alone could resolve this question; but he kept the secret. . . . He did not answer it; and without even appearing to hear, he again repeated: 'If a man has any love for me, he will be true to my word; and then he will win my Father's love, and we will both come to him, and make our continual abode with him' (John xiv, 23-24). As though he had said: 'O, Jude, ask not what it is not given to you to know; do not seek the cause of the preference; adore my counsels; all that concerns you in this is that you keep my commandments; all the rest is my Father's secret; the unfathomable secret the Sovereign reserves to himself' " (*Meditations on the Gospel*, ninety-second day).

According to a certain tradition, Jude and Simon evangelized Persia and were martyred there. The first is invoked in desperate cases; the second has been taken as patron by curriers and pit sawyers.

St. LUDARD

Was a baker at Soissons (8th century).

St. FARO

Brother of St. Fara, was bishop of Meaux for forty-six years, after having been chancellor or referendary of King Clotaire II (7th century)

St. DODO (d. about 750)

Godson and disciple of St. Ursmar, was a native of the Laon district and abbot of Valers-en-Fagne.

October 29th

ST. NARCISSUS (d. about 212)

NARCISSUS must have been not less than eighty when he first occupied the episcopal see of Jerusalem. It is known that with Theophilus of Caesarea he presided over a council where the custom of always celebrating Easter on a Sunday was approved. Eusebius tells that one feast day when the oil needed for the liturgical unctions was lacking, he had water brought from a nearby well and that it was changed to oil by his benediction. He also reports the circumstances in which Narcissus laid aside his duties:

To clear themselves of some crime, three knaves accused their bishop of some infamous deed or other. "Burn me alive, if I am lying!" said the first. "May leprosy devour me!" said the second. "Strike me blind!" added the third. Narcissus' pain at seeing himself thus slandered led him to give way to his former taste for retreat; without saying where he was going, he left Jerusalem. He seemed to have vanished so completely that Dius was named his successor, and he was succeeded by Germanion and Gordios. Meanwhile, it was not long before our three slanderers were stricken with the punishments which they had called down upon themselves: the first perished in a fire, the second died a leper, and the third lost his sight, bewailing his sin.

Some years later, Narcissus reappeared in his episcopal city. The saintliness of his conduct was never again called in question, and so it was with transports of joy that Jerusalem greeted its old bishop. And he, with the aid of a helper named Alexander, continued, Eusebius tells us, to govern his church up to the age of a hundred and sixteen.

St. AELFLEDA

Daughter of Oswy, king of the Northumbrians, and granddaughter of St. Edwin, succeeded St. Hilda as abbess of Whitby in 680; her own mother came and placed herself under her guidance (d. 713).

St. THEODORE or THEUDART

Native of Vienne in Dauphiny, was a disciple of St. Caesarius of Arles, and founded some monasteries (d. 575).

St. ZENOBIUS

Priest and doctor, martyred at Tyre in Phoenicia (d. 310).

St. EUSEBIA OF BERGAMO (Lombardy)

Niece of St. Domnius and martyr (d. end of 3rd century).

October 30th

ST. DOROTHEA (1347–1394)

A CONTEMPORARY of Bridget of Sweden and of Catherine of Siena, Dorothea Swartz was, like them, favoured with ecstasies and visions and has left numerous revelations.

She was born at Montau, near Marienburg, of a family of peasants who had nine children. Marienburg, like Danzig and Marienwerder, where Dorothea later lived, belonged to the Teutonic Knights, then at the height of their power. She lived somewhat under their obedience and jurisdiction, and it was they who, in 1404, introduced the process of her canonization at the court of Rome.

Married to a Danzig workman named Adalbert, Dorothea gave birth to nine children of whom only one daughter survived and became a Bene-dictine. Her conjugal life was rather difficult. Adalbert, irascible and stupid, was often brutal to his wife; however, they went on long pilgrimages to-gether. In 1389, Dorothea left for Rome alone, in order to arrive for the jubilee the following year. She travelled under the guidance of God, begging her bread, scarcely seeing the countries she traversed. At Rome she fell ill and was cared for, during many weeks, at the hospital of Maria Auxiliatrix. Her husband had been dead some months when she reached home. Then she was able to think about the realization of her old dream of entering religion. For two years she was on probation, after which, on May 2nd, 1393, she was immured in a cell built into the cathedral of Marienwerder. It was a square hole, six feet wide and nine feet high, pierced by three windows, one giving on to the sky; another on to the altar where she took her Communion; the third, on to a cemetery, through which her food was brought. It was in this kind of tomb that Dorothea received the innumerable visits and heavenly communications which her confessors have related. She died there, racked with sufferings and austerities, at the end of a year, June 25th, 1394.

A whole literature has been dedicated to the visionary of Marienwerder; numerous miracles were attributed to her; and the Prussians have chosen her as their patron.

St. ZENOBIUS

Bishop and doctor, was martyred at Aegea in Cilicia, with St. ZENOBIA, his sister, between 285 and 304.

St. MARCELLUS

Soldier of the Trajan legion, was martyred at Tangier in 298.

St. ALPHONSUS RODRIGUEZ (1531–1617)

After the death of his wife and his two children, he entered the Society of Jesus and for forty years worked as porter at Palma, Majorca.

St. EUTROPIA

Suffered martyrdom at Alexandria (3rd century).

St. LUCANUS

Was martyred, it is believed, at Lagny in the 5th century. Formerly, in times of public calamity, his relics were carried in procession.

St. FOILLAN

Friend of St. Gertrude of Nivelles, brother of St. Ultan and St. Fursey, was on his way to the abbey of Fosses (Belgium) when he was massacred by infidels or by thieves at Soignies (d. 655).

October 31st

ST. QUENTIN (d. between 282 and 287)

IN 641, the year of his elevation to the episcopal see of Noyon, St. Eligius, the skilled metal smith, discovered the body of this martyr in the town where he had died. He enlarged the church dedicated to him and placed the saint's relics in a tomb which he himself enriched with gold and precious gems.

A century before, Gregory of Tours testified to the widespread devotion to St. Quentin and to the efficacy of his intercession. He tells the story of a man condemned to death for theft upon the complaint of a priest. Appalled at the severity of this sentence, the priest regretted having made the complaint and begged the judges to soften the punishment. As they refused to reconsider, he hastened to the Church of St. Quentin and prayed the saint to intervene. And, Gregory writes, St. Quentin came to the rescue, for before the man was dead, the rope of the gallows broke; the judges, seeing this as a sign from heaven, set the thief at liberty.

The *Acts* of St. Quentin were recast around 620, from a text written about 327, that is, some fifty-five years after his martyrdom.

It seems certain that he was an historical personage, the son of a Roman senator named Zenonius, and was put to death for his faith between 282 and

286. He had come from Rome with St. Lucian, and evangelized the districts around Beauvais and Amiens. Imprisoned in the latter city, he was dragged from his dungeon to be tortured and beheaded in a place then called Augusta Vermanduorum, afterwards known as Saint-Quentin.

St. LUCILLA

Daughter of St. Nemesius, deacon of the Roman church, was a victim with her father and numerous other Christians of the persecution of Valerian (254–260).

St. BEGGA OF EGREMONT (7th century)

It is told how this daughter of the king of Ireland, who had determined to remain a virgin, was promised in marriage to the king of Norway. On the eve of her wedding she fled, received the veil from the hands of St. Aidan, and founded a convent at Copeland. She was venerated for many centuries in the northwest part of England and in Norway.

St. ULTAN (d. about 868)

Also a native of Ireland, was a monk like his brothers St. Fursey and St. Foillan. Like them, he came to France after having lived in England. Helped by St. Gertrude of Nivelles, he founded the abbey of Fosses and then ruled at the same time those of Péronne and Saint-Quentin.

THE SAINTS OF NOVEMBER
November 1st
ST. BENIGNUS (2nd or 3rd century)

 T is said that St. Benignus came from Smyrna. Having landed at Marseilles he made his way to Autun, where he stayed for some years; then, going by way of Langres, he reached Dijon, where he exercised his apostolate and endured martyrdom. Some place his death in the time of Marcus Aurelius, others in the following century under Emperor Aurelian. According to some, it took place in the most curious circumstances. Accused of magic, his body torn by flagellation, the apostle was led before the idols and stuffed to choking with the consecrated meats. At that very moment, the statues of the idols and all the accessories of their cult vanished in smoke. He was confined in prison for six days, his feet sealed into a stone, with three mad dogs for company, but not one of them did him the least harm. They had to beat the martyr on the head with an iron bar finally to kill him.

His cult only began to spread after the barbarian invasions. By the time of St. Gregory of Tours it was flourishing. The latter tells how, appearing to Gregory of Langres, Benignus enjoined him to open the crypt where his remains had been placed. The bishop of Langres obeyed, and upon his crypt, happily rediscovered, a church was built which gave rise to a celebrated abbey and became one of the religious centres of Burgundy.

Telling of a pilgrimage which he made there, Gregory of Tours, the greatgrandson of Gregory of Langres, affirms that he had benefited from the power of St. Benignus. "The stone," he wrote, "in which the feet of the martyr had been sealed in molten lead, is at the present day pierced with small holes. People pour some beer or some wine into them and afterwards they apply it to their ailing eyes or to other sores. Thanks to this, their ills are soon cured. I myself made the experiment one day when I was suffering cruelly from my eyes; no sooner had I bathed them in this holy liquid than I was completely relieved"

St. LUDRE (5th century)

This child, son of a senator of Bourges, died almost immediately after his baptism, still wearing the white robe in which he had been dressed. His remains are honoured at Déols on the Indre.

St. AMABILIS (d. 475?)

Since the time of Gregory of Tours, his tomb has been venerated in Auvergne at Riom, of which town he is said to have once been pastor.

ALL SAINTS

It is known that in the Eastern Church from the 1st century onwards the Christian community of Antioch consecrated a day to the celebration of "all the martyrs". At Rome, the feast of "all saints" was established at the beginning of the 9th century; other countries adopted it in turn.

November 2nd
ST. MALACHY (1095-1148)

ST. MALACHY is known chiefly for a prophecy on the succession of the popes which has been falsely attributed to him. Born at Armagh in Ireland, he received his spiritual education from a recluse named Imhar and became a priest at twenty-five, although the canons of that time required priests to be thirty years of age. After having tried to reform the monks of Bangor who had chosen him as abbot, he was elected to the bishopric of Connor; but he did not occupy it for long as this town was destroyed by war. Nor was he more successful in maintaining his place as archbishop of Armagh, a rival having been set up against him before whom he effaced himself. Nevertheless, his virtues, his trials, his apostolic success and the miracles attributed to him finally gave him tremendous authority. He twice went to Rome with the object of setting the religious affairs of his country in order; he took the opportunity to visit Clairvaux of which he had introduced the reform into Ireland, and stayed there with his friend St. Bernard. He died in his arms on November 2nd, 1148.

The archbishop of Armagh was supposed to have applied himself in his last days to designating, by mottoes which render them recognizable, all the popes who were to succeed one another in the future. The mottoes, which run from 1143 to 1590, do in fact permit of our recognizing the persons to whom they apply; here the prophet is informed by the historian. The mottoes which follow are vague to the point of fitting all cases; here the prophet is hard put to it. This demarcation line in the series of formulae which constitute the prophecy is explained by the date of its publication, which was also that of its fabrication. Unknown until 1595, it appeared in that year through the good offices of a French Benedictine, Arnold Wion. Where did he get it? Nobody knows. It is thought that the author of that lucubration attempted to favour the chances of Cardinal Simoncelli in the conclave of 1590. As this prelate was bishop of Orvieto (*urbs vetus,* ancient city) the forger put out the formula: *De antiquitate urbis,* thus clearly designating his favourite, who, however, was not elected.

Although valueless, the prophecy of St. Malachy is still frequently cited in our day.

St. EUDOXIUS

Martyred in Armenia with nine other Christian fellow soldiers, about 315.

St. MAURUS

Founder of the abbey which gave rise to the Scottish town of Kilmore (d. 899).

Blessed MARGARET OF LORRAINE

Duchess of Alençon and great-grandmother of Henry IV, king of France had married Duke René of Alençon, twenty-three years older than she. Widowed at twenty-nine, she fulfilled her duties as sovereign until the day when she could become a Poor Clare at the convent of Argentan (1463–1521).

The COMMEMORATION OF THE FAITHFUL DEPARTED or
ALL SOULS' DAY

This feast which St. Odilo established at Cluny (*see January 1st*) began
to spread throughout the Western Church in the 11th century.

November 3rd

ST. HUBERT (d. 727)

WHEN he became bishop of Tongres in 705, that diocese comprised not
less than two-thirds of the present Belgium. Hubert succeeded St. Lambert,
who had just been murdered. His origins are unknown; some say he was a
duke of Aquitaine, others believe that he was of humble extraction, born in
the country around Liége.

His encounter with a miraculous stag in the forest of Ardennes seems to be
quite legendary. This had been for a long time a feature of the biography of
St. Eustace before it began to adorn that of St. Hubert. None the less, it is
true that in the 11th century our saint was already said to protect hunters
and to cure madmen.

For more than twenty years Hubert ruled the diocese of Tongres with both
firmness and good nature; a friend of Pepin of Heristal and Charles Martel,
he enjoyed universal popularity. He travelled widely, sometimes on horseback,
sometimes by boat; burned idols, built sanctuaries, preached everywhere,
led the most recollected of lives. Prisoners were especially dear to him and he
would secretly put food through the windows of their dungeons. Liége was
then only a fishing village. By taking the body of St. Lambert there, Hubert
made it a centre of pilgrimage, around which the city rose.

He fell ill in his forest residence of Tervueren near Brussels. Before he
breathed his last, to those who were present he said: "Stretch the *pallium* over
my mouth, for I am going to give back to God the soul which I received
from him." His body was interred at Liége, in the Church of St. Peter, as
he had wished.

St. PAPOUL (3rd century)

He died a martyr in Lauragais, after sharing St. Saturninus' labours (*see
November 29th*).

St. FLORUS (d. about 389)

From the 14th century on, he is credited with having spread the Gospel
in Languedoc and Auvergne. Upon his tomb, St. Odilo of Cluny built

a monastery which was the origin of the town of Saint‑Flour, birthplace of the celebrated Abbé Migne.

Blessed MARTIN DE PORRES (1579–1630)

Dominican lay brother, born in Peru of a Spanish gentleman and a negress; he was overseer of the infirmary of a monastery at Lima and, although he had never studied, he was frequently consulted on theological questions by the learned of his order and by bishops.

St. GWENAEL

Successor of St. Gueholy as abbot of Landevenec (Brittany); reformed various monasteries in England and in Ireland; then returned to die in Brittany (6th century).

November 4th

ST. CHARLES BORROMEO (d. 1584)

BORN on October 2nd, 1538, at the castle of Arona on Lake Maggiore, of Gilbert Borromeo and Margaret de' Medici, Charles studied the humani‑ ties at Milan and took the university course at Pavia.

On December 26th, 1559, his uncle, Angelo de' Medici, became pope under the name of Pius IV. Five days later, Charles Borromeo, aged twenty‑ two, was named cardinal and, on February 8th of the following year, arch‑ bishop of Milan. From that time on he lived at the Roman court loaded with honours and enjoying notable power. Indeed, his influence was always used in what he judged were the best interests of the Church. He played a prepon‑ derant part in the final decisions of the Council of Trent, and in the con‑ clave which brought about the election of St. Pius V.

The sudden death of his elder brother in 1562 deeply affected him. Until that time he had lived virtuously; from that moment he lived the life of a saint. Far from giving way to his family, who urged him to re‑enter the world and to marry, he soon took holy orders and was ordained priest; then he planned to leave the pontifical court. His uncle's death in 1565 restored his freedom. He returned to his diocese, the reform of which occupied him almost entirely from that time on. With his own fortune he founded seminaries, schools, hospitals; he faced unpopularity, slander, even death; he fought and succeeded in suppressing abuses which existed among the monks and clergy; he created all kinds of institutions to revive religious fervour.

Every day he himself made two meditations of an hour, said his office on his knees, fasted almost continually on bread and water, slept fully clothed on the ground. Two priests were charged with pointing out his failings to him; to have wounded him was sufficient to ensure becoming the particular object of his solicitude. He helped thousands of the poor, selling his gold plate for them and even giving them his bed. The plague of 1576 was an opportunity for him to display a heroism and a charity which are still famous.

He died at the age of forty-six, saying *"Ecce venio,* Behold, Lord, I come."

St. GILBERT

Abbot of Fontenelle. He came from Germany like his friend, St. Maurilius, archbishop of Rouen, with whom he lived for some time in a solitary section of Normandy (d. end of the 11th century).

St. GERARD

Monk of St. Albinus (d. 1123).

St. VITALIS (d. about 304)

Slave of Agricola, who had converted him, he was martyred at Bologna with him and interred at his side. St. Ambrose found their tombs in 393.

St. AMANTIUS

Bishop of Rodez. His life was written by the poet Venantius Fortunatus. It is not known if he lived in the 1st or the 5th century.

November 5th

ST. BERTILLE (d. between 705 and 713)

BORN of a landowning family near Soissons, Bertille became a nun at the abbey of Jouarre, founded by Ado, St. Ouen's brother. There the severe rule of St. Columbanus was followed. Some leagues away rose the little convent of Chelles, built by Queen Chrodegilde. About 658 it was rebuilt on a more ample plan by Queen Bathilde. At her request, Bertille undertook direction of it, and was brought from Jouarre to Chelles by Genesius, future bishop of Lyons. Did Bathilde suspect that she was choosing a superior for herself, and that, driven from the throne, she herself would pass the last fourteen years of her life under her obedience?

We know that Bertille was abbess for forty-six years, and had under her guidance, in addition to a queen and a number of Merovingian princesses, many nuns of the Anglo-Saxon nobility.

STS. ZACHARY AND ELIZABETH (1st century)

WHAT is known about the parents of St. John the Baptist comes from the third Gospel.

"In the days when Herod was king of Judaea, there was a priest called Zachary, of Abia's turn of office, who had married a wife of Aaron's family, by name Elizabeth; they were both well approved in God's sight, following all the commandments and observances of the Lord without reproach. They had no child; Elizabeth was barren, and both were now well advanced in years. He . . . had been chosen by lot . . . to go into the sanctuary of the Lord and burn incense there. . . . Suddenly he saw an angel of the Lord, standing at the right of the altar where incense was burnt. . . The angel said, Zachary, do not be afraid; thy prayer has been heard, and thy wife Elizabeth is to bear thee a son, to whom thou shalt give the name John. . . . many hearts shall rejoice over his birth, for he is to be high in the Lord's favour. . . . And Zachary said to the angel, By what sign am I to be assured of this? I am an old man now, and my wife is far advanced in age. The angel answered, My name is Gabriel, and my place is in God's presence; I have been sent to speak with thee, and to bring thee this good news. Behold, thou shalt be dumb, and have no power of speech, until the day when this is accomplished. . . .

"And so, when the days of his ministry were at an end, he went back to his house. It was after those days that his wife Elizabeth conceived. . . . Meanwhile, Elizabeth's time had come for her childbearing, and she bore a son. . . . And now, when they assembled on the eighth day for the circum‑cision of the child, they were for calling him Zachary, because it was his father's name; but his mother answered, No, he is to be called John. And they . . . began asking his father by signs, what name he would have him called by. So he asked for a tablet, and wrote on it the words, His name is John. . . . Then, of a sudden, his lips and his tongue were unloosed, and he broke into speech. . . .

"Blessed be the Lord, the God of Israel; he has visited his people, and wrought their redemption. He has raised up a sceptre of salvation for us. . . . And thou, my child, wilt be known for a prophet of the most High, going before the Lord, to clear his way for him; thou wilt make known to his people the salvation that is to release them from their sins. Such is the merciful kindness of our God, which has bidden him come to us, like a dawning from on high, to give light to those who live in darkness, in the shadow of death, and to guide our feet into the way of peace" (Luke i, 5–79).

St. GUIRAUD

Bishop of Béziers (d. 1123).

St. LYE

Recluse in Sologne and in Beauce, died in his hermitage of La Forêt-aux-Loges (6th century).

St. NATALINE

Is honoured in the diocese of Pamiers. She was, her legend tells, second daughter of Fredelas, governor of that town, and he did not know that she was a Christian; learning of it, he himself condemned her to death. She had been denounced to him by a lieutenant, Alydanus, who thus avenged himself because he had not succeeded in marrying her.

November 6th

ST. LEONARD (d. about 559)

HE is patron of prisoners, to whom he is considered to give the grace of resignation and often even deliverance. As early as the 12th century, Geoffrey de Vigeois wrote that "almost the whole world recognized this power of his." At Saint-Léonard-de-Noblat in Limousin, numerous stone crosses could be seen where former captives had come to hang their manacles and chains. Today, St. Leonard is still invoked in Germany, Belgium, Spain, Italy, and Poland; and in France a host of churches have been dedicated to him.

He was, they say, a Frankish lord who had gone to the wars with Clovis and, like him, was baptized at Rheims in 496. He then placed himself under the spiritual direction of St. Remigius, who conferred the tonsure on him.

Seeing that he had decided to renounce the world, Clovis wished to give him a bishopric, but in vain; as the greatest of favours the old warrior only asked to be allowed to withdraw into solitude, to be authorized to visit the prisons, and to give their liberty to those prisoners whom he selected. The king assented to his request and made him a present of the forest of Pauvain, near Limoges. Leonard then made his way towards Aquitaine. At Orléans he was ordained deacon and lived for some time in the abbey of Micy, with St. Mesmin; and longer in Berry where he achieved numberless conversions and worked several miracles.

The place which he chose by way of a retreat, in the forest of Pauvain, he called Nobiliacum or Noblat; the sanctuary which he raised there to the Virgin

Mary he named "Our Lady beneath the Trees." During the twenty years he still lived, Leonard saw many disciples come to him, former convicts now converted, former soldiers now freed; and when he died, they interred him in the chapel of Our Lady beneath the Trees.

Blessed CHRISTINA OF STOMMELN

Was born in the village of that name, in the duchy of Juilliers, and died in an almshouse in Cologne after a long life of suffering. She was a great ecstatic. She has left numerous letters (1242-1313).

St. WINNOC

Entered the abbey of Sithiu governed by St. Bertin, and later founded that of Wormhoult, in Flanders. The hagiographers made him out to be the son of a Breton king and named as his brothers, Brodanoc, Igénoc, and Madoc, who like him became monks at St. Bertin (d. 717).

St. THEOBALD

Born in Limousin; died a canon of the collegiate church of Dorat, in 1070.

November 7th
ST. ERNEST (d. 1148)

ERNEST, baron of Steisslingen, had governed the monastery of Zweifalten for six years when the signal was given for the second crusade. ThisWürttemberg abbey had seventy choir monks and more than a hundred and three lay brethren. Taking leave of them, the abbot said: "I do not expect to see you again here below, for God will grant me, I trust, soon to shed my blood. The death I am destined to die matters little so long as it allows me to suffer for the love of Christ."

The preceding year, at Vézelay, St. Bernard had shown how the Christian kingdom of Jerusalem was about to fall back into infidel hands, and such had been the effect of his words that King Louis VII of France, Eleanor, his wife, Robert de Dreux, his brother, the great vassals of Toulouse, Champagne, and Flanders, and a host of knights and commoners had sworn to make a crusade. His success was no less at Speyer, where the German princes, previously reconciled among themselves, also had resolved to take the Cross. They set out in 1147, with Emperor Conrad III at their head, accompanied by his brother, Bishop Otto of Freisingen and the holy abbot of Zweifalten.

Going ahead of the French, the Germans took the road through the valley of the Danube towards the Byzantine Empire. We know the fate of each of these two armies, to which were added a crowd of women and unarmed pilgrims. The crusade was a disaster from every point of view; as for the two or three hundred thousand Christians who reached the East, only a few hundred returned to Europe two years later.

Ernest himself did not reach Jerusalem, having been taken captive in the advance guard by an emir of Ambronius, king of Persia. With four hundred prisoners he was taken to Mecca, where the Persian king then resided. There, called upon and refusing to embrace Islam, he suffered a long and frightful martyrdom. "The executioners finally made incisions in his skull and removed the skin from his head; they then opened up his stomach and plucked out his intestines, the end of which they affixed to the bottom of a stake driven into the ground; and they made their victim turn about the stake, until he fell dead at their feet." These details are taken from a letter to the Abbot Berthold, successor of Ernest at Zweifalten, by the Armenian priest Marsilius, an eyewitness.

St. Engelbert of Cologne (1180–1225)

To within a few months, the dates of his birth and death correspond to those of St. Francis of Assisi. Belonging to the family of the counts of Berg, and receiving ecclesiastical dignities while still very young, he first took sides with an emperor excommunicated by Innocent III and himself suffered excommunication. The pope removed this in 1203 and in 1216 confirmed the choice of the church of Cologne which had elected Engelbert as bishop. Frederick II, detained in Italy, confided to him the guardianship of young Henry, his son, and also the administration of all the Cisalpine part of the Empire. Engelbert, who had always been a friend of the poor and had become a pious prelate, then showed himself a politician of a high order. He was killed at Swelm by Frederick of Isenburg, his cousin, against whose simoniacal intrigues he was fighting.

St. Willibrord

A native of Northumbria, disciple of St. Wilfrid and St. Egbert, he went to Frisia and worked for the conversion of that country. He founded the monastery of Echternach (Luxemburg) and died archbishop of Utrecht in 738.

St. Florentius

Native of Ireland, was bishop of Strassburg (d. 687).

November 8th

ST. GEOFFREY (d. 1115)

GEOFFREY or Godefroid was the son of a notable of the village of Moulicourt, called Frodon, and his godfather was Abbot Godefroid, who then ruled the monastery of Mont-Saint-Quentin near Péronne. At the age of five he entered that abbey, wore the Benedictine habit and enjoyed the exercises of monastic life. Having become a monk, he discharged the duties of infirmarian, hospitaller, and bursar; was ordained priest by Radbod II, bishop of Noyon; then was entrusted with rebuilding the abbey of Notre Dame at Nogent, in the diocese of Rheims. In this house, fallen into ruins and overrun with brambles, there remained only six nuns and two children; a few years sufficed for Geoffrey to restore it and to attract numerous recruits.

The abbot of St. Remigius at Rheims being dead, this rich benefice was offered in 1097 to the man who had rebuilt Notre Dame. But he answered that, in accordance with the canon of the Council of Nicaea, he did not at all wish, for his part, "to slight a poor woman in order to marry a rich one."

In 1104 the clergy and the people of Amiens elected Geoffrey head of their church; he was then forced to accept appointment as bishop, the Council of Troyes and King Philip having formally ordered him to do so. His episcopate was carried on under political and religious difficulties of every kind. No room was given the bishop to remain neutral in the midst of factions, for whichever party he joined he made enemies. These rendered his life so unbearable that he communicated his wish to resign to St. Ivo of Chartres. This celebrated personage doubtless encouraged him, for in November 1114 we find Geoffrey setting out, via Cluny, towards the Grande Chartreuse where he intended to end his days. But he stayed there only a few months; then he was obliged by the Council of Soissons to return to his see.

The prelate was back in his episcopal city for Lent in 1115. In his Palm Sunday homily he adjured King Louis VII to seize the castle of Amiens by force; in June he took part in the Council of Châlons; on October 29th, he fell ill at Soissons. As soon as they learned of it, the monks of St. Crispin came to fetch him and carried him into their abbey, at death's door. It was in their midst that Geoffrey drew his last breath, on the following November 8th, aged about fifty.

St. CLAIR

Monk of Marmoutiers, disciple of St. Martin, and friend of Sulpicius Severus (d. about 397).

St. DROUET

Bishop of Auxerre (d. 532).

The FOUR CROWNED MARTYRS

A group of martyrs honoured at Rome, on the identity of whom there is no agreement. For some say they are Sts. Claudius, Castor, Nicostratus, and Nictorinus; others, Sts. Severus, Severianus, Carpoforus, and Victorinus (date uncertain).

Blessed JOHN DUNS SCOTUS

A Franciscan of Anglo-Saxon birth, taught at Oxford, Paris, and finally at Cologne where he died in 1308, aged thirty-four. He built up a system in many respects opposed to that of St. Thomas and caused the triumph, in the schools, of the doctrine of the Immaculate Conception. His two master works are the *Opus Oxoniensis* and the *Reportata Parisiana*. The Scotists consider Duns Scotus, the "subtle Doctor," to be the greatest genius of scholastic theology, while the Thomists reserve this title for the "angelic Doctor," St. Thomas Aquinas.

November 9th

ST. MATHURIN (4th century ?)

THE following biographical note on St. Mathurin is not very reliable but as there exists no other, we shall give it for what it is worth.

His father's name was Marin; his mother's, Euphemia. They lived at Larchant in Gâtinais not far from Fontainebleau. They were pagans, and Marin, an imperial official, had the duty of prosecuting and exterminating the Christians. Nevertheless, a holy bishop of Sens, named Polycarp, had come to baptize twelve-year-old Mathurin in secret. From that time on the child never ceased to implore God to convert his father and mother. Euphemia was the first to be touched by grace. Marin resisted a long time, but finally he embraced the faith and from that time he protected those whom he had persecuted.

Polycarp, having baptized all the family, became their close friend. When Mathurin was twenty, he ordained him priest and when Polycarp had to absent himself, Mathurin administered the diocese.

Numerous miracles are attributed to our saint. Notably, he had the power of driving out demons and calming the possessed. It must have been due to this reputation as exorcist that he was called to Rome to cure the demoniac daughter of a nobleman. There he did what was expected of him and, having edified the Eternal City for three years, he died universally venerated.

St. Mathurin is invoked in cases of madness, epilepsy, and fears. He is also patron of buffoons and others whose business it is to amuse the public. There used to be a church in Paris dedicated to him, and as it was served by Trinitarians they came, in France, to be called the Mathurins.

St. VITONUS

Bishop of Verdun (d. about 525).

St. RANULFUS

Martyr in Artois; father of St. Hadulfus, bishop of Arras (d. about 700).

St. URSICINUS

Supposed to have been the first bishop of Bourges (3rd century).

November 10th

STS. NYMPHA, RESPICIUS, and TRYPHON
(3rd century)

It is believed that Nympha was a virgin of Palermo. According to some, she underwent martyrdom in Sicily; others say she fled from that country on the invasion of the Goths and came to live at peace in Rome; others again say she died at Soana in Tuscany.

The fact is that at Rome her relics were united with those of St. Respicius and St. Tryphon, a circumstance which led the Roman Church to join her with these two martyrs in one common feast day.

As for Tryphon, it appears he was an old man, native of Apamea, who devoted himself to the persecuted Christians, striving to prevent their losing courage and apostasizing. Making no secret of it, he was arrested and condemned to death. His companion in torture at Nicaea was the tribune Respicius who, seeing Tryphon's sufferings, proclaimed himself a Christian.

ST. ANDREW AVELLINO (1521-1608)

AT Rome and in Italy, St. Andrew Avellino is very popular, and he is especially invoked against sudden death and apoplexy.

Born at Castronuovo, he became a doctor of law and was ordained priest at Naples; then he began to plead there in the ecclesiastical courts. A little lie, slipped into a speech, caused him such remorse that, renouncing the profession of advocate for ever, he resolved to devote himself from that time on solely to the conversion of souls. He was given a community of women to reform and was completely successful. On that occasion he called upon himself the vengeance of a libertine who tried to assassinate him. Wounded and with his face disfigured, Andrew obtained from the vice-regent his attacker's pardon; but the latter soon afterwards was killed by an outraged husband.

St. Andrew Avellino entered the Theatines in 1556; there he filled for ten years the duties of novice master and founded houses of his order in Piacenza and Milan. He refused a bishopric offered him by Gregory XIV and returned to Naples where his virtues, preaching and miracles brought him universal veneration. He was the friend of St. Charles Borromeo, converted a number of noted courtesans, directed the consciences of many personages of high rank, and counted among his disciples, Scupoli, celebrated author of the *Spiritual Combat*. He himself wrote much on the subjects of asceticism and edification. He was struck at the foot of the altar with an attack of apoplexy as he was reciting the first prayer of the Mass and died a few hours later after having, as he had predicted, struggled with the demon till the last.

St. ALDA

Lived in the neighbourhood of Paris. Her feast is often celebrated on November 18th (d. 8th century).

Sts. FLORENCE, TIBERIUS, and MODESTUS

Martyrs of Languedoc (3rd century).

St. JUSTUS

Archbishop of Canterbury, companion of St. Augustine (d. 627).

November 11th

ST. MARTIN OF TOURS (d. 397)

BORN at Sabaria in Pannonia about 325, Martin was enrolled at fifteen in the imperial horse guards. It was at Amiens, where he was on garrison duty, that he divided his cloak with a stroke of his sword to clothe a poor man. Shortly afterwards, at about twenty, he was baptized, left the army, and was made an exorcist by St. Hilary at Poitiers.

Warned in a dream of the approaching death of his parents, Martin returned to his own far-off country where he had the happiness of converting his mother. While on the road returning to Gaul, a rumour reached him that the bishop of Poitiers had been exiled. He then withdrew to the island of Gallinaria and lived there as a solitary until the day when he heard that St. Hilary had been set at liberty. After stopping in Rome, he again arrived in Poitou and there led for ten years the cenobitic life according to the rule of St. Basil. Thus came to be founded Ligugé, the most ancient monastery in the West.

In 371, the people of Tours, seeking a bishop, carried off Martin by force and took him to their town. His episcopate lasted for twenty-six years, during which he converted not only Touraine but also Berry, Anjou, Beauce, Paris, Trier, Luxemburg, Sennonais, and even far-off Dauphiny. He travelled light, always followed by a party of monks, sometimes riding on a donkey, ordinarily on foot or by boat; praying, preaching, accomplishing many miracles and good works; converting families, villages, whole tribes; casting down temples and idols, raising monasteries and churches in their place; consolidating his gains, and everywhere leaving monks or priests to carry on his work.

In 397 he collapsed from exhaustion at Candes. As his disciples begged him not to leave them, the old man began to weep and said: "If God finds that I can still be of use to his people, I do not at all refuse to work and to suffer longer." He died with his face turned to the window to see the sky, and at once became the most popular saint of the West. In France, four thousand churches are dedicated to him and more than five hundred villages bear his name.

St. BERTUIN

Of Anglo-Saxon origin, founded the abbey of Malonne in Belgium (d. about 698).

St. Véran

After having led a life of solitude in Gévaudan, was nominated bishop of Cavaillon by Sigebert, king of Austrasia (d. end of 6th century).

St. Menas

Hermit of the country round Benevento, whose virtues were praised by St. Gregory the Great (6th century).

St. Theodore of Studium

One of the greatest figures of the Eastern Church by reason of his virtues, his knowledge, his resistance to the Byzantine emperors, and the persecutions he suffered at their hands. The monastery of Studium, over which he ruled at Constantinople, had a thousand monks. His works include ascetic writings, poetry, discourses, and hundreds of letters (759–826).

November 12th

ST. RENATUS (d. 450?)

As his name tells (*renatus,* reborn), this saint was twice born; and his double birth was attributed to the prayers of St. Maurilius.

One day when passing through the village of La Poissonnière, the bishop of Angers saw a patrician named Bononia coming towards him who threw herself at his feet and begged him to pray that heaven might make her a mother. Maurilius prayed, and the following year Bononia gave birth to a child.

Seven years later, Maurilius was officiating in the cathedral when he again saw Bononia coming towards him in tears. Her child was dying, and this time she adjured Maurilius to restore him to health or at least to baptize him. The bishop had first to finish reading the liturgy, so that he reached the child's bedside only to find that he was dead, and dead without baptism.

This event so affected him that, considering himself guilty, he left his bishopric, said farewell to the world, and buried himself in a forest where all trace of him was lost. There he lived seven years at the end of which an inspiration came to him to return to his episcopal town. Going straight to the Church of St. Peter, he prayed for a long time, then had the tomb of Bononia's son opened. Then it was that the child arose to be baptized and to begin his life anew.

At the school of Maurilius, who had taken up the duties of his ministry once more, Renatus acquired all the ecclesiastical virtues, and on his master's death in 437, he became his successor. But he was not to end his days in the episcopal see of Angers. One day he set out for Italy, settled in a deserted place near Sorrento, became bishop of that town, and died there; it was only some centuries after his death that his relics were taken back to Angers.

All this, which may be found recorded in a *Life of St. Maurilius*, written in the 10th century, is no doubt legendary, but nothing else is known about St. Renatus.

St. CHRISTIAN

Hermit; assassinated by thieves at Brennava (Poland) in 1004.

St. MARTIN I

Pope, died exiled to the Chersonese by Constans II. This emperor of Byzantium bore the Roman pontiff a grudge for having condemned the Monothelites whom he protected (d. 655).

St. EMILIAN

Pastor of Vergegium in Aragon (d. 574).

St. NILUS (d. about 430).

Abandoning his duties as governor of Constantinople, he became a monk with his son Theodulus, while his wife and his daughter entered a convent in Egypt. He has left numerous writings and enjoys great authority in ascetical matters.

St. OR

Abbot of a monastery in Egypt (4th century).

November 13th

ST. BRICE (d. 444)

ST. BRICE is a remarkable example of the divine mercy; during the first part of his life he was, according to Sulpicius Severus, like a man possessed by a demon; then, having been made a bishop, he showed himself edifying in all things and underwent courageously the most humiliating trials.

He was a child whom St. Martin had rescued and placed among his clerics. Growing up, he became wicked, proud, ungrateful, and disorderly in his life. The suffering he caused his master cannot be imagined, but when St. Martin was pressed to get rid of him, he observed that Jesus had borne with Judas, and that divine grace would change Brice in the end.

About 397, Brice was designated to succeed St. Martin, but the people of Touraine would have nothing to do with him and substituted the priest Justinian. Brice fled to avoid stoning. Justinian having died, he tried, about 430, to take back the see, but accused of bad morals, he was again driven out of the town and forced to give place to the priest Armentius. The Council of Terni in 401, and Pope Zosimus in 417, however, cleared him of all blame. It was not until 437, on the death of Armentius, that he could go back to Tours. Forty years had passed since he had been elected bishop; hatred had been disarmed, and for the seven years he survived, Brice could govern his church in peace.

ST. DIDACUS or DIEGO (d. 1463)

THE humble friar who bore this name among the Spanish Franciscans was born of poor parents at San Nicolás del Puerto (Andalusia) in the early years of the 15th century. He was first a porter in the monastery of St. Francis at Arizafa, then he was chosen to accompany some missionaries to the recently discovered Canary Islands. He stayed there four years, a simple lay brother at the head of the monastery of Fortaventura. During the jubilee year 1550, that of the canonization of St. Bernardine of Siena, four thousand friars minor came from all parts of the world to Rome. An epidemic broke out among them, the great monastery of Ara Coeli was transformed into a hospital, and Didacus was given direction of it. Wonder-worker that he was, he mysteriously multiplied the bread and medicines; he cured even the dying. Caught kissing the sores of those affected with a contagious disease, he replied that it was the best way to treat this kind of illness. After returning to Spain, he lived in the monastery of Seville, then in that of Salceda, finally in that of Alcala de Henares where he died, leaving a reputation as one of the great ecstatics of his time.

St. HOMOBONUS

Pursued the calling of merchant at Cremona (Lombardy). He died at the Church of St. Giles where, every night, he attended matins, leaving only after high Mass (d. 1197).

St. SIARDUS

Of the Premonstratensian order, abbot of Mariengarten (d. 1230).

Sts. VALENTINE, FELICIAN, and VICTOR

Martyrs of Ravenna (4th century).

November 14th

ST. JOSAPHAT (1580–1623)

BORN at Vladimir (Volhynia) of a very pious mother and a father who was a municipal counsellor, John Kuncevyc was baptized and brought up in the Orthodox Ruthenian Church. He was in his sixteenth year when, on November 23rd, 1595, this Church was officially united to the Roman Church. After having learned something of commerce, John entered the Basilian monastery of the Trinity at Vilna where the community was reduced to one archimandrite, Samuel. The presence of John, now become brother Josaphat, restored life to this house, and recruits were not long in coming. Meanwhile Samuel, the superior, remained secretly attached to Orthodoxy, and, like many others, was awaiting the possibility of fighting with impunity against the Uniat or Roman Catholics. Unmasked by Josaphat, he was deposed by the archbishop of Kiev, a measure which might have cost the latter his life.

Placed at the head of the monastery of the Trinity, Josaphat never ceased proclaiming his fidelity to the pope or recruiting new subjects for him through his preaching. For this he became one of the best loved and most hated men in the country. In 1617, he was appointed to the archbishopric of Polotsk, which included almost the whole of White Ruthenia. For six years Josaphat displayed great activity in favour of the Roman primacy, by annual synods where he assembled his clergy and gave them most detailed instruction, and by a thousand other courageous actions. But the pact of unity between the king of Poland and the Holy See continued to be fiercely opposed. In 1620, while the archbishop was at the Diet of Warsaw, the enemies of the union, supported by the Cossacks, consecrated as many Orthodox as there were Uniat bishops and installed them in opposition to the latter. Josaphat found a usurper at Polotsk when he returned. His protests only served to infuriate the populace which, but for the army's intervention, would have assassinated him then and there.

In October 1623, at Vitebsk, on a pastoral tour, he cried out in a sermon: "Please God I will give my life for the holy union, for the supremacy of Peter and of the Holy Father, his successor." God permitted this wish to be realized two weeks later in the same town where it had been pronounced. Following an incident between supporters of the bishop and an Orthodox priest, the populace invaded the bishop's palace and beat Josaphat to death with their staves.

St. Sidonius

A native of Ireland, became a monk at Jumièges and founded an abbey in Caux (d. about 689).

Sts. Philomenus, Theodotus, and Clementinus

Martyred in Thrace (period unknown).

St. Emmerich

Son of St. Stephan, king of Hungary (1002-1032).

November 15th

ST. GERTRUDE (d. about 1302)

St. Gertrude is one of the mystics whose works, so highly esteemed by St. Teresa and St. Francis de Sales, have always enjoyed wide appreciation. The work comprising her life and revelations is entitled *The Herald of Divine Love* and is divided into five books; the first is a sort of introduction written by one of her companions; she was herself author of the second; and the three last were edited from notes made at her dictation.

The words of the mystics have a special virtue; those who have met God naturally speak about Him better than those from whom He has remained hidden. Thus it was with Gertrude to whom "heaven had accorded," as her biographer wrote, "the gift of moving hearts to their very depths and saying things so sensible, agreeable, and penetrating, that she compelled everyone to think of nothing but God, raising the most downcast souls, and adding flames to those which already possessed the fire of divine love."

It is not known who her parents were, the place or date of her birth, or the year in which she died. She had been brought to the Cistercian abbey of Helfta, near Eisleben (Saxony) at the age of five. She was immediately noted for her excellent memory and extraordinary intelligence and was allowed to follow her bent for study. She learned Latin and what were then called the liberal arts. All her sisters loved her for her docile, competent, and sparkling character; all were edified by her virtues. Her fervour, however, suffered in the end from too great an application to philosophy. On January 27th, 1281, Our Lord appeared to her and reproached her with this. From then on she had no other books than the Holy Scriptures and the works of the Fathers of the Church. It was from that apparition, followed by countless others, that Gertrude dated her "conversion." Her whole life was full of ecstasies, sufferings, and heavenly communications. Sufferings and joys she received alike with gratitude and humility. "Lord," she cried, "surely the greatest of your miracles is to compel the earth to bear such a sinner as I am."

St. Gertrude died one Easter Wednesday, about the age, it is believed, of forty-five.

St. LEOPOLD

Margrave of Austria, grandfather of Frederick Barbarossa, surnamed "the Valiant" for his victory over the Hungarians (d. 1136).

St. ARNOUL

Bishop of Toul from 847 to 871.

St. DESIDERIUS

Bishop of Cahors, friend of St. Eligius and St. Ouen (d. 655).

St. VALERIA

Martyr of Hippo, honoured by St. Augustine (3rd century).

St. EUGENE

Martyr, companion of St. Denis of Paris (period uncertain).

St. ALBERT THE GREAT

Doctor of the Church (d. 1280). Son of the count of Bollstaedt and born at the castle of Lauingen (Swabia), he studied at Padua, became a Dominican in 1223, then taught in the monasteries of his order at Hildesheim, Freiburg in Breisgau, Ratisbon, Paris (1245), and Cologne (1248). He contributed to "Christianizing" Aristotelianism and to spreading it in the schools; he was also interested in the natural sciences. In Paris and Cologne, he counted St. Thomas Aquinas among his disciples. From 1254 to 1257, he was superior of the Dominican province of Germania. In 1256, we find him at Anagni, taking up the defence of the mendicant orders before Alexander IV. In 1256, at the chapter of Valenciennes, with Thomas Aquinas and Peter of Tarentaise, he elaborated a programme of studies for the monks of his order. The following year he became bishop of Ratisbon, but resigned two years later; from 1263 to 1265, he preached the last crusade in Germany; then, following a stay in Würzburg, he again began to teach theology at Cologne, interrupting this, however, by journeys to Antwerp, Paris, Lyons, and elsewhere. He died at Cologne, leaving the reputation of a true saint, an able negotiator, and one of the most learned men of his time. He has been given the surname of the "universal doctor." Pius XI, in virtue of his supreme authority, canonized him in 1931 "by equipollency," that is to say, without recourse to the usual formalities. He fixed his feast upon November 15th, moving that of St. Gertrude to the following day.

November 16th
ST. EDMUND (d. 1240)

AT Abingdon, not far from Oxford, the parents of St. Edmund had always led an almost monastic life in the midst of the world. His mother, Mabel, wore a hair shirt and attended matins every morning. His father, Reginald Rich, a former merchant, entered the monastery of Evesham with his wife's consent; thus the care of their four children, Edmund, Robert, Alice, and Margaret, fell to Mabel. She early accustomed them to fasting on Friday on bread and water, and on feast days to reciting the whole psalter.

Edmund was teaching literature at Paris when Mabel, feeling that she was dying, recalled him to give him her last benediction. "I bless you," she said to him, "and in you I bless my other children, over whom you will henceforth watch."

To be near his sisters, whose beauty was a source of anxiety to him, Edmund had himself appointed professor of sciences at the University of Oxford. Recognizing soon that Alice and Margaret had a religious vocation, he had them received into the convent of St. Gilbert at Catesley. He himself decided to embrace a priestly calling as the result of a dream in which he heard his mother pledge him to give up geometry for theology. He returned to Paris and studied the sacred sciences; he taught them there, became a priest and then, about 1214, went back to England where for seven years the University of Oxford reckoned him among her most brilliant professors of theology

In 1228, Edmund was entrusted with preaching the sixth crusade in Britain. Five years later he was appointed to the archbishopric of Canterbury; then began for him a period of trials which was to last until his death. King Henry III, who had at first been favourable to him, could not long endure this prelate who showed himself to be inflexible and incorruptible in defence of ecclesiastical immunities. Monks, bishops, the chapter of Canterbury, and even the pontifical legate, who had been circumvented by Edmund, ranged themselves beside the sovereign. Abandoned by all and believing that he should withdraw, Edmund left England secretly in 1240 and sought asylum in the Cistercian abbey of Pontigny, in Burgundy. He left there some months later for Soissy in the diocese of Meaux and there died in the same year.

St. AGNES OF ASSISI

Fled from her father's house fifteen days after her sister Clare. St. Francis cut off her hair and received her profession. After having been abbess of the Poor Clares of Monticelli, near Florence, she returned to St. Damian's in Assisi, where she died in 1253, three months after St. Clare.

St. EMILION

A native of Vannes, lived in solitude in the Bordelaise. A church and a town there bear his name, which is also that of a celebrated wine (d. 767).

St. OTHMAR

Abbot of St. Gall (d. 758). Two lords who had seized certain goods of his abbey and wished to keep them, accused him of immoral conduct and had him condemned by an ecclesiastical court to perpetual con‑ finement.

November 17th

ST. AIGNAN (d. 453?)

HISTORY honours St. Aignan as having prevented the capture of Orléans by Attila and thus having helped to save Europe from occupation by the Huns.

What the hagiographers add to this is not easily verified. If they are to be believed, Aignan was born at Vienne in Dauphiny, of a Roman family which came from Pannonia. He profited so well from the lessons of his teacher, St. Euvertius, that the latter, feeling his death approaching, chose Aignan to succeed him as the head of the church of Orléans. As this choice was contested by some, Euvertius ordained three days of fasting and prayers in order to learn the divine will. After this interval, a child was led before the assembly of the Christians; he was made to dip his hand into an urn which contained the names of the proposed candidates, and he drew out that of Aignan.

The biographers dwell on the zeal displayed by the new pastor in the conversion of the idolatrous Gauls and the immoral Romans, who composed almost his entire flock. Then they depict Attila approaching Orléans by forced marches. The people of Orléans were in despair, expecting that, as was his wont, the barbarian leader would have them all massacred. Aignan galloped to Toulouse to call on Aetius for help; but the latter who was fighting with Theodoric against the Vandals would promise nothing. Returning to Orléans, the bishop nevertheless announced that the Roman general would soon be there. While this was taking place, Attila appeared beneath the city walls with 500,000 men. Thinking that by opening the gates to him they would perhaps mollify him, the inhabitants of Orléans talked more than ever about surrender. But Aignan displayed confidence, and by fasting, praying, preaching, holding many processions and expiatory ceremonies he encouraged the defenders of the ramparts to hold out for a few days more. He was received by Attila, who conceded nothing to him except a safe conduct. Fortunately a storm broke which prevented the Huns from carrying out their work of siege for three days. This respite allowed Aetius to arrive in time and, reinforced by Theodoric, to compel the Huns to fall back towards the north; there at Châlons, as we know, the defeat of the Catalaunian plains awaited them.

Aignan, it is said, died at the age of ninety-five.

St. GREGORY OF TOURS

Was cured of a grave illness at St. Martin's tomb. He lived at the court of Neustria before being appointed bishop of Tours. His writings are of the highest importance for information on the Merovingian epoch (d. 593 or 594).

St. GREGORY THE WONDER-WORKER

Father of the Church (d. about 272). He became bishop of Neo-caesarea, his native city, and completely converted it by his miracles and his virtue. Of this great man, who recognized that he owed everything to Origen, there remain unfortunately only a few writings.

St. SALOME

Daughter of the duke of Cracow, married the son of King Andrew of Hungary and, widowed, entered the order of the Poor Clares (1201–1269).

November 18th

ST. ODO (879–942)

His noble family lived near Château-du-Loire (Sarthe) and attributed his birth to the intercession of St. Martin. While he was still quite a child he was sent to the court of Foulques the Good, count of Anjou, and when thirteen, to that of William, duke of Aquitaine. Odo has told how, about his sixteenth year, he was seized with such fearful headaches that they had to take him back to Touraine. "I still suffered for three years," he wrote, "without any of the thousand remedies used doing any good. Finally my father declared that I had already been consecrated to St. Martin and that doubtless he was demanding fulfilment of his promise."

The young man had no sooner resolved to enter the chapter of St. Martin at Tours than he recovered his health permanently. For several years he gave himself up to the study of the classics and of the holy Fathers; from 901 on, he followed at Paris the philosophy course of the famous Remigius of Auxerre. There he applied himself also to poetry and music, which he pursued all his life. Returning to Tours he was appointed chief cantor of the chapter, and he composed various works, such as an abstract of the *Moralia* of St. Gregory the Great and a life of St. Gregory of Tours.

It was in 909 that Odo became a Benedictine at Baume-les-Messieurs in Burgundy, which St. Berno then ruled. He took with him his library which comprised about a hundred manuscripts. Shortly afterwards, Cluny was founded, and he became its abbot in 927. The schools which he established there soon attracted everyone of distinction in the West. "Even a prince in his father's palace," it was said, "was not brought up better than a child at Cluny." Thanks to the abbot, the influence of Cluny began to extend to all Christendom. Popes had recourse to him in their difficulties; princes appealed to him to reform the monasteries of their domains.

In the summer of 942, when he was in Rome, Odo was attacked by malaria. He wished to return to Tours to die. On the way he stopped to teach some anthems to the mountain shepherds and rewarded them after a good performance; to the poor he gave, as was his wont, abundant alms. He died at Tours, near the tomb of St. Martin, on November 18th, the very day of the octave of his feast.

St. HILDA

Northumbrian princess, foundress of Whitby abbey in Yorkshire (d. 680).

St. MANDEZ

Hermit, native of Ireland, who died in Brittany (7th century).

Sts. ROMANUS and BARULAS

Were martyred at Antioch in Syria in 304. Barulas was a young child.

November 19th

ST. ELIZABETH OF HUNGARY (1207-1231)

A DAUGHTER of Andrew II, king of Hungary, and of Gertrude of Meran, Elizabeth was promised shortly after her birth, to Louis, hereditary duke of Thuringia. At the age of four she was taken in a silver cradle to the castle of Marburg, where her eleven-year-old betrothed awaited her. They were married in 1220, he being twenty, she thirteen. They lived together until 1227, when Louis IV went on the crusade and there died. Four children were born to them, one son and three daughters.

Even before her marriage Elizabeth had much to suffer. Her future father-in-law being dead, his widow and his brother tried to send her back to Hungary; so much did her betrothed love her that they did not succeed, but at least they did their best to persecute her. On Assumption Day, when her future mother-in-law had taken her to church, Elizabeth, taking off her crown, prostrated herself at length before the crucifix. The shrewish woman taunted her with flinging herself on the ground "like an old tired mule." "Is your crown too heavy?" she said. "You look like a clown, folded in half that way." Getting up, Elizabeth simply replied that she could not keep on her crown of pearls before Christ on the cross, wearing a crown of thorns.

When news came of the death of Louis IV, Elizabeth was driven from the court by the dead man's uncle, now the regent. She left at night, her youngest in her arms, her other children clinging to her robe. She had to take shelter in a pigsty; then the Franciscans of Eisenach rescued her as a pauper. No others would help her for fear of displeasing the regent; even the beggars and the sick whom she had helped thought they did well by insulting her. It was her uncle, the bishop of Bamberg, who finally took her in.

Meanwhile the companions of her husband returned from the crusade. As he was dying, Louis had left to them the duty of protecting his wife. They were preparing to do this when the usurper and his mother changed their attitude towards Elizabeth. She found herself recalled to the court, the rights of her son were recognized, and nobody from that time on behaved other than well towards her and her children.

Never did she forget the spouse she had cherished from her cradle. "Thou knowest, my God," she said, "that of all the joys of the world I preferred his presence which was so sweet to me; I fain would have lived all my life in misery, he a beggar and I a beggar, two paupers begging from door to door, for the happiness of being with him, if thou hadst permitted it."

She became a Franciscan tertiary in 1227, founded a convent of Francis-cans in 1229, and died at the age of twenty-four, November 19th, 1231.

St. MECHTILDE (d. about 1310)

She lived in the same convent of Hedelfs as her sister, St. Gertrude, and there, like her, had revelations which have been preserved (*see November 15th*).

St. CITROINE

Is honoured near Loudon in Poitou (d. about 580).

Sts. EXUPERIUS, FELICIAN, and SEVERINUS

Were martyred at Vienne in Dauphiny, about 178.

St. PATROCLUS

Lived as a hermit in Berry (d. 577).

November 20th

ST. FELIX OF VALOIS (d. about 1212)

AT the end of the 12th century there lived in a forest of Valois a hermit called Felix, who had been seen there as long as men could remember. He received one day a visit from a Paris doctor named John of Matha, who came to share his thoughts with him. God, he believed, had called him to succour the numerous Christians at that time being taken to Africa by the Mediter-ranean pirates. Felix confided to him that he himself had had the same inspiration from heaven. They resolved to found together, in the name of the Holy Trinity, an institution devoted to ransoming these unfortunates, and they left for Rome to obtain sanction of their project. Pope Innocent III accorded them his approval; thus the order of the Trinitarians was founded. A monastery of these monks was founded in Rome, of which John of Matha became superior, and another at Cerfroid (Aisne) which Felix ruled until his death.

And that is all that is known for certain about St. Felix. Some authors have, however, composed a more extensive biography. It was not, they say, because he lived as a solitary in the Valois, but because he was the issue of an illustrious family of the same name, that the founder of the Trinitarians was called Felix of Valois. They represent him as a near relative of Louis VII and friend of St. Bernard; take him in the king of France's train on the second crusade; show him in company with his uncle, Thibaud of Blois, travelling through the countryside in search of the indigent. One day he came across one who was going half naked in wintertime:

"What do you want me to give you?" said Thibaud to him.

"First your mantle, lord count."

"Here it is. And then?"

"Your ring which is so beautiful."

"It is yours! Do you want anything else?"

"You are rich, I am poor; you could give me the knightly insignia you are wearing?"

"True," said the count, "I will give it to you and with good will. And also take my gloves. Will that be all for today?"

"I think so, sir, but I would also have your hat."

"That, no. It is impossible," said Thibaud, "for I am bald and I cannot bear to be laughed at."

In fact, this beggar had no need of a hat nor anything else, since, as was found later, he was an angel travelling in that country to test the charity of the Christians.

St. Edmund of England

King of East Anglia, was conquered, made prisoner, and put to death by the Danes, invaders of his country (d. 870).

St. Hippolytus

Bishop of Belley, died at Condat, where he had retired (d. 769).

St. Mamas

Martyr in Persia under Sapor II (d. 343).

St. Octavius (d. 286)

A discourse of St. Maximus refers to him as a soldier of the Theban legion who was martyred at Turin.

November 21st
ST. GELASIUS (d. 496)

OF African origin, Gelasius was pope from 492 to 496, at the time when Acacius, Peter Mongus, and their friends had just dragged the Oriental Church into schism. This caused the pontiff to defend all the more actively the prerogatives of the Roman see. Of his literary work only six treatises and about sixty letters have been preserved. These are about Oriental affairs and ecclesiastical discipline. As regards the treatises, three of them combat schism; two others set out the true Christological doctrine; and the last joins issue with Andromachus, a pagan senator, who was urging the re-establishment of licentious processions, called "lupercalia."

ST. COLUMBANUS (d. 615)

HE was one of the powerful personalities of his time; a man passionately devoted to Christ, moderately intelligent, heroic and obstinate, loving poetry and nature, a friend of animals. He remained faithful to the customs and love of his country.

Born in Ireland about 540, Columbanus had been trained at the monastery of Bangor by the austere and rigorous St. Comgall. He landed in France about 590, with twelve monks of Bangor. He had been invited by the king of Burgundy to spread the Gospel there in its strictest terms and to found monasteries on the Irish model. The first which he established were those of Annegray, Fontaine, and Luxeuil. Others were afterwards built at Coutances, Faremoutiers, Jouarre, St. Gall, and elsewhere. The rule which he imposed on them predominated in Gaul until it was replaced by that of St. Benedict. Columbanus sent his sick monks to winnow the wheat on the threshing floor; he wished the healthy to be exhausted before going to bed. "They should," he said, "sleep on their way there and rise before having slept enough."

The influence of Luxeuil at that epoch was considerable; from it came many holy bishops and great missionaries. Columbanus ruled there for a score of years. He attempted to impose piety and virtue on the Austrasian court; reproached the bishops for not celebrating the feast of Easter on the same date as in Ireland; wrote the pope vehement letters, while describing himself as "the most timid of men" and signing: "Columbanus the sinner." From his country he brought the custom of private confession which he succeeded in imposing on the Burgundian churches.

Although venerated by all, he shocked many. Queen Brunehaut and King Thierry, reproached by him for their debauches, finally, without incurring too much opposition, made him leave their lands in 610. Agilulfus, king of the Lombards, gave him the territory of Bobbio in Italy; it was there that Columbanus built his last monastery in 614 and died the following year.

St. ALBERT OF LOUVAIN

Son of Godfrey III, count of Louvain, had been elected bishop of Liége in 1191, but the Emperor Henry VI appointed to that see Lothaire of Bonn. Albert departed for Rome where the pope confirmed his election. Returning, he stopped at Rheims to be consecrated, and there it was that two months later some partisans of Lothaire of Bonn, come from Liége, assassinated him (d. 1192).

Sts. CELSUS and CLEMENT

Roman martyrs (period unknown).

The PRESENTATION OF THE BLESSED VIRGIN

Tradition has it that Mary, when still a child, was presented at the Temple at Jerusalem to live there wholly consecrated to God. Today's feast, which already existed in the East when it was extended to the Roman Church by Sixtus V in 1585, recalls this tradition.

November 22nd

ST. CECILIA (period unknown)

WE still may see in the cypress-wood coffin at Trastevere the beheaded body of St. Cecilia, wearing the robe of cloth of gold in which the virgin was dressed when she was taken to the catacombs. But the story of her martyrdom is full of doubtful details. We do not even know at what epoch she lived; some make her a contemporary of Marcus Aurelius, others a victim of the persecution of Diocletian or that of Julian the Apostate.

She was, it is said, a very cultivated young patrician whose ancestors were illustrious in Rome's history. Although she had vowed her virginity to God, her parents married her to Valerian, who lived at Trastevere. "*O dulcissime et amantissime juvenis*—O very sweet and very loving youth," said Cecilia to him after the wedding ceremony, "there is a mystery which I will confide to you if you swear to guard if faithfully." He swore to do so. She then revealed to him that an angel watched over her. "But in order to see him," she added, "you must first be purified."

On her advice Valerian went to find old Urban, who lived in hiding among the Christian tombs, and received baptism from him. On returning, he found Cecilia at prayer and an angel at her side. The latter, who held in his hand two crowns, placed one on Cecilia's brow, the other on Valerian's, and in addition he offered the latter to grant him a favour. All that Valerian asked was that the grace of baptism should also be given to his brother Tiburtius.

As the persecution became more rigorous, and the two brothers undertook to inter the faithful to whom the imperial police refused burial, they were arrested and decapitated. Cecilia was in her turn apprehended for having interred their bodies at her villa on the Appian Way. She was given no alternative but to sacrifice to the gods or to die. She chose death. To the prefect Almachius, who recalled to her that he had the power of life or death over her, she answered: "It is untrue; for if you can give death, you cannot give life." Almachius had condemned her to die by suffocation; but this torture not succeeding, he had her beheaded.

The *Acts* of St. Cecilia contain the following passage: "While the profane music of her wedding was heard, Cecilia was singing in her heart a hymn of love for Jesus, her true spouse." It is this phrase, read without due attention, which aroused belief in the musical talent of St. Cecilia, and has made her the patron saint of musicians.

Sts. PHILEMON and APPIA (1st century)

They lived at Colossus. It is on behalf of a fugitive slave whom St. Paul urged Philemon to take back, that he wrote to him the beautiful epistle which is a part of the New Testament.

St. CALMIN (beginning of the 8th century)

Stopping at Lérins on a pilgrimage to Rome, he there secured some monks to form the nucleus of the abbey of Moustier-Saint-Chaffre in Velais. He also founded the monastery of Mauzac in Auvergne.

Blessed TYGRIDE

Daughter of Sancho, count of Castile, a Spanish abbess honoured at Ogne, near Burgos (11th century).

November 23rd

ST. CLEMENT OF ROME (d. about 100)

ON the authority of St. Irenaeus, it is generally believed that Pope Clement was the third successor of St. Peter and that he occupied the see of Rome during the last ten years of the 1st century. According to some he was a Jew; according to others he was a freed slave or the son of a freed slave of the household of the consul, Clemens. One thing is sure: that he was well educated and that his literary training had been good. A tradition, going back to the beginning of the 4th century, says that his life ended in martyrdom.

Of all the writings which have been attributed to him, the only authentic one is his *Letter to the Corinthians*. It was addressed, about the year 96, to the Christian community at Corinth where troubles had broken out. In it the pope speaks as though in possession of a superior authority and charged with promoting peace throughout the whole Church. This letter ends with an admirable prayer:

"God of all flesh, who givest life and death, thou who castest down the insolence of the proud and turnest aside the scheming of men, be our help! Oh, Master, appease the hunger of the indigent; deliver the fallen among us. God, good and merciful, forget our sins, our wrongdoing and backsliding; take no account of the faults of thy servants. Give us concord and peace, as to all the inhabitants of the earth. It is from thee that our princes and those who govern us here below hold their power; grant them health, peace, concord, stability; direct their counsels in the way of goodness. Thou alone canst do all this and confer on us still greater benefits. We proclaim it by the high priest and master of our souls, Jesus Christ, by whom to thee be all glory and power, now and in endless ages."

St. FELICITAS

Roman martyr whose identity has been much discussed (2nd century?).

St. TROND or TRUDO (d. 693)

A native of the Liége country and disciple of St. Cloud, bishop of Metz, he founded a Benedictine monastery, cradle of the Belgian town which bears his name.

St. GOBERT

Is honoured in the diocese of Rheims (period uncertain).

Blessed JOHN THE GOOD

Founder of the Hermits of St. Augustine, was born and died at Mantua (1168-1249).

November 24th

STS. FLORA and MARIA OF CORDOVA (d. 851)

BORN at Cordova of a Mohammedan father and a Christian mother, Flora was baptized clandestinely and practised her religion in secret. When she became an orphan, her brother denounced her to the cadi, who had her arrested and soundly beaten. She was whipped till the blood ran, struck on the head, then given back to her denouncer for him to make her apostasize. She succeeded in escaping from his hands and sought refuge with her sister who was at Ossaria.

The Moors of the Cordova caliphate were then unloosed against the Christians, and those who hid them were exposed to the worst annoyances. Flora's sister and her household feared that some misfortune would befall them and advised the refugee to leave their home. The poor girl went back to Cordova; like a trapped animal she did not know which way to turn. She entered the Church of St. Acicle to weep. A girl like herself, named Maria, was praying there. A few days before, her brother, the deacon Valabonse, had been executed; she herself was wanted and perhaps on the eve of arrest. The two unfortunates, seeing no way out but death, decided to go to meet it and to face it courageously together. Presenting themselves to the cadi, they declared that they would never deny their faith. The cadi had them put in a dungeon in the midst of prostitutes. St. Eulogius, imprisoned near them, managed to send them words of encouragement. As they had hoped, they were not separated, and they suffered martyrdom together on November 24th, 851.

Six days later Eulogius left prison and, in *The Memorial of the Saints*, in telling the foregoing he attributes his deliverance to the intercession of St. Flora and St. Maria. It was only for a time, for a few years later Eulogius also shed his blood for the faith.

St. JUSTUS
Bishop of Jerusalem (2nd century).

St. MARIUS
Benedictine monk, who led the solitary life in Maurienne and was killed by the Saracens in 731.

St. JOHN OF THE CROSS
Doctor of the Church. Son of a poor weaver, John Yepes was born near Avila in 1542. Twice in his childhood the Blessed Virgin miraculously

saved him from drowning. Helped by Alvarez of Toledo, his benefactor, he received an excellent education with the Jesuits. He entered the Carmelites in 1563 and took his vows at Salamanca. He was thinking of becoming a Carthusian when he met St. Teresa and determined to work with her for the reform of Carmel. He was the saint's confessor and her friend. In 1577, the Carmelites, opposed to the reform, had him imprisoned at Toledo. It was in prison that he outlined *The Ascent of Mount Carmel*, *The Spiritual Canticle*, and *The Dark Night*, which have placed the great ecstatic in the front rank of Western mystical writers and of his country's poets. In 1580 the work of the reformer received the support of the Roman Curia, and John died in peace at Ubeda in 1591.

November 25th

ST. CATHERINE OF ALEXANDRIA (period uncertain)

Born of Costus, king of Cilicia, and Sabinella, Samaritan princess, Catherine was the most beautiful girl and the most learned person of her time. Having no more to learn in the schools and libraries of Alexandria, she left that city and at the age of seventeen years settled in Armenia. Soon she let it be known that she was ready to marry. "Only," she added, "I must have a husband who is as handsome and learned as I am." This last condition sufficed to discourage the numerous princes who were already thinking of asking for her hand.

The hermit Ananias came to tell her that he had found her the spouse she dreamed of. "Let him present himself," said Catherine. "He will present himself tomorrow night in your room," replied the hermit, "provided you first address this prayer to the Virgin. 'Our Lady, show me thy Son, I pray thee.'" Catherine prayed in this manner, and the Virgin appeared to her with the Infant Jesus. "Do you want him?" she said. "Oh, yes," said the girl, "I am not worthy to be his slave." "And thou," Mary continued, addressing Jesus, "dost thou wish it?" "Oh, no!" said the child, "she is too ugly." Immediately the sun had risen, Catherine ran to the hermit. "He found me too ugly," she said to him, weeping. "It is not the ugliness of your body but of your proud soul, of which he spoke," replied Ananias. He instructed her in Christianity, baptized her, and succeeded in making her humble; then Catherine prayed the Blessed Virgin to return. Mary came back with her son. "And now," she said to Him, indicating Catherine, "do you want her?" "Yes," replied Jesus, "for I find her perfectly beautiful." The

Virgin placed a golden ring on the finger of the humble fiancée and there took place what has been called since then "the mystical marriage of St. Catherine."

The following year, having achieved a great victory, Maximinus ordered that all the subjects of the Empire should offer a sacrifice to the gods. In her palace at Alexandria where she was living, Catherine learned that many of the Christians were apostasizing. She went to the emperor and showed him, by syllogisms and quoting the philosophers and poets, the falseness of paganism. Finding no answer to confound her, Maximinus assembled fifty of the most famous university professors. She it was who confounded them and converted them all to the last one. It was noticed that during this debate the archangel Michael stood at her side to comfort her. Maddened with rage, Maximinus had the fifty learned men burned alive. Two hundred soldiers, converted by their example, also suffered martyrdom, as well as the Empress Constance and the soldier Porphyrius who, having visited Catherine in her prison, had been persuaded to embrace the faith.

When the time came for Catherine to face torture, divers miracles again took place. One of the learned men was seen coming down from heaven to place a crown upon her forehead. Then a machine, invented for the occasion, was brought forward. It had four wheels, armed with points and saws, which turned in opposite directions. Into it was put the beautiful body of Catherine, and there came forth a bleeding mass which the angels received and carried up to Sinai.

Such is the legend of St. Catherine, as the middle ages have handed it down to us. Of her story, properly speaking, almost nothing is known. Devotion to her seems to have started at Mount Sinai; her feast was put on the calendar by John XXII about 1335. Philosophers and scholars on one hand; grinders, millers, wheelwrights, tanners, turners, and spinners, on the other hand, have taken her as patron; the first because of her reputation for learning, the others because of the four-wheeled machine of which we have spoken. Formerly there existed a custom of crowning her statue on November 25th; the privilege was reserved for maidens who alone, as the expression recalls, might "bonnet St. Catherine."

St. FINTAN (d. 878)
  Former slave, became a Benedictine monk at Rheinau (Switzerland).

St. BARBARY (period unknown)
  Abbot of Moutier-Roseille (Creuse).

St. JUCUNDA
  Was, it is said, the spiritual daughter of St. Prosper of Reggio (d. 466).

Blessed ELIZABETH THE GOOD (1386-1420)

Nun of the Franciscan third order, celebrated for the demoniac persecutions she endured. She lived and died at Reute near the Waldsee (Swabia).

November 26th
ST. DELPHINE (1283-1366)

DELPHINE of Glandèves, daughter of Sinna of Puy-Michel, had been betrothed at the age of twelve to Elzéar of Ariano, son of Hermengaud de Sabran. The marriage took place four years later and the pair settled in the castle of Ansois in Provence, where they lived for seven years. God had inspired them both to keep continence. Moreover, they loved each other tenderly, received their guests agreeably, and made none suffer for their virtues.

The time came when Elzéar had to exercise his rights of sovereignty over the county of Ariano in the kingdom of Naples. Delphine accompanied him and showed herself by her charm and goodness to be the perfect partner of her husband. She succeeded in conciliating several among the vassals who were partisans of the house of Aragon and were always in revolt against the French, and they became for a time loyal servants of the count of Ariano.

However, political conditions compelled Elzéar to return to Provence, and he again settled with his wife in the castle of Ansois. It was then that both joined the third order of St. Francis. From this time on, they led the existence of the truly religious. Clad in the Franciscan habit, they practised austerities, together recited the canonical hours of both day and night, received the poor and visited the lepers whom they tended with their own hands.

Widowed in 1323, Delphine, in spite of her love of retirement, had to appear again at the court of Robert, king of Naples, where she lived for twenty years. The monarch's death allowed Queen Saucia, his wife, to become a Poor Clare and Delphine to follow her to her convent. She stayed there for ten years, until Saucia's death, then went to spend the last thirteen years of her life at the castle of Ansois. Elzéar, who had been dead for more than half a century, had just been canonized. Delphine wished to rest at his side and, like him, was interred in the Franciscan church of Apt.

St. LEONARD OF PORT MAURICE

A celebrated Franciscan preacher, born on the Genoese coast in 1677, died at Rome in 1751. He spread the devotion of the Way of the Cross.

St. BASLE

Lived for forty years as a solitary in the neighbourhood of Rheims (d. 620).

St. VICTORINA

Martyr in Africa (period unknown).

St. PETER

Patriarch of Alexandria, put to death for his orthodoxy. A few frag, ments of his theological writings have come down to us (d. 310).

November 27th

ST. MAXIMUS OF RIEZ (d. 460)

A NATIVE of Decomeum, the present Château-Redon in Provence, Maximus became a monk at Lérins, and succeeded St. Honoratus, the founder, as abbot of the monastery.

At that time, when the Roman Empire of the West was falling into ruin, Lérins was unrivalled as a centre of the religious and intellectual life of Christendom. There flourished, in addition to Vincent and Salvianus, so famous for their writings, a number of persons whose renown later went far beyond the churches which they were called to rule: St. Eucherius, bishop of Lyons; his son St. Véran, bishop of Vence; St. Hilary, bishop of Arles; St. Lupus, bishop of Troyes; St. Valerius, bishop of Nice, and still others.

"Dear abbey, I love and will always honour you," wrote St. Eucherius from Lyons to the monk Hilary, his friend. "What angels I have seen there! The alabaster jar of the Gospels did not exhale a sweeter perfume. The light of the inner man lit up their faces. Humble, charitable, with gentle piety and serene gaze, these men journeyed towards that heaven which they already held in their heart. Work was joy for them, for in it they found God who would reward them . . . Honoratus, now bishop of Arles, in whom the majesty of the patriarchs reappeared, directed us. Now, it is Maximus, great by the very fact that he was judged worthy to succeed him, who is at your head. . . ."

Such Gallo-Roman churches as had lost their bishops often approached Lérins to find a successor. Thus it was that one day Maximus saw a delega, tion of Christians from Fréjus approaching the island. Their bishop had just died, and they wanted him as his successor. He fled into the forest and hid among the rocks for three days and that time escaped the episcopate.

Again in 433 deputies from Riez landed on Lérins in order to offer him the rule of their church. He jumped into a boat and vigorously rowed towards the coast of Provence. But he was overtaken, conducted to Riez, and had to give way to the wish of the Christians who demanded him as their shepherd.

He returned to die at Lérins, having edified all by his penitence and his charity for twenty-seven years. His presence has been noted at the Council of Orange in 441 and at that of Arles in 454.

St. ODA or ODETTE (d. 713)

This daughter of an Irish king heard of the miracles which were said to have been accomplished at the tomb of St. Lambert at Liége. Overtaken by blindness, she made a pilgrimage thither, obtained her cure, and passed the remainder of her life in Belgium. It is believed that she died near Brussels.

St. ACHAR

Former monk of Luxeuil; preceded St. Eligius in the bishopric of Noyon-Tournai (d. 640).

St. JAMES INTERCISSUS (d. 421)

His surname came from his having been hacked to pieces on the orders of Varanus V, king of Persia. He had first apostasized out of ambition; afterwards he repented and voluntarily exposed himself to martyrdom.

November 28th

ST. SOSTHENES (1st century)

SOSTHENES was at St. Paul's side when he wrote his first Epistle to the Corinthians. This letter, in fact, began thus: "Paul, whom the will of God has called to be an apostle of Jesus Christ, and Sosthenes, who is their brother, send greeting to the church of God at Corinth, to those who have been sanctified in Jesus Christ, and called to be holy; with all those who invoke the name of our Lord Jesus Christ, in every dependency of theirs, and so of ours. Grace and peace be yours from God, who is our Father, and from the Lord Jesus Christ" (I Cor. i, 1-3).

The name of Sosthenes recurs in the Acts of the Apostles after the sojourn of Paul at Corinth. Paul was living there with Aquila and Priscilla, tent-makers like himself. During the week he worked with them; on Sundays he went to preach in the synagogue. Sometimes his sermons made converts; at others they only succeeded in arousing anger and riots. Thus one day, weary of the blasphemies of his hearers, Paul shook the dust off his garments on them and cursed them, saying: "Your blood be upon your own heads, I am clear of it; I will go to the Gentiles henceforward." Another time the Jews seized him and dragged him to the tribunal of Gallio, proconsul of Achaia. "This fellow," they said, "is persuading men to worship God in a manner the law forbids." Paul wished to justify himself but Gallio stopped him, addressing himself to his accusers. "It would be only right," he said, "for me to listen to you Jews with patience, if we had here some wrong done, or some malicious contrivance; but the questions you raise are a matter of words and names, of the law which holds good among yourselves. You must see to it; I have no mind to try such cases." And he drove them away. It was then that, furious at seeing the preacher escape them, the Jews took Sosthenes, the ruler of the synagogue who had allowed him to preach, and beat him in the full tribunal. "But all this," adds St. Luke, "caused Gallio no concern" (Acts xviii, 1–17).

Is the Sosthenes in the Epistle to the Corinthians the same as he of whom the author of the Acts is speaking here? It seems that he was favourable to the apostle since he allowed him an opportunity to preach the Gospel and to attack the obdurate Jews in the synagogue over which he had charge. Was he already a Christian at that time? Or was it ill-treatment which brought him close to Him for whom he had endured it?

These are all questions which have not been answered. Neither do we know what to think of the tradition according to which Sosthenes died later, a bishop and a martyr, in Ionia.

St. Gregory III

He was pope from 731–741. He had made an appeal to Charles Martel against Liutprand, king of the Lombards who was threatening to occupy Rome.

St. James of the Marches (1389–1479)

Born in the Marches of Ancona, this celebrated Franciscan missionary travelled through Italy, Germany, Austria, Bohemia, Pomerania, Albania, and the Scandinavian countries, and died near Naples.

St. Stephen the Younger

A Greek monk, one of the leaders of the resistance to Constantine Copronymus, was massacred by the Iconoclasts in the streets of Constantinople about 764.

November 29th

ST. SATURNINUS or SERNIN (3rd century)

IT was formerly believed in France that St. Saturninus was a Greek, disciple successively of St. John the Baptist and of Our Lord, who had accompanied St. Peter to Rome, and going from thence into Gaul and Spain, there founded many churches.

Today he is placed in the 3rd century, with the same merits and miracles attributed to him. He came, it is said, from Rome and made his way among the Gauls by the Rhône Valley. At Arles he made innumerable conversions; at Nîmes, as many again, and notably that of a farmer, Honestus, on whom he conferred the priesthood and who from that time became, with St. Papoul, his companion. All three went towards Carcassonne, where they were imprisoned by the prefect Rufinus and delivered by an angel, and finally arrived safely at Toulouse. Saturninus there met St. Martial, bishop of Limoges, and together they cured of an incurable illness the daughter of the town's governor. Saturninus was also called to the house of the wife of the president of the Senate, whom he likewise restored to health. We omit the other miracles which he worked in great numbers both in Toulouse and Auch and in the neighbouring districts.

Invited to Spain, St. Saturninus crossed the Pyrenees with St. Honestus, having left the care of communities in Gaul to St. Papoul. In Navarre he baptized St. Firminus, the future bishop of Amiens, pushed on as far as Toledo and into Galicia; then, learning of the martyrdom of St. Papoul, he went back to Toulouse, after consecrating Honestus bishop of Pampeluna.

Wherever he appeared the devil suffered innumerable defeats. At the capitol of Toulouse the priests of the false gods found that they received no more oracles. They took counsel and said: "Our gods are silent, because they are angry that we tolerate the presence of their enemy Saturninus amongst us. Let him disappear and the tutelary deities will restore their favours to the city." Just at that moment the bishop was passing before the capitol. The priests pointed him out to the crowd, who wished to compel him to sacrifice; he refused, while the idols fell in pieces at his feet. Then the crowd tied him with a rope to a bull which was awaiting immolation; the animal fled wildly through the town; and so it was that, dragged over the cobbles, his head shattered and his body in shreds, Saturninus met his death.

St. Radbod (d. 917)

Grandson of the last king of the Frisons, he was brought up by his uncle Günther, bishop of Cologne, lived for some time at the court of Charles the Bald, then became bishop of Utrecht. The few writings of his which remain, attest his knowledge and his literary gifts.

St. Brendan of Birr, or the Younger

Of Irish origin, disciple of St. Finnian and friend of St. Columcille, founded the monastery of Birr and died there about 710.

The Blessed Denis of the Nativity, and Redemptus of the Cross, discalced Carmelites (d. 1638)

The first was a Frenchman named Berthelot, born at Honfleur in 1600; he had been a sailor since the age of twelve and bore the title of pilot-in-chief and cosmographer to the king of Portugal when he became a Carmelite at Goa in 1635. The second was a former Portuguese officer. The viceroy of the Indies obtained from their superiors permission for them to accompany an embassy sent by him to the king of Achin. They fell into an ambush laid for them by the Mussulmans of the Malay archipelago and, refusing to embrace the Koran, were tortured to death.

November 30th

ST. ANDREW (1st century)

Although a native of Bethsaida in Galilee, Andrew bore a Greek name which signifies "courageous." Like his father Jona and his brother Simon Peter, he was a fisherman by calling and he lived at Capharnaum on the lake of Tiberias. His first meeting with the Saviour took place at Bethany, where John was baptizing, and where, on that day, two disciples accompanied him: "Watching Jesus as he walked by, he said, Look, this is the Lamb of God. The two disciples heard him say it, and they followed Jesus. Turning, and seeing them follow him, Jesus asked, What would you have of me? Rabbi, they said (a word which means Master), where dost thou live? He said to them, Come and see; so they went and saw where he lived, and they stayed with him all the rest of the day, from about the tenth hour onwards. One of the two who had heard what John said, and followed him, was Andrew, the brother of Simon Peter. He first of all found his own brother Simon and told him, We have discovered the Messias (which means, the Christ), and brought him to Jesus" (John, i, 35-42).

Andrew and Peter none the less continued to pursue their habitual occupations until the day when Jesus, learning that John had been imprisoned, left Nazareth, came to live at Capharnaum, and began to preach. "Repent, he said, the kingdom of heaven is at hand. And as he walked by the sea of Galilee, Jesus saw two brethren, Simon who is called Peter, and his brother, Andrew, casting a net into the sea (for they were fishermen); and he said to them, Come and follow me; I will make you into fishers of men. And they dropped their nets immediately, and followed him" (Matt. iv, 17–20).

From then on, Andrew fades into the apostolic group and the Gospel does not mention him again except in passing. On the occasion of the feeding of the five thousand, Andrew said to Jesus: "There is a boy here, who has five barley loaves and two fishes; but what is that among so many?" (John vi, 8). On the eve of Jesus' triumphal entry into Jerusalem: "There were certain Gentiles . . . who approached Philip . . . and made a request of him; Sir, they said, we desire to see Jesus. Philip came and told Andrew, and together Andrew and Philip went and told Jesus" (John xii, 20–22). Andrew is, finally, cited among the apostles who asked the Saviour when the destruction of Jerusalem would take place and did not obtain from him the desired reply (Mark xiii, 3).

Tradition has it that Andrew carried the Gospel into the districts around the Black Sea and died at Patras in Achaia on a cross in the form of an X. This kind of cross always bears his name.

Fishermen and fishmongers have chosen St. Andrew as patron, and barren women invoke him in order to have children.

St. MAURA (period unknown)

Martyred at Constantinople, she gave her name to an island in the Ionian Sea. Julian the Apostate tried to destroy the devotion to her, very widespread in the East.

St. CONSTANTIUS

A Roman priest who suffered at the hand of the Pelagians. He died about 418.

THE SAINTS OF DECEMBER

December 1st

ST. ELIGIUS OR ELOI (d. 659)

NATIVE OF Limoges, Eligius there learned the craft of goldsmith which he later exercised in Paris. Bobo, the treasurer of Clotaire II, having ordered from him a royal throne, he managed to make two out of the gold given him, and this was the origin of his good fortune. Clotaire appointed him his own goldsmith and the master of his mint. Many coins signed by Eligius have come down to us, and we know that at one time he also minted coin in Marseilles.

Under Dagobert I, son and successor of Clotaire II, Eligius became one of the king's most influential counsellors. We are told that the envoys of foreign princes were interviewed by him before being officially received by the sovereign. He was a clever diplomat, and many times was able to prevent war. He reached such a point in his master's favour that he could advise him on his dress as well as on his private life which, it is known, left even more to be desired.

When this courtier was not in conference or at prayer, caring for the poor, redeeming prisoners, freeing slaves, he spent his time honouring with his art the relics of the saints. To him are attributed the shrines of St. Germain of Paris, St. Piat, St. Severinus, St. Martin, St. Columba, and St. Genevieve. He is also said to have decorated with goldsmith's work the tomb of St. Denis. Moreover, he founded monasteries, notably one near Solignac in Limousin, another dedicated to St. Martin at Noyon, and a third six miles from Arras on a hillside called Mount Saint-Eloi.

Eligius, who had been ordained priest by Deodatus, bishop of Le Mans, was consecrated bishop at Rouen on May 14th, 641, and thenceforth occupied the episcopal see of Noyon. Like many other prelates of the Merovingian era, he was a great organizer and zealous apostle, full of wisdom and goodness. His activity spread to Flanders and Holland and even, it is said, to Sweden and Denmark. Learning that he was at the point of death, the saintly Queen Bathilde came speedily from Chelles to see him once again, but she only arrived at Noyon the day after her friend's death.

St. Agericus

Bishop of Verdun (d. 588). He was given this name because his mother, a poor woman, gave birth to him in a field where she was working (*agricola*).

St. Florentinus (6th century)

This holy man who lived at Amboise, in Touraine, was the friend of St. Germain of Paris. This latter brought him one day to the court of Clotaire II, where Florentinus was the edification of everyone.

St. Nahum

One of the twelve minor prophets. He preached against Ninive and predicted its ruin.

St. Agnofleta or Nofleta (7th century)

Lived in Maine, where she was the friend of St. Longis, who gave her the veil and was somewhat maligned and persecuted on her account.

St. Simon of Cyrene

"As for his cross, they forced a man of Cyrene, Simon by name, whom they met on their way, to carry it" (Matt. xxvii, 32). "As for his cross, they forced a passer-by who was coming in from the country to carry it, one Simon of Cyrene, the father of Alexander and Rufus" (Mark xv, 21).

December 2nd

ST. BIBIANA OR VIVIAN (d. 363)

JULIAN the Apostate, Caesar in 355, Augustus in 360, sole master of the Empire from 361, died in battle against the Persians on June 26th, 363. He had denied his baptism and, during his brief reign, had attempted to annihilate Christianity by substituting for it a kind of pagan revival in which it is not certain that he himself believed. He restored liberty to all the Christian sects, hoping they would destroy each other; he made school laws likely to provoke the apostasy of Christian children; he reserved all civil and military jobs for pagans alone, ostracizing all those who were supposed to profess the Christian religion. Without going so far as to publish sanguinary edicts against the Christians, he made them so much disliked that it was often possible to torture them and to put them to death with impunity.

Thus it may be said that St. Bibiana was a victim of Julian the Apostate. In 362 her father Flavian, formerly prefect of Rome, had been branded on the forehead as a slave and sent to the Aquae Taurinae in Tuscany; there he died of privations. Her mother, Dafrosa, was beheaded. She herself, it is said, was handed over to a procuress who had been told to corrupt her. As she failed, the pretor Apronianus had her tied to a pillar, and executioners beat her with leaded cords until she succumbed.

St. CONSTANTINE

Lived as a hermit in the forest of Javron (Maine), after having been a monk at Micy, near Orléans (6th century).

Sts. AURELIA and PAULINA

Members of a group of Roman martyrs who perished under Valerian (3rd century).

St. SILVANUS

Bishop of Troas in Phrygia after having been a monk at Constantinople. He forbade his priests to act as members of a law court (d. after 450).

St. PONTIAN

Roman martyr, victim, with his companions, of Valerian's persecution (d. 259).

Blessed JOHN RUYSBROECK (1295-1381)

Born near Brussels, he was for twenty-six years chaplain of St. Gudula in that city; then retired to Groenendael, in the forest of Soignes, where he founded and directed a community of canons regular of St. Augustine. Author of *The Spiritual Espousals, The Mirror of Salvation, The Seven Cloisters, The Kingdom of Loving Souls*, etc., Ruysbroeck the Admirable is one of the greatest mystical writers of the West, and his influence still endures.

December 3rd

ST. FRANCIS XAVIER (1506-1552)

PROFESSOR of philosophy at the University of Paris, Francis Xavier met Ignatius Loyola there and joined the nascent Society of Jesus. On August 15th, 1534, in the church of Montmartre, Ignatius and his companions vowed to leave at the end of a year for the Holy Land. But the war between the Venetians and the Turks prevented this, and the pope detailed them to other tasks. For his part, Francis Xavier exercised his zeal for some time at Padua, Bologna, and Rome. Then he went to Portugal, embarked for India with two colleagues, and arrived at Goa on May 6th, 1542.

His missionary activity lasted ten years, during which he covered immense distances, accomplished all sorts of miracles, founded churches and colleges, and achieved apostolic successes which have become a legend. His biographers relate that he baptized not less than forty thousand Palawars; that in the kingdom of Travancore, as later in Japan, he was granted the gift of tongues; that he raised several people from the dead, calmed tempests, often foretold the future, and healed countless persons. It has even been said that he converted a million souls. The history of the missions surely has few pages so glorious.

In 1549, Francis Xavier arrived in Japan, where his travels were no less fecund than in India; he stayed there twenty-eight months, after which he returned to Goa and, on April 14th, 1552, he embarked for China. His dream of evangelizing that country was never realized; the apostle fell ill on the island of Sancian, within sight of Canton. He would have died abandoned on the shore had not a poor man, named George Alvarez, rescued him and carried him to his hut. There he drew his last breath, December 2nd, 1552.

St. ANTHEMIUS

Bishop of Poitiers, apostle of the Saintonge, accompanied Charlemagne to Spain and was killed by the Saracens (8th century).

Blessed BERNARD OF TOULOUSE (d. 1320)

A Dominican and a victim of the Albigensians, who sawed his body in half.

St. LUCY THE CHASTE (d. 1420)

A Dominican tertiary of French origin, she died in Spain whither she had followed St. Vincent Ferrer.

St. VERANUS (5th century)

His brothers are supposed to have been Sts. Gibrian, Helan, Tressan, Abran, Petran, and Germain, and his sisters Sts. Promptia, Franca, and Possenna, honoured on May 8th. Coming from Ireland, their native land, they all arrived at Rheims, wishing to lead the eremitic life in France. St. Remigius designated solitary places for them on the banks of the Marne and, under the direction of Gibrian, they practised sanctity until their deaths.

St. MIROCLES

Bishop of Milan, whose life and writings have been praised by Ennodius and St. Ambrose (d. about 318).

Sts. CLAUDIUS and HILARIA, his wife, Sts. JASON and MAURUS, their sons

Put to death for the faith at Rome under Numerian in 283.

December 4th

ST. BARBARA (d. about 235)

THE *Acts* of St. Barbara are of a doubtful era and little worthy of credence. It would seem that her martyrdom took place at Nicomedia, under Maxi-minus of Thrace, whose persecution only lasted three years but was in certain places extremely cruel. This former prize-fighter, built like Hercules, who drank an amphora of wine a day and amused himself by breaking horses' jawbones with one blow of his fist, had Alexander Severus, his predecessor, assassinated; he persecuted the Christians, Eusebius tells us, for the sole reason that Alexander had left them in peace; and he was completely indifferent to the fact that his orders were executed with the most barbarous refinements.

The romantic author of the *Acts* tells us that Barbara was placed by her father Dioscorus in a palace topped with a high tower and surrounded by marvellous gardens. There she received philosophers, orators, and poets, appointed to teach her the secrets of all things. The only result of their lessons was to make her see the absurdity of polytheism. Origen, whom she consulted, sent her his disciple Valentinian, who taught her the mysteries of Christianity and secretly baptized her. Barbara then resolved to remain a virgin and to dedicate herself entirely to God. She threw out of the window the statues of the false gods which filled her palace, traced the sign of the cross over almost all the walls, and to the two openings which were pierced in the high tower she added a third in honour of the Blessed Trinity.

For Dioscorus these were all horrible sacrileges, worthy of death. He drew his sword to strike the blasphemer, but she fled to the mountains. He caught up with her and dragged her home by her hair; then he handed her over to the prefect Marcian, to whom Maximinus had confided the suppression of Christianity in that neighbourhood. On Marcian's orders, Barbara was beaten with rods, torn with iron hooks, and suffered other torments; then, since an end had to be made, her father asked for the honour of dispatching her. Dioscorus led his daughter out of town and cut off her head with a blow from an axe.

St. Osmund

A companion of William the Conqueror, was created count of Dorset; became chancellor of England; was consecrated bishop of Salisbury in 1078, where he died in 1099.

St. Meletius

Bishop in Pontus, not far from the Red Sea (died end of the 4th century).

St. Cyran

Lived as a hermit in the forests of Brenne (7th century).

Blessed Francis Galvez, Spanish friar minor, Jerome de Angelis, Sicilian Jesuit, and Simon Yempo, Japanese Jesuit

Martyred in Japan in 1623.

St. Peter Chrysologus

Doctor of the Church, bishop of Ravenna from 433 until his death. There remain to us more than two hundred discourses by this eloquent orator. They were published in the 8th century, and it was then that their author was dubbed *Chrysologus*, or "the man of golden speech."

December 5th

ST. SABBAS (439-532)

SABBAS, from Metalala in Cappadocia, became at twenty years of age the disciple of St. Euthymius in the Judaean wilderness. For ten years Euthymius followed his spiritual progress in the cenobitic life, then allowed him to lead that of an anchorite. Thenceforth Sabbas lived in a cave, devoting himself to prayer and to manual labour. He made ten baskets a day, which he brought each Saturday to the monastery; he spent Sunday with his brothers, and in the evening went back to his cave with his ration of food and willow wands for the week.

On the death of Euthymius, he himself became the leader, and many solitaries placed themselves under his guidance. Up to one hundred and fifty of these anchorites settled in the gorges formed by the Cedron flowing from Silo towards the Dead Sea; later there were a thousand. The patriarch of Jerusalem gave them Sabbas as superior, and at the same time appointed St. Theodosius to rule the cenobites.

Troubles broke out one day in Sabbas' cell-community. Some reproached him with his ignorance, others with his excessive severity. Sixty or so of the anchorites informed the patriarch of Jerusalem that Sabbas had been devoured by a lion and should be replaced. The truth was that, weary of their opposition, Sabbas had taken refuge in Transjordania where a lion, it seems, had first disputed, then ceded, his den to him. He reappeared at Jerusalem at the very moment he was reported dead, and this, coupled with the patriarch's firmness, restored order completely.

On several occasions Sabbas intervened with the emperors of the East for the public good and the liberty of the Church. Under Anastasius I, ten thousand monks rose at his request to intervene in favour of the persecuted Palestinian bishops. He was seen again at Constantinople, aged ninety, having come to plead for Justinian's clemency towards the revolting Samaritans, and he succeeded in obtaining their pardon.

St. NICETIUS

Bishop of Trier (d. about 506).

St. APER or AVRE (7th century)

It is said that he was first pastor of La Terrasse, in the diocese of Grenoble; then, weary of the calumnies which the people of that country heaped upon him, he left them to lead a hermit's life in the mountains of

La Chambre, in the diocese of Saint-Jean-de-Maurienne. His name means wild boar (*aper*); and he had a disciple called Aprunculus (little wild boar).

St. BASILISSA

Benedictine abbess of Horren near Trier (d. 780).

December 6th
ST. NICHOLAS (d. 324)

FEW saints enjoy such great popularity and few are credited with so many miracles. Sts. John Chrysostom, Peter Damian, and Bonaventure have vied in eloquence with one another in telling of the merits and the goodness of St. Nicholas. Born at Patara in Lycia, he visited the Thebaid, ruled a great monastery, was imprisoned for a time for his faith, and ended his life as archbishop of Myra.

It is doubtless the story of his restoring life to the children put in the salting tub which caused him to become the patron and the annual benefactor of school children. St. Bonaventure tells the story in a sermon. St. Nicholas was, it seems, on his way to the Council of Nicaea, when he entered an inn whose owner, not content with having killed two young boys for the sake of their meagre purse, had cut them up and was about to sell them piecemeal to his clients. The bishop restored them to life and then converted this murderer.

Another famous tale is that of the three marriageable girls who did not succeed in getting married. Poor and not knowing what to do with them, their father was about to put them into a house of ill fame. Nicholas took advantage of the fact that this odious man slept with his window open, to go one night and throw a purse filled with gold into his room. A few days later, the eldest daughter was married. In the same way, Nicholas delivered to the second the dowry she needed. Soon she, too, found a husband. The saint was discovered at the moment when he was throwing up from the street the purse destined for the third. The father, who had been hiding in the shadow, recognized him; he fell at his feet, weeping in penitence and gratitude, and from then on did not cease to sing his praises everywhere.

St. ASELLA (d. about 406)

St. Jerome relates that this little Roman girl lived from the age of twelve in a cell from which she only emerged to visit churches and the tombs of the martyrs.

Sts. MAJORICUS, DIONYSIA, and AEMILIANUS

Suffered for the faith in Africa, under Huneric, the king of the Vandals. Dionysia, a lady of the nobility, was ignominiously whipped on the public square. Majoricus was her son; he had at first trembled a little at the sight of the instruments of torture, but thanks to his mother's encouragement he died with courage. Aemilianus was a doctor who refused to become an Arian and was for that reason put to death.

St. PETER PASCHAL (1227–1300)

A canon of Valencia and doctor of the University of Paris, he entered the Order of Mercy in 1250 and became tutor to Don Sancho, son of the king of Aragon, in 1253. Nominated bishop of Jaén in 1289, he was taken prisoner in an ambuscade in 1297 and led captive to Granada, where King Mouley Mohammed had his head cut off.

December 7th
ST. AMBROSE (d. 397)

AMBROSE resided at Milan as governor of Aemilia and Liguria when, in 374, the Christians of that city joined together to elect a successor to Bishop Auxentius who had recently died. The assembly, composed of both Catholics and Arians, was tumultuous and divided. Ambrose spoke in an effort to calm the crowd and obtain a decent election. Suddenly a child's voice called out: "Ambrose, bishop." That cry cleared the air and brought unity. He whom the child had named was unanimously elected; this choice was ratified by the neighbouring bishops and by the emperor. The high Roman functionary thus elected, who was only a catechumen, immediately received baptism, and a few days later, episcopal ordination.

It is believed that Ambrose was born at Trier about 333. His father had been prefect of the Gauls; his sister Marcellina had been leading the cloistered life since 353; after serious juridical and literary studies, he himself had for some time been a lawyer. After becoming a bishop, he studied exegesis in Origen and theology in the Greek Fathers.

His admirable intelligence, his goodness, his noble bearing, his gift of oratory, and his political genius served admirably in the post in which Providence, in that decisive hour, had placed him. He won the confidence of the Emperors Gratian, Valentinian II, and Theodosius, who made Milan their residence. If Ambrose did not actually govern the Empire, at least one can say that he dictated to the emperors their conduct in ecclesiastical affairs. He drew up the statute which for long centuries regulated the relations of Church and State, notably emphasizing the following principles: the Church is independent of the State in its teaching, its hierarchy, and its representatives; it is the Church which is the guardian of morals; the Church has a right to the protection of the State, which must refuse its favours to other cults. Scriptural and dogmatic works, moral and ascetical treatises, ninety-one letters, and hymns such as *Aeterne Rerum Conditor* and *Veni Redemptor Omnium*, which are still in use in the Roman liturgy, have come down to us from St. Ambrose.

St. MARIA JOSEPHA ROSELLO

Franciscan tertiary, founded the congregation of Daughters of Our Lady of Mercy, devoted to the education of youth and the care of the sick; she died at Savona (Italy) in 1880 at the age of sixty-nine years.

St. GERARD

Reformed the abbey of Joigny, founded Benedictine monasteries in several French provinces, and ended his days as a simple monk at La-Charité-sur-Loire (11th century).

December 8th

THE IMMACULATE CONCEPTION OF THE VIRGIN MARY

THE dogma of the Immaculate Conception teaches that Mary was conceived without original sin and thus exempted from the consequences of the fault of our first parents, in virtue of the merits of Jesus Christ. Since, according to Bossuet, Our Lord had decided to become man He took upon Himself all the feelings of a man: in that case, could He "forget those of a son which are the most natural and the most human," and let His own mother share the fallen state of all the other posterity of Adam?

In the 12th century this doctrine was formally affirmed by the Eastern Church, which had long celebrated a liturgical feast in honour of the "Conception of the Virgin." In the 10th century, when this feast began to be adopted in the West, questions arose regarding its doctrinal significance. Great doctors like St. Bernard, St. Bonaventure, and St. Thomas Aquinas refused to admit that Mary had been conceived without sin. The first to

teach the doctrine of the Immaculate Conception were Eadmer of Canterbury and Osbert of Clare; it was Duns Scotus to whom its triumph in the
schools is due. The Sorbonne rallied to its support and remained constant to
it. In 1482, Sixtus IV forbade the partisans of the contrary opinion to censure
their adversaries; Gregory XV in 1622 and Alexander VII in 1661 forbade
that this contrary opinion be taught; in 1854, Pius IX proclaimed *ex cathedra*
that the Immaculate Conception was an article of faith.

St. Eucharius

Those who say he was the first bishop of Trier place his existence in the
1st century of our era.

St. Gunthildis

She was one of those English nuns who came to help St. Boniface
evangelize Germany. She became abbess of a convent in Thuringia
about 748.

St. Romaric (d. 653)

He was a great lord of Austrasia who had been married and who was
much tried by political and military vicissitudes. We have seen (*see
September 13th*) how, after becoming a monk at Luxeuil, he left that
monastery to found two houses at Remiremont (*Romarici mons*), a convent
and a monastery. Romaric directed them and several members of his
family embraced the religious life there, namely his two daughters, Azel-
truda and Zeberga, his granddaughter Gebetruda, and his grandson,
Adelphus.

December 9th
ST. LEOCADIA (d. about 303)

ONE of the most popular of Spanish saints, she was living at Toledo when
a functionary of Diocletian, named Dacian, arrived in town with orders to
ensure the execution of the edicts issued against the Christians. Leocadia had
to appear before Dacian, who required that she should abjure her faith. As
she refused, he had her publicly beaten as a slave, then thrown half dead into
a dungeon to await further tortures. There she learned of the ignominious
torments which at that very moment the little Eulalia, a child of thirteen, was
enduring at the hands of the same persecutors at Mérida. She prayed God to
let her leave a world where such horrors were committed, and her prayer was
granted, for she soon died in prison.

BLESSED CLARA ISABELLA FORNARI (1697-1744)

BORN in Rome on June 25th, 1697, Anna Felicia Fornari entered at fifteen the novitiate of the Poor Clares of Todi; under the name Clara Isabella she made her profession the following year. From that time her life was a sequence of the strangest phenomena. These, related in her process of beatification, were sworn to by her fellow nuns, her confessor, and her doctor.

Her ecstasies were long and frequent; frequent also were the visits she received from Our Lord, Our Lady, St. Clare, and St. Catherine of Siena. During one of these, Jesus placed on her finger the ring which symbolized their spiritual marriage. He liked to call her His "spouse of sorrow."

Clara Isabella indeed had her share, a large one, in the sufferings of the Crucified Saviour. Her hands, her feet, and her side were marked with visible stigmata which sometimes bled. Her head bore a crown whose thorns grew inwardly until they came out on her forehead, broke loose, and fell out bleeding.

The trials and persecutions of the devil which she endured recall those that the Curé d'Ars had to support a hundred years later. From the beginning of her novitiate the devil tried to drive her to despair and to suicide; later he rained blows upon her, threw her down stairs, attempted to take away her faith. During the last months of her life she appeared abandoned by God, having lost even the memory of past consolations. She found joy again only a little while before her death.

St. BALDA

Third abbess of Jouarre (7th century).

St. VALERIA

Is supposed to have been a spiritual daughter of St. Martial and to have been martyred in Limoges.

St. CYPRIAN

A hermit who flourished in Périgord in the 6th century.

St. PETER FOURIER (1565-1640)

Pastor of Mattaincourt (Vosges), founder of the Daughters of Our Lady.

Sts. PHILOTHEUS and LOLLIAN and five other Christians

Crucified out of hatred for the faith in 297, before the town ot Samosata.

December 10th

ST. EULALIA (d. 303)

THOSE who distinguish between St. Eulalia of Mérida and St. Eulalia of Barcelona (*see February 12th*) and wish to write a biography of her, must seek its elements in a hymn Prudentius wrote in her honour. Never, cried this poet, was a human creature endowed with more grace and fascination. Yet, "in spite of the twelve winters and the thirteen springs she had spent on earth, she had not become less of a stranger here below. One might not speak to her of espousals nor of the marriage bed; her body belonged to Christ. The games of her age had no charm for her; the weakening delights, the sweet smell of roses, the brilliant jewelry of women, she was horrified by them all. Her reserve compelled the same respect as the white hair of the aged."

As soon as Diocletian's edict of persecution reached Spain, Eulalia showed a wish to be a martyr. Her parents then moved her thirty miles out of Mérida to a castle whose key they confided to the priest Felix. Reinforced by a troop of slaves, Felix was told not to let her out of his sight. A lady-in-waiting, called Julia, completed the watch. During this time, the prefect Calpurnian was putting to death at Mérida all the Christians who refused to burn incense or pig's liver before the idols. Meanwhile Eulalia had won Julia over to her plan: together they hurried to present themselves to the prefect Calpurnian. Eulalia reproached him with his cruelty and even spat in his face. Julia was the first to endure martyrdom. That of Eulalia, as Prudentius describes it, was of interminable length and marked by many miracles. The little girl endured all the tortures imaginable as though they were a game. At the moment when she was thrown on to a pyre, she was seen to breathe in the flames and to swallow them avidly, in order to reach God's presence more quickly.

This martyr's legend became as popular in Gaul as in Spain. In Wallonia in the 9th century *The Cantilène of St. Eulalia* was sung, and these verses are still the most ancient example we have of Romanesque poetry.

OUR LADY OF LORETO

The translation of Our Lady's house from Nazareth to Loreto.

St. VALERIA

Roman martyr, whose cult was already in favour in Paris in the time of St. Elegius.

St. Guitmarus

Fourth abbot of St. Riquier in Normandy (d. around 750).

St. Miltiades (d. 314)

Pope. St. Augustine said of him that he was a great son of peace and a true father to Christians.

December 11th
ST. DAMASUS (d. 384)

St. Damasus occupied the see of Rome from 366 to 384. His father, of Spanish origin, had embraced the ecclesiastical state and exercised his priestly functions in the Roman basilica of St. Lawrence. Before his election to the pontificate, Damasus was the collaborator of Pope Liberius and when Liberius was exiled, that of Felix II. At the same time he directed a community of women dedicated to God on the Aventine hill. His pontificate was disturbed by the onslaughts of Arians and by the schisms which broke out at Antioch, Constantinople, Sardinia, and Rome. The Roman schismatics had as their chief the anti-Pope Ursicinus, whose life and reign lasted as long as that of Damasus himself.

There remain to us some ten of St. Damasus' synodal letters relative to doctrinal or personal questions, as well as twenty-four "anathematizations" against the heresies of the time. He was a benefactor of the learned, notably of St. Jerome, whose scriptural works he patronized. He himself composed some metrical inscriptions for the catacombs and poems in honour of the martyrs. He would have liked to repose among their tombs. "I avow," he wrote, "I would ardently have desired this honour, but I fear to profane the august places where sleep the saints."

St. Daniel the Stylite (409–493)

Born at Maratha in Mesopotamia, he entered a monastery at the age of twelve and lived there until he was thirty-eight. During a voyage he made with his abbot to Antioch, he passed by Tellnesin and received the benediction and encouragement of Simeon Stylites. Then he visited the holy places, stayed in various convents, retired in 451 into the ruins of a pagan temple; then, in 460, he established himself near Constantinople on a pillar to begin his stylitic life. This column, surmounted by a wooden balustrade, was about twelve feet high. Daniel was ordained priest upon it, and there passed thirty-three years, without ever sitting or lying down, absorbed in prayer and often in ecstasy. He had many disciples, for whom a monastery was built close by. Daniel sometimes came down from his column to bring his help to those who fought the Arians. People came from far-off places to see him and to be edified at the sight of his penances and by hearing his discourse. The Emperors Leo the Thracian, Zeno the Isaurian, and Anastasius, as well as the Empress Eudocia, held him in veneration and often were governed by his counsel.

December 12th

ST. CORENTINUS (6th century)

ST. CORENTINUS is thought to have been the first bishop of Quimper. Was he one of those British emigrants who, in the 5th and 6th centuries, fled before the Saxon invaders and came to seek refuge in Brittany? His biographers' accounts have so stated, but they do not merit great credence. What can, however, be gathered from them is that this saint was always held in great veneration among the Bretons, that he accomplished numerous miracles in their favour, and that he was among those who developed the Christian faith in their country.

His two principal biographers are two 17th-century monks. One, Albert Le Grand, was a Dominican of Morlaix; the other, the Venerable Julien Maunoir, was a Jesuit missionary who wrote in Latin verse. The latter grew lyrical over the soil of Brittany which St. Corentinus evangelized and over the Armorican language which he used in his sermons: "It is this venerable tongue which served you as your medium, O great apostle, to implant the faith in Cornouaille. Never in the succeeding thirteen centuries has any infidelity soiled the language in which you preached Jesus Christ; and he who can find a Breton teaching anything other than the Catholic religion is still to be born. . . . In your bishopric, beyond Cape Sizun, there is an island called the Sein, where no poisonous beast can live; it is an image of this blessed earth watered with your sweat, which never produced the least poison contrary to the sentiments of our holy mother Church."

For his part, Albert Le Grand relates a fine miracle with which St. Corentinus was favoured during his life as a hermit. "For his nourishment and sustenance God caused a continuing miracle, for, although he was content with some pieces of coarse bread begged in the villages and with a few wild herbs and roots that the earth produced of herself, God sent a fish to his fountain, which each morning offered itself to the saint, who caught it and cut off a piece for his pittance, then threw it back into the water, and in that instant the fish found itself whole again, without wound or scar, and never failed the following mornings to present itself to St. Corentinus, who always did the same thing."

St. COLUMBA

Abbot of Terryglass in Ireland (d. 548).

Blessed CONRAD OF OFFIDA

A Franciscan, died at Bastia in 1306. He had at first given up his studies in order to become the cook in a convent. But soon his superiors obliged him to devote himself to preaching, at which he was very successful.

Blessed CALLISTUS (d. 1124)

A near relative of the German emperor, cousin of the king of England, uncle of the queen of France, Guido of Burgundy had been archbishop of Vienne in Dauphiny for more than thirty years when, in 1119, he became pope under the name of Callistus II. He put an end to the Conflict of the Investitures and presided over the first Lateran Council.

December 13th
ST. LUCY (d. 303?)

ST. LUCY, patroness of Syracuse, is supposed to have suffered martyrdom in that city during Diocletian's persecution. Certain painters show her in the company of Sts. Thecla, Barbara, Agatha, Agnes, and Catherine. Like these, Lucy had vowed her virginity to God. She was clever enough to put off for three years the nobleman who wished to marry her. Other painters have represented her as kneeling before a tomb or yoked to a pair of oxen, sometimes also with her neck pierced by a dagger. These pictures recall episodes in her biography, true or legendary. It is said that, to avenge himself for being refused, her suitor denounced her as a Christian as she was on her way back from praying for the conversion of her mother at the tomb of St. Agnes. Upon her refusal to apostasize, she was condemned to a house of ill fame. But it proved impossible to make her leave the tribunal; an invincible force kept her rooted to the spot. Even a yoke of oxen was unable to drag her thence. To get rid of her it was necessary to light a pyre in the pretorium and, as she remained alive in the midst of the flames, for an executioner to pierce her throat with his dagger.

ST. ODILIA or OTTILIA (8th century)

ADALRIC, her father, was duke of Alsace; Beresinde, her mother, was the niece of St. Leodegar, bishop of Autun. They had hoped for a son to perpetuate their line; a daughter was born, and as the height of misfortune, a blind daughter. Considering himself disgraced, Adalric wanted to do away with her. Beresinde saved her by confiding her to a former wet nurse who lived at Scherwiller, two leagues from Selestat. This latter took her with her to the Burgundian abbey of Baume-les-Dames, where, aged twelve, Odilia received baptism and at the same instant recovered her sight.

A few years later, Odilia returned to Obernheim, in Alsace, to her parents. Her father received her with kindness but was determined to marry her to one of his friends, a German duke. Odilia, who did not wish for this marriage to take place, fled disguised as a beggar. She only returned to her parents' home when she was assured of permission to follow her vocation to be a nun. Adalric then gave her a fine castle which he possessed on the mountain of Hohenburg. She transformed it into a great convent, where soon a hundred and thirty devout girls sang the divine praises. Then she built, at the foot of the mountain, a hospital for the poor and a lazaret. Long did Odilia rule these two houses; her name became popular in Alsace-Lorraine and in the Baden country; she died stretched out on a bearskin, urging her daughters to serve God and to love the poor.

St. JODOCUS

A king in Brittany who became a priest after his abdication (d. about 668).

Blessed BARTHOLOMEW (d. 1300)

A Franciscan tertiary and a priest, who died a leper after twenty years of severe suffering. He has been nicknamed "the Job of Tuscany."

St. AUBERT

Was named bishop of Arras and Camorai in 603. He founded several monasteries in Flanders and Hainaut (d. about 669).

St. ROSE ELIZABETH

Formerly a nun at Chelles, was authorized to become a hermit, and lived for a long time in a hollow oak (d. about 1130).

December 14th

ST. FORTUNATUS (d. about 600)

VENANTIUS FORTUNATUS lived for a long time as a troubadour, travelling widely, eating at the best tables, making rhymes in honour of the princes and prelates who gave him hospitality. Born about 530 at Duplavilis, near Treviso, he studied grammar, law, and rhetoric at Ravenna. Cured of an eye ailment by the intercession of St. Martin, he wished to make a pilgrimage of thanksgiving to the tomb of his benefactor. He set off about 565 and, taking the longest way, first went to sing his songs in Germany where, he admits, they were but half appreciated. He was better liked at the Austrasian court, which received him at Metz in 566; the mythological epithalamium which he composed there for the marriage of Sigebert and Brunehaut greatly enhanced his reputation and was the beginning of his career as official court poet of the Merovingians.

After visiting the tomb of St. Martin at Tours, Fortunatus went on to venerate that of St. Hilary at Poitiers. It was there that the friendship of the queen St. Radegunde and the abbess St. Agnes brought him to a standstill in his travels. He became a priest and passed the remainder of his life near their monastery. In his spare time he sent them verses and tiny offerings; on special occasions he addressed pieces to the great men at court and to the bishops; he lavished eulogies upon the kings and queens who ordered poems from him; sometimes his muse and St. Radegunde inspired him to write admirable poems as, for example, when he deplored the assassination of Galeswintha by Chilperic or the destruction of the kingdom of Thuringia by Clotaire and Thierry, or again, when a relic of the True Cross arrived at Poitiers, sent by the Empress Sophia from Constantinople. It was on this occasion that he composed the *Vexilla Regis* and the *Pange Lingua*. Among the ten thousand other verses of his which have come down to us are 2245 hexameters in honour of St. Martin, turned out in two months at the request of Gregory of Tours. Moreover, he wrote the lives of four saints, among which is that of St. Radegunde.

Venantius Fortunatus had been ordained priest after his arrival at Poitiers and, in 597, three or four years before his death, he became bishop of that town.

St. Agnellus

Abbot of Abitini, in the country of Naples (d. 596).

St. VIATOR

Said to have been a disciple of the apostles, who became bishop of Bergamo (d. 78?).

St. SPIRIDION (270–344)

His legend shows him as holy from his youth, even when he was still only a little shepherd boy. His wife and his daughter having taken the veil he became a monk at Mount Carmel, and later became bishop of Tremithus (Cyprus). During the persecution of Galerius, his right eye was pulled out, the calf of his left leg was amputated; then he was sent to work in the Spanish mines. The Edict of Milan allowed him to occupy his see once more. Among the miracles attributed to him, we will cite two which are of a didactic nature. One day he ordered a gold ingot to take on again its original shape, and the ingot was changed into a serpent. Another time he silenced a deacon who was reading the Gospels in a worldly and affected manner; the deacon suddenly became a stammerer and remained one always, and the desire to call people's attention to his diction left him for good and all.

December 15th

ST. NINA or CHRISTIANA (4th century)

THE Georgians regard her as the woman who was the instrument of their conversion. She was a slave who lived in Georgia at the beginning of the 4th century. Had she been led captive into this land by victorious soldiers? Or had she voluntarily sought refuge from the persecution waged in her country? The fact is that it was not certain whence she came, and she was only known by the name of Christina or Nina (*cristiana*). She was humble and charitable and made herself loved.

When a child fell ill in that district, its mother would carry it from one neighbour's house to another to consult them on the best remedies to administer. A poor woman came one day bringing to Nina her dying child. "I can do nothing for him," said Nina, "but Almighty God, if He wishes, can restore his health." She laid the unconscious child on her mat, covered him with her hair-shirt, prayed to God in Christ's name, and gave back the child, cured, to his mother.

The fame of this miracle came to the ears of the queen of Georgia, who was dying of a rare disease. She ordered Nina to her bedside. "My place is not in a palace," replied the young woman, whose innocence had already survived many dangers. The queen went to seek out the slave and recovered her health. She wanted afterwards, as did King Mirian, to reward her with rich presents, but Nina refused them, saying: "The only thing which could make me happy would be to see you and the king embrace the Christian religion." Mirian took a long time to make this decision, but one day, faced by mortal danger while hunting wild animals, he promised that if he escaped, he would become a Christian. It is a known fact that about the year 325 he requested the Emperor Constantine to send him missionaries to evangelize his country.

St. Urbicius

Was born at Bordeaux and died as a hermit near Huesca in Aragon, about 805.

St. Silvia or Silviana of Constantinople

Made great efforts to defend the true faith against heretics. Some consider her to have been the most learned woman of her day (d. about 420).

St. John Discalceat (1280–1349)

His surname (*discalceatus*) was given him from his going barefoot when he was pastor of Saint-Grégoire in the diocese of Rennes. He had formerly been a mason. In 1316 he became a Franciscan in the monastery at Quimper, and in 1349 died of the plague at St. John in Quimper (Brittany).

December 16th

ST. ADELAIDE (931–999)

"This woman was a marvel of grace and beauty," wrote Odilo of Cluny, who was her spiritual director and biographer.

A daughter of Rudolf II, king of Burgundy, Adelaide married at the age of fifteen Lothaire II, king of Italy. There was born to them a daughter named Emma, who became queen of France. Adelaide was eighteen when Lothaire II died, poisoned, it is believed, by Berengarius II, his rival. Soon, the latter proclaimed himself king of Italy and offered his son's hand to his victim's widow. As Adelaide refused, Berengarius despoiled her of her estates and held her prisoner in the château of Garda. There, says Luitprand, she suffered a thousand outrages, was cuffed and kicked, without, however, making her change her views. She succeeded in escaping and in reaching the castle of Canossa, which was church property. From this impregnable fortress she appealed to Otto I, king of Germany, who came at the head of his army. He donned at Pavia the crown of Italy, while awaiting consecration as emperor at Rome. Meanwhile he had married Adelaide.

Their son, Otto II, succeeded his father in 973 and then turned against his mother. Fearing for her life, she took refuge in Burgundy. It was then that she knew St. Odilo, and spread her bounty to the French abbeys of the surrounding country. Notably, she rebuilt the monastery of St. Martin of Tours which had been destroyed by fire. Later, from Germany whither she had returned, she again sent presents to Tours, among them the finest cloak of her son, the repentant Otto. "When you reach the tomb of the glorious St. Martin," she wrote to the person to whom she entrusted the mission, "say, 'Bishop of God, receive these humble presents of Adelaide, servant of the servants of God, sinner by her nature, empress by divine grace. Receive also this cloak of Otto, her only son. And pray for him, thou who hadst the glory of covering with thine own cloak Our Lord, in the person of a beggar.'"

When she felt her end approaching, Adelaide had herself taken to the monastery of Sehl on the Rhine, to die and to be laid to rest near the tomb of Otto the Great, her second husband.

St. Albina

According to the Roman martyrology, a victim of the persecution of Decius.

St. Bean

Bishop of Mortlach in Scotland (11th century).

St. Eusebius

Bishop of Vercelli, was exiled to Palestine and Cappadocia for his ardour in combating the Arians. His numerous written works have been lost (d. 371).

St. Judicael

Assumed the title of king on the death of his father, prince of Domnonia. He abdicated, became a monk, again resigned and spent the last twenty years of his life in the monastery of Gael (d. 658).

December 17th

ST. OLYMPIAS (d. about 410)

CONSTANTINOPLE, her native city, was at that time torn by heresies and factions. Her father, Count Anycius, occupied a high official post; her mother was a relative of Arsaces the Great, king of Armenia. She herself was brought up by the sister of St. Amphilochius, friend of St. Basil. She also received lessons from St. Gregory of Nazianzus, to whom her family was related. When she was eighteen, Olympias married Nebridius, steward of the estates of Theodosius the Great. Invited to the wedding, Gregory, who had then retired to Arianzus, excused himself by a letter in which he said: "It would be neither easy nor decent for a gouty old man like myself to take his place at a nuptial feast." He added: "My daughter, may your husband be always first in your heart next to God; share your joys and sorrows together; let his be external business affairs, yours the spinning wheel, wool, and meditation on the divine oracles in the home. . . . May you see your children's children born and grown up to praise the Lord!"

This wish was not to be realized, for twenty months later Nebridius died, leaving his widow of twenty in control of an immense fortune. Suitors presented themselves, but she sent them away. The Emperor Theodosius urged her to marry a certain Elpidius, who was also refused; the goods of Olympias were then sequestered, but it was seen that their owner would never change her views.

From the resignation of St. Gregory of Nazianzus in 381 to the election of St. John Chrysostom in 397, the patriarchal see of Constantinople was occupied by St. Nectarius. He received Olympias as a deaconess; thenceforth her life was entirely devoted to works of zeal and charity.

Olympias was the friend of St. Chrysostom for the five years of his episcopate, and still more so during his exile. The seventeen letters he addressed to her show the friendship he felt for her. She was finally driven from Constantinople for having remained faithful to him. Her little community of deaconesses was dispersed; her goods were confiscated; she found herself insulted by those whom she had covered with benefactions; and after wandering from place to place, she died in exile at Nicomedia about 410.

St. FLORIAN

One of the sixty Christians massacred in Palestine by the Saracens, about the year 638.

Blessed YOLANDA

Became a Dominican nun at Marienthal after having suffered much from her father, the count of Vianden, because of her vocation (d. 1283).

St. BEGGA

Daughter of Blessed Pepin of Landen and of Blessed Ita, was the sister of St. Gertrude of Nivelles. The death of Auseghisel, her husband, the son of St. Arnulf of Metz, allowed her to retire to the convent, which she had founded at Andénne (Belgium). She died there in 698.

December 18th

ST. GATIANUS (4th century)

ST. GATIANUS is said to have brought Christianity to Tours and to have been its first bishop. Formerly it was suggested by some that he was one of the shepherds who, learning from the angel of the birth of the Saviour, went to adore Jesus in the stable at Bethlehem. It is better to place him in the 4th century, and his place of origin in Touraine, a few decades before St. Martin.

When the latter came to Tours, the traces of his predecessor's apostolate had almost vanished for, says Sulpicius Severus, "No one, so to speak, any longer knew even the name of Christ." St. Gatianus was, however, remembered; it was told how he had brought the Gospel to the region and there had ended his days. Sulpicius Severus adds that God revealed to St. Martin the place where Gatianus' body rested, and afterwards the great apostle never failed, on returning to Tours, to prostrate himself upon the tomb of St. Gatianus.

ST. FLAVITAS (d. about 630)

TAKEN prisoner after the Lombard invasion in 568, Flavitas was led from Italy to Gaul and sold as a slave in Champagne. His master, named Montain, paid thirty sous for him, at that time the price of a horse. He placed him on his estate of Marcilly-le-Hayer, near Troyes, married him to a slave named Aponia, and made him his steward.

Twice Flavitas lost and twice regained the favour of his master. The first time he was accused by the wife of Montain of having tried to seduce her; it was pure vengeance and calumny; the virtuous steward, like Joseph of old in Putiphar's house, had done nothing but resist the advances of this wicked wife. Another time, Montain was warned that Flavitas was dissipating his goods and planned his ruin; the truth, which later was acknowledged, was that in spite of what he gave to the poor, the steward had doubled his master's fortune. The latter finally set free Flavitas and his wife, who thenceforth could devote themselves to God. From St. Lupus, bishop of Sens, she received the nun's veil; and he, while waiting to be ordained priest, the hermit's garb.

St. Desiderius

Son of St. Waningus, the founder of Fécamp, was a monk at Fontenelle, Normandy (7th century).

Sts. Victurus, Victor, Victorinus, Adjutor, and Quartus

Members of a group of thirty-five African martyrs about whom no details are known.

St. Winebald

Brother of St. Willibald and of St. Walburga, left England to aid St. Boniface in the evangelization of Germany and founded a monastery at Heidenheim (d. 761).

December 19th

BLESSED URBAN V (1310–1370)

BORN at the castle of Grisac in the Cévennes, Guillaume de Grimoard, son of the knight of the same name, and of Amphélise de Montferrand, showed from his childhood a character hostile to every frivolity. Seeing him avoid the games proper to his age to withdraw into the chapel, his mother said: "I do not understand him, but, after all, it is enough that God understands him." He entered the Benedictine abbey of Chirac, near Mende; made his vows at that of St. Victor at Marseilles, and later joined the congregation of Cluny. On October 31st, 1342, he became doctor of canon law; taught in the universities of Toulouse, Montpellier, Paris, and Avignon; exercised the functions of vicar-general at Clermont and Uzès; was named abbot of St. Germain of Auxerre on February 13th, 1352, and on July 26th of the same year was appointed by Clement VI as pontifical legate in Lombardy. Later, becoming abbot of St. Victor of Marseilles, he was entrusted with the same mission to the kingdom of Naples by Innocent VI.

The popes were then living at Avignon; but they were already contemplat⁄ing their return to Rome, and it was in order to prepare this return that Guillaume used all his diplomatic skill in Italy. At the end of 1362, he himself succeeded Innocent VI under the name of Urban V. His pontificate was marked by the sending of missionaries to India, China, and Lithuania; by the preaching of a new crusade; by the support he gave to the development of ecclesiastical studies, and by various reforms which he effected in the administration of the Church. Having renewed the excommunication pro⁄nounced by Innocent VI against Peter IV, king of Castile, murderer of his wife and a polygamist, he authorized Henry of Trastamare, his brother, to dethrone him. At the same time he urged Du Guesclin and his "white companies" to help him, thus assuring the success of this dynastic revolution.

In 1367, Urban V thought the time was ripe for his return to Rome. On May 19th he embarked from Marseilles with twenty⁄three galleys; on June 3rd he landed at Corneto; on October 16th, he made his triumphal entry into the Eternal City. He could not, however, maintain himself there, and he was obliged, on September 26th, 1370, to return to Avignon. He died the following December 19th, clothed in the Benedictine habit. He had himself carried into his brother's house, not wishing to draw his last breath in a palace; on his orders, the doors of this house were left open, so that all might enter freely and see, as he said, "how a pope dies."

St. ADAM

Our first father.

Sts. THEA and MEURIS

Martyred at Gaza, in Palestine, about 307.

St. GREGENTIUS

Bishop of Dhafar, in Arabia, has left a treatise against vice (d. 552).

St. TIMOLEON or TIMOTHEUS

Deacon, preached the Gospel in Mauretania, and was burned alive there under Diocletian.

December 20th

STS. THEOPHILUS, ZENO
AND THEIR COMPANIONS (d. 249)

THE following scene was enacted during the persecution of Decius at Alexandria; all the *Acts* do not tell the story in exactly the same fashion, but by and large things happened roughly in this way:

A poor man whose sole crime was to be a Christian was brought to judgement in this town. Some of the soldiers in the governor's guard were among the spectators. The accused had at first behaved well; but now, as torture was being applied, his resistance was ebbing visibly, and it was thought at one moment that he was about to apostatize. It was then that a veteran called Theophilus began by sign and look to encourage him so strongly that the crowd, seeing the prisoner regaining mastery of himself, called out indignantly: "Do you, too, happen to be a Christian?"

"Yes, that I am," he replied in a voice like thunder, approaching the judges, "let me also be judged, and with me those of my comrades who profess the religion of Christ."

Four other soldiers, Ammon, Zeno, Ingenius, and Ptolemy were then seen proudly marching towards the tribunal. Either from surprise, from admiration, or because they feared that some misfortune might befall themselves, the president and his assessors hurriedly declared that they did not in any way wish to judge Theophilus and his friends, and that the five soldiers were free to withdraw. They did withdraw, and the crowd, suddenly calmed, respectfully hastened to make way for them. Some *Acts* affirm that later they all had an opportunity to shed their blood for the faith; but others say that they died of a peaceful old age.

Blessed JULIA DELLA RENA (d. 1367)

Of noble origin, she became a servant in Florence, then took the habit of the hermits of St. Augustine, and spent the last thirty years of her life in a cell built into the Church of St. Michael of Certaldo in Tuscany.

Sts. BAJULUS and LIBERATUS

Martyrs whose relics are honoured in Rome and who suffered, it is believed, in the East.

St. DOMINIC OF SILOS (1000–1073)

He restored the Benedictine abbey of Silos, in Spain. Expectant mothers invoke him for a happy delivery. When a queen of Spain was on the point of giving birth to a child, the abbot of Silos took St. Dominic's staff and carried it into the royal palace, and this relic remained there until the happy event had taken place.

St. URSICINUS (d. about 650)

Obliged, like St. Columbanus, his master, to leave Luxeuil, he took refuge in the Swiss mountains and lived there some years as a solitary; then he founded the monastery of St. Peter on the borders of the Doubs.

December 21st

ST. THOMAS (1st century)

THE only evangelist who speaks of St. Thomas specifically is St. John. He mentions him three times.

The first time is when Lazarus was raised from the dead. Learning that Jesus wished to go to Bethany, in that part of Judaea where He had just escaped from His enemies, the disciples said to Him: "Master, the Jews were but now threatening to stone thee; art thou for Judaea again?" Jesus replied: "Come, let us make our way to him. Thereupon Thomas, who is also called Didymus, said to his fellow-disciples, Let us go too, and be killed along with Him" (John xi, 8-16).

In the long farewell address which He made to them before going to His death, Jesus promised His own to return one day to fetch them: "There are many dwelling-places in my Father's house; otherwise, should I have said to you, I am going away to prepare a home for you? And though I do go away, to prepare you a home, I am coming back; and then I will take you to myself, so that you too may be where I am. And now you know where it is I am going; and you know the way there. Thomas said to him, But, Lord, we do not know where thou art going; how are we to know the way there? Jesus said to him, I am the way; I am truth and life; nobody can come to the Father, except through me" (John xiv, 2-6).

On the occasion of one of the apparitions of the risen Jesus to His apostles, "Thomas was not with them when Jesus came. And when the other disciples told him, We have seen the Lord, he said to them, Until I have seen the mark of the nails on his hands, until I have put my finger into the mark of the nails, and put my hand into his side, you will never make me believe. So, eight days afterwards, once more the disciples were within, and Thomas was with them; and the doors were locked. Jesus came and stood there in their midst; Peace be upon you, he said. Then he said to Thomas,

Let me have thy finger; see, here are my hands. Let me have thy hand; put it into my side. Cease thy doubting, and believe. Thomas answered, Thou art my Lord and my God. And Jesus said to him, Thou hast learned to believe, Thomas, because thou hast seen me. Blessed are those who have not seen, and yet have learned to believe" (John xx, 24–29).

A tradition has it that after Pentecost, St. Thomas went to evangelize the Parthians, Medes, and Persians, and that he penetrated as far as India and was martyred at Calamine. He is sometimes represented with a square rule in his hand, and both architects and masons have chosen him as their patron. His apocryphal *Acts* relate that during the course of his travels he laid out for Guduphara, king of India, a magnificent palace of a peculiar type, the plan of which no architect of the country had been able to draw.

St. Paul of Latros (d. 956)

Celebrated anchorite and monastic legislator of the Greek Church. He lived successively on Mount Latros, in Bithynia, and on the island of Samos.

St. Honoratus

Bishop of Toulouse (3rd century).

St. Themistocles

A shepherd who was peacefully tending his sheep when he was arrested by mistake instead of one Dioscorus, who was sought as a Christian. Themistocles took no steps to clear up the misunderstanding, and was happy to take Dioscorus' place and to die in torment (d. about 250).

December 22nd

BLESSED GRATIAN (1439–1503)

HE was the only son of an honest couple who lived in the village of Mulla near Kotor (Cattarro), in one of the most beautiful spots on the Dalmatian coast. His surname is unknown. His mother's name was Bonna; his father, Benedict, earned his living as a fisherman and a water carrier. He himself was plying the coastal trade along the Adriatic, when at the age of thirty, he heard a sermon in the Church of St. Christopher at Venice. When the sermon was over, he went to find the preacher in the sacristy and, as though it were a perfectly natural thing, asked to be received as a lay brother in his order. His request was immediately granted.

He returned to Mulla, sold the hut his parents had left him, his boat and his nets, and, a few weeks later, entered the novitiate of the hermits of St. Augustine, at Monte-Ortono, near Padua. There he was given the maintenance of the garden as his principal occupation, but he was also tailor, mason, carpenter, and shoemaker for the community. He slept under the rafters in an attic, with a stone for pillow; he added three fasts a week to those prescribed by the Church and his rule; he spent all his free moments in chapel; wore, next to his skin, a rough hair shirt, which is still shown today in the cathedral of Kotor. The biography devoted to him was written a century after his death, and is full of the miracles he accomplished and of the prodigious graces with which he was favoured. As in the life of St. Pascal Baylon, we see the walls of the church opening at the moment of the elevation to permit him to adore the Holy Eucharist; as in the *Fioretti*, we hear of the flames coming out of his heart, making people think that a fire was breaking out in the convent; there, too, are related the diabolical persecutions he long suffered. Demons beat him unmercifully; threw him against the walls; inflicted wounds upon him, of which one made him lame for the rest of his days. Brother Gratian spent his last years at the convent of St. Christopher of Venice and died there on November 9th, 1503.

St. FLAVIAN (d. 362)

All that is known about him was told on the occasion of the feast of his daughter, St. Vivian or Bibiana (*see December 2nd*).

St. FRANCES XAVIER CABRINI

Foundress of the Missionary Sisters of the Sacred Heart of Jesus, was born at Lodi (Italy) in 1850, and died at Chicago (U.S.A.) in 1917. From Codogna (Italy) where it was founded, her institute spread to France, Spain, England, the United States and South America, and counted, at the death of its foundress, seventy houses and three thousand members devoted to the care of the sick and to education. It was Pope Leo XIII who urged Mother Cabrini to send her daughters to America to aid the numerous Italian emigrants to that part of the world. She crossed the Atlantic twenty-five times to visit the different establishments of her congregation.

December 23rd

ST. VICTORIA (d. 253?)

ST. VICTORIA is supposed to have been martyred at Rome during the persecution of Decius. She and her sister Anatolia both belonged, it is said, to one of the noblest families of Tivoli. Christians, and both remarkably beautiful, they had been promised by their parents to local pagan noblemen. Victoria, promised to Eugenius, saw her wedding day approach with pleasure. Anatolia, on the contrary, betrothed against her will to Titus Aurelius, sought all possible occasions for delay. Urged by Eugenius, who had been himself urged by Titus Aurelius, Victoria tried to bring Anatolia to make a decision. She proved to her, from Holy Writ, that marriage was agreeable to God, because that had been the state of the patriarchs and prophets, and heaven had blessed their posterity. Anatolia retorted with such persuasive arguments in favour of virginity that Victoria immediately broke off her engagement, and on the same day sold her jewels and ornaments for the benefit of the poor.

Begged to intervene, the emperor allowed the disappointed suitors to carry off the young girls to their country houses, and there to persuade them to become their wives and to deny their faith. However, neither the gentleness nor the violence which they used could prevail against their constancy. It was Titus Aurelius who first lost patience, and Anatolia who first suffered martyrdom. As for Eugenius, he hoped that time would restore to him the heart of his betrothed. For years he employed, to win her back, treatment that was alternately harsh and kind. He went so far as only to give her for food daily one piece of dry bread. It was in vain; far from apostasizing, Victoria converted everyone who came near her. Exasperated, Eugenius finally asked Julian, prefect of the Capitol and count of the temples, to send him the executioner Liliarcus, and he it was who pierced Victoria's breast with one blow of his sword. The hagiographers add that Liliarcus immediately became a leper, and died, devoured by worms, six days later.

Blessed HARTMANN

Governed the church of Brixen (Tyrol) for twenty-four years and had the merit of frequently showing his independence of Frederick Barbarossa. He was found dead in his bath in 1164.

St. SERVULUS (d. about 590)

A paralytic beggar who long was the edification of the city of Rome. St. Gregory the Great relates in the eulogy he made of him that he knew the whole of the Holy Writ by heart.

December 24th

STS. ADELA (d. 735) AND IRMINA (d. about 716)

THEY were two sisters, daughters of St. Dagobert II, who was himself a son of St. Sigebert, king of Austrasia.

At the death of Sigebert in 656, Dagobert, aged seven, succeeded him, but Grimoald, mayor of the palace, soon dethroned him in favour of his own son, and the young prince had to take refuge in Ireland. He hid himself so well that the usurpers were able to spread the rumour that he was dead; but in 673, he reappeared at Metz and took possession of his throne again. Meanwhile, Dagobert in his exile had married an Anglo-Saxon princess called Matilda, who had given him one son and four daughters. St. Irmina and St. Adela were two of these.

Irmina was betrothed to Count Herman, who died before the date set for their wedding. She then became a nun and founded, in the old castle of Horren, at Trier, a convent which she placed under the Benedictine rule. An epidemic broke out which threatened to wipe out the entire community. Irmina sought the help of St. Willibrord, whose prayers brought about the cessation of the disaster. In gratitude, Irmina gave him the land of Echter- nach where the great missionary established the abbey which later bore his name.

Adela had married the nobleman Alberic, who gave her a son and left her a widow a few years later. Her riches and her beauty brought many suitors for her hand; but following the example of her elder sister, she, too, became a nun and founded, about 690, not far from Trier, the convent of Palatiolum, on the site of the present town of Pfalsel. Adela was its first abbess and died there on December 24th, 735.

Sts. LUCIAN, ZENOBIUS, and THEOTIMUS

Were members of a group of Christians martyred at Tripoli, about whom details are lacking.

St. DELPHINUS

Bishop of Bordeaux, was a friend of St. Ambrose and St. Paulinus of Nola and a staunch adversary of the Priscillianists (d. 404).

Blessed FRANCESCO DEI MALEFICII

A Florentine Franciscan, apostle of Corsica (d. 1290).

December 25th

ST. EUGENIA (d. about 258)

BEGUN under fortunate auspices, the reign of Valerian ended in grave economic difficulties. This emperor was persuaded that by enriching itself on its own account, the Church contributed to the ruin of the fortune of the State. This was the reason which drove him, in 257, to issue severe edicts against the Christians. The richest among them were those who had most particularly to suffer; they saw their goods confiscated and they themselves were often bidden to abjure their faith under pain of death.

Eugenia, a noble young girl, died for the faith during this persecution and her body was buried in the cemetery of Apronianus. She is thought to have been converted by the martyrs Hyacinth and Protus. Whatever else is told about her is legendary.

Her *Acts* make her a daughter of Philip, governor of Egypt, who at seventeen knew Greek, Latin, and philosophy, and who, moreover, was incomparably beautiful. Urged by her father to marry a young man who was rather mediocre although of noble lineage, she asked: "Is it with his ancestors or with him that I must live?" Her father thereafter left her free to choose for herself.

She chose to embrace Christianity one day when, passing a monastery with her servants, Hyacinth and Protus, she heard this verse of a psalm being sung: "The gods of the gentiles are demons; He whom we adore is the true God, creator of heaven and earth."

For reasons which could not be generally approved, her *Acts* relate, the bishop of Heliopolis allowed Eugenia to don men's garments and to become a monk with Hyacinth and Protus. All three lived for a certain time in a monastery of Heliopolis without the secret being discovered. They only left it in the wake of circumstances which it would take too long to relate. Eugenia then converted her whole family, founded a convent of Christian virgins in Africa; then she returned to Rome, still accompanied by Hyacinth and Protus. Under Valerian, she was finally beheaded.

CHRISTMAS

This is the oldest specifically Christian feast. From the beginning of the 4th century, the birth of the Saviour was commemorated at Rome. Sixty years later, it was similarly so in the East. Christmas began the liturgical year, and the custom was introduced of preparing for it by several weeks of penance, a period which took the name *Advent*.

Blessed NERA

Dominican tertiary, vowed herself to the care of the sick in the hospitals of Siena (1230–1287).

St. ANASTASIA

A martyr whose name occurs in the canon of the Mass (d. about 304).

St. ROMULUS

A Breton priest, founded a monastery in Berry (d. about 700).

December 26th

ST. STEPHEN (d. 33)

ST. STEPHEN is called "the first martyr"; it was he, indeed, who first shed his blood for the faith. The Acts of the Apostles relate that he was "full of grace and power, performed great miracles and signs among the people." He belonged, it seems, to that group of Hellenized Jews who had lost the use of Hebrew because they remained abroad after the Babylonian captivity. He had become a Christian, had been ordained deacon by the apostles, and as such was given the care of feeding the poor and the widows to whose support the Christian community in Jerusalem was committed.

"There were those who came forward to debate with him, some of the synagogue . . . but they were no match for Stephen's wisdom, and for the Spirit which then gave utterance. Thereupon they employed agents to say they had heard him speaking blasphemously of Moses, and of God. Having thus roused the feelings of the people, and of the elders and scribes, they set upon him and carried him off, and so brought him before the Council. There they put forward false witnesses, who declared, This man is never tired of uttering insults against the holy place, and the law. We have heard him say that the Nazarene, Jesus, will destroy this place, and will alter the traditions which Moses handed down to us."

The High Priest asked him if this were true. Then, in a long speech recorded in the *Acts*, Stephen showed them that this Jesus of Nazareth was indeed the Messias announced by Moses and the prophets, and come on earth to call all men to salvation.

"At hearing this, they were cut to the heart, and began to gnash their teeth at him. But he, full of the Holy Spirit, fastened his eyes on heaven, and saw there the glory of God, and Jesus standing at God's right hand; I see heaven opening, he said, and the Son of Man standing at the right hand of

God. Then they cried aloud, and put their fingers into their ears; with one accord they fell upon him, thrust him out of the city, and stoned him. . . . Thus they stoned Stephen; he, meanwhile, was praying; Lord Jesus, he said, receive my spirit; and then, kneeling down, he cried aloud, Lord, do not count this sin against them. And with that, he fell asleep in the Lord. . . . Stephen was buried by devout men, who mourned greatly over him" (Acts vi–viii).

St. THEODORE

Sacristan of the Church of St. Peter in Rome. St. Gregory the Great relates that he was often favoured with apparitions of the angels (6th century).

St. ZOSIMUS

Pope, condemned Pelagius and Pelagianism (d. 418).

St. ARCHELAUS

Bishop of Charcar in Mesopotamia; left anti-Manichaean writings valued by St. Jerome (d. about 280).

December 27th

ST. JOHN THE EVANGELIST (d. 101)

A NATIVE of Galilee, John was the son of Zebedee and Salome. With his brother, James the Greater, he followed the calling of fisherman, and was among the disciples of St. John the Baptist when he was called to follow Our Lord. Jesus had a predilection for him; he was "the disciple whom Jesus loved" (John xxi, 7), as the Gospel sometimes describes him. At the Last Supper, he was seen leaning his head against the breast of the Master who was about to die. It was to him that Jesus, at the point of death, confided the Virgin Mary, and he took her into his house; finally it was he who, the first of the apostles with St. Peter, ran to the tomb which Magdalen had found empty, and who first of them all recognized the risen Saviour on the shores of the lake of Tiberias.

However, he had not always been perfect. "Master," he said one day, "we saw a man who does not follow in our company casting out devils in thy name, and we forbade him to do it. But Jesus said, Forbid him no more; the man who is not against you is on your side." And later when some Samaritans having shut their door against the Saviour, James and John said to him:

"Lord, wouldst thou have us bid fire come down from heaven, and consume them? But he turned and rebuked them, You do not understand, he said, what spirit it is you share. The Son of Man has come to save men's lives, not to destroy them" (Luke ix, 49–56). Another time, the two brothers asked for themselves the first places in the kingdom of heaven. "Master, we would have thee grant the request we are to make. And he asked them, What would you have me do for you? They said to him, Grant that one of us may take his place on thy right and the other on thy left, when thou art glorified," which offended the other apostles, and led Jesus to say, "Whoever has a mind to be first among you, must be your slave" (Mark x, 35–44).

The Acts show us Peter and John remaining united in friendship after Pentecost; together they went up to the temple to pray; together they preached and were thrown into prison; both were sent together to Samaria there to bring down the Holy Ghost upon the newly baptized.

At the end of the 1st century, St. John was bishop of Ephesus. There it was, according to tradition, that he died, aged over a hundred. Tradition also adds that he was plunged into boiling oil during a voyage to Rome and was later exiled to the island of Patmos.

St. Nicarete

Cared for the poor at Constantinople. It is thought that she practised medicine and healed St. John Chrysostom, her spiritual father, of a stomach ailment (4th and 5th centuries).

St. Fabiola (d. 399)

She belonged to the illustrious Roman family of the Fabii and at first, in spite of being a Christian, took married life somewhat lightly. Widowed, she did penance and went to place herself under the direction of St. Jerome at Bethlehem. She left Palestine, fearing an invasion of that country by the Huns, and returned to Rome, where she founded hospitals for the poor and a hospice for pilgrims.

Sts. Theodore (d. 841) and Theophanes (d. 845)

These two brothers, both monks and both poets, endured atrocious tortures at Constantinople because they had remained faithful to the veneration of images. Theodore died in prison of his injuries. Theophanes was set free, became archbishop of Nicaea, surviving his elder brother by four years.

December 28th

THE HOLY INNOCENTS (1st century)

WHEN, guided by a mysterious star, the wise men arrived at Bethlehem, "they found the child there, with his mother Mary, and fell down to worship him and, opening their store of treasures, they offered him gifts, of gold and frankincense and myrrh. Afterwards, because they had received a warning in a dream forbidding them to go back to Herod, they returned to their own country by a different way. As soon as they had gone, an angel of the Lord appeared to Joseph in a dream, and said, Rise up, take with thee the child and his mother, and flee to Egypt; there remain, until I give thee word. For Herod will soon be making search for the child, to destroy him. He rose up therefore, while it was still night and took the child and his mother with him, and withdrew into Egypt, where he remained until the death of Herod, in fulfilment of the word which the Lord spoke by his prophet, I called my son out of Egypt.

"Meanwhile, when he found that the wise men had played him false, Herod was angry beyond measure; he sent and made away with all the male children in Bethlehem and in all its neighbourhood, of two years old and less, reckoning the time by the careful enquiry which he had made of the wise men. It was then that the word spoken by the prophet Jeremy was fulfilled: A voice was heard in Rama, lamentation and great mourning; it was Rachel weeping for her children, and she would not be comforted, because none is left." (Matt. ii, 11–19).

It is thought that a score of children were massacred by Herod's order. A feast was established in their honour in the 5th century, and many churches soon claimed to possess their relics.

In the middle ages, there originated the "Feast of the Little Clerics", which began at vespers on December 27th and ended with vespers on the 28th. On this occasion the choir boys and the children in the chapter schools were honoured. They chose a bishop, took over the canons' stalls, and sang in their stead. This improvised bishop presided over the offices, the intoning of the *Invitatorium* and the *Te Deum*, and accomplished various other functions which the liturgy reserves to great prelates. The pastoral staff was only taken from his hands at the verse in the Magnificat: *Deposuit potentes de sede* at the end of the second vespers. After this, he gave a banquet to his colleagues at the chapter's expense and returned with them to their benches.

Sts. CASTOR, VICTOR, and ROGATION

African martyrs whose names alone have reached us.

Blessed GASPARE BUFALO (1786-1837)

Son of a servant of Prince Altieri, Gaspare studied at the Collegium Romanum and first thought of entering the recently established Society of Jesus. He was ordained priest in 1808, and because he refused to take the oath of fidelity to Napoleon, he spent the next five years in prison. In 1815, he founded the congregation of Priests of the Precious Blood, devoted to the preaching ministry, and in 1834, a congregation of sisters of the same name devoted to the education of girls.

December 29th

ST. THOMAS BECKET (1117-1170)

IN 1155, Henry II, king of England and of a part of France, took as his chancellor Thomas Becket, archdeacon of Canterbury. This prelate, of Norman origin and possessor of an immense fortune, was considered one of the most capable men of his age. Some have compared him with Richelieu, whom he resembled by his statesmanlike qualities and his love of pomp. The visit which he paid, in 1158, to Louis VII, king of France, long remained famous. Thomas Becket crossed the Channel with six frigates and two thousand men. On his way to Paris, he traversed the cities preceded by two hundred and fifty musicians, surrounded by his many greyhounds, followed by eight carriages each pulled by six horses. Then came carts bearing his bedroom, his kitchen, his chapel, and his silver; then, on high chargers, hundreds of horsemen composed of the flower of the nobility, bedecked with gold and silver.

When the episcopal see of Canterbury fell vacant, Henry II gave it to his chancellor. Thomas was ordained priest, June 1st, 1162, and consecrated bishop two days later; after this he became the second person in the kingdom; and after this, too, he changed his life entirely and became the most austere of prelates.

Persuaded that the office of prime minister and that of chief of the Church in England were not reconcilable, he had resigned his functions as chancellor, to the king's annoyance. Henry II was still more displeased with him when, in 1164, on the occasion of the "Councils" of Clarendon and of Northampton, the archbishop took the pope's part against him. Thomas had to flee, disguised as a lay brother, and sought refuge at Compiègne with Louis VII. Then he stayed at the abbey of Pontigny and at that of St. Columba, near Sens. Four years passed at the end of which, upon the request of the pope and of the king of France, Henry II finally gave permission to Thomas to return to England. He counted thenceforward on a blind submission from him, but he was quickly disabused when he discovered that the archbishop continued to defend the prerogatives of the Roman Church against the royal pretensions. "Cursed be they that eat my bread unless they deliver me from this insolent priest," he cried one day. Some courtiers took upon themselves to carry out this cruel wish. Thomas, who was expecting to be killed, wished to be immolated in his cathedral, and it was there, on the night of December 28th, 1170, that he was cut down and hacked to death with swords.

St. DAVID (1084–1015 B.C.)

Born at Bethlehem, he had while young watched over his father's flocks and shown his courage. At the age of twenty-two, he was anointed king of Israel by Samuel. His sensuality drove him to kill the husband of the woman he coveted. This frightful crime was punished by the misfortunes which the prophet Nathan predicted to him. The psalms which David composed under divine inspiration to express his confidence in God and his sorrow for his sins are among the most beautiful prayers in use in the Church.

St. ELEANOR

Martyred in Ireland (16th century).

Blessed REGIMBERT

Became a monk after having been the intimate counsellor of Otto I (d. 964).

December 30th
ST. SABINUS (d. 304)

WHEN, in 304, Diocletian and his colleagues of the tetrarchy decided to prosecute the Christians, orders were sent to the provincial governors notifying them of the edict of persecution. That addressed to Venustian, governor of Etruria and Umbria, has come down to us. "We order," it ran, "that those who profess the Christian superstition be obliged to sacrifice to the gods; if they refuse, they shall be put to death, and their properties confiscated by the treasury." It was in virtue of this order that Bishop Sabinus, the deacons Exuperantius and Marcellus, and several other members of the clergy were arrested and imprisoned. Venustian summoned them before his tribunal in the forum of Assisi. He asked the bishop: "By what right do you urge the people to leave our gods to follow a dead man?"

"Knowest thou not that Christ, after being dead and buried, rose the third day?" replied Sabinus.

"You can choose between sacrificing to the gods or dying in torment," replied the governor, "after which, you have only to rise up again like the Christ, your master, on the third day."

Venustian had the bishop's hands cut off; then he turned to the two deacons, who, the *Acts* tell us, were trembling all over. However, assisted by their pastor's encouragement, they resisted his threats and died gallantly, their sides torn by iron hooks.

In the dungeon to which he was then returned, Sabinus received the assistance of a matron named Serena, and he cured one Priscian, born blind. Learning of this, Venustian, who suffered from an eye ailment, went to visit the martyr in his prison. This latter, not content with curing his eyes, healed his soul also and opened it to the faith. He baptized him, as also his wife and his sons, and found refuge in his house. The rumour of this came to Rome, where Maximianus Herculius directed the tribune Lucius to punish the governor and finish off the bishop. And thus it was that Venustian, his wife, and his two sons had their heads cut off at Assisi, and that Sabinus, taken to Spoleto, died under the rod. Although somewhat embellished with later additions, the *Acts* which relate these happenings are considered worthy of credence.

St. RAYNERIUS

Honoured as bishop of Aquila (epoch unknown).

December 31st

ST. SYLVESTER (d. 335)

POPE ST. SYLVESTER'S life is entirely unknown to us. Nothing more is known of him than that he was a Roman by origin, that his father was called Rufinus, and that he governed the Church of Rome from 314 to 335. This was, indeed, one of the great moments of ecclesiastical history. The Edict of Milan had just ended the era of persecutions; the conversion of Constantine was to allow the Christian religion to replace paganism throughout the whole Empire. The three councils held, then took on the highest importance. At Arles, in 314, the bishops of the West declared that the validity of the sacraments did not depend on the faith nor the virtue of the ministers conferring them. That same year, at Ancyra (Angora), the Eastern bishops decided thenceforward to admit to Communion all repentant sinners, whatever had been their sins. Finally, there took place in 325 the œcumenical Council of Nicaea (Isnik) which pronounced the condemnation of Arius, and proclaimed the divinity of Christ. Sylvester was represented by Vitus and Vincent, Roman priests, and by Hosius, bishop of Cordova.

ST. COLUMBA OF SENS (d. 374?)

ST. COLUMBA is honoured for having suffered martyrdom at Sens under Aurelian. Her *Acts*, written in the 8th century, relate that she had always had an insurmountable horror of idols. That is why, still a child, she fled from Spain and reached France, where, she had been told, a more beautiful religion flourished. The good people who welcomed her, baptized her and brought her up in the most perfect manner. However, the Emperor Aurelian passed through Sens and had all the Christians put to death. Alone, Columba found favour in his eyes, such was the nobility and the beauty of her features revealing her high origin. To his blandishments, however, she replied with words so proud that Aurelian ended by losing his temper and giving her over to persons of ill repute. But a bear came out of a wood, knelt at her feet, and kept at a respectful distance those who wished to approach her; the animal never left her, and the executioners themselves were for a long time unable to carry out their orders. It was not until Columba dismissed her rough protector that they succeeded in cutting off her head.

St. BARBATIAN

Priest of Antioch (5th century). During a voyage to the West he met Placidia Augusta, mother of Valentinian III, who took him as her spiritual director and built him a monastery at Ravenna.

St. CATHERINE LABOURÉ (1806–1875)

Sister of Charity, a native of Yonne, spent her life caring for the sick in the region of Paris. In 1832, the Virgin Mary appeared to her three times in the chapel of her convent on the Rue du Bac in Paris. During these visions Catherine was commanded to have a medal struck in commemoration of the merciful goodness of the Mother of God extended to the whole human race—this is the origin of the "Miraculous Medal."

Sts. MELANIA THE YOUNGER (383–439) and PINIANUS (d. 435)

Born in Rome, Melania was only thirteen when she married Pinianus. They had several children who all died in infancy. They then took the vow of continence, set their numerous slaves free and in order to give the value of their goods to the poor, they sold their possessions in Spain and Gaul, reserving those which they had in Italy, Sicily, and Africa. Then they went to visit St. Augustine, founded two monasteries in his diocese, and afterwards settled in Jerusalem. Melania lost her husband in 435. She took on the direction of a convent for some time, journeyed to Constantinople to convert her uncle Volusianus there, and came back to die in Jerusalem.

LIST OF SAINTS SPECIALLY INVOKED

St. ACACIUS is said to cure headaches (May 8th).

St. ADAM has been taken as patron by gardeners (December 19th).

St. AGATHA, patroness of nurses, is invoked against breast diseases and against fire (February 5th).

St. AGIA is invoked in lawsuits (April 18th).

St. ALBERT THE GREAT was given as patron by Pius XII, in 1941, to students of natural sciences (November 15th).

St. ALOYSIUS GONZAGA, named as patron of youth by Pius XI in 1926 (June 21st).

St. ALPHONSUS LIGUORI. Pius XII has given him as patron to confessors and professors of moral theology (August 2nd).

St. AMBROSE is the protector of bees and domestic animals (December 7th).

St. ANDREW AVELLINO is one of the patrons of a holy death, and is also invoked against sudden death (November 10th).

St. ANDREW THE APOSTLE, patron of fishermen and fish dealers, is also invoked by women who wish to become mothers (November 30th).

St. ANNE is the patroness of old-clothes dealers, of seamstresses, laceworkers, housekeepers, of carpenters, turners, cabinetmakers, stablemen, and broommakers. She is also invoked against poverty and to find lost objects (July 26th).

The ANNUNCIATION OF THE BLESSED VIRGIN is the feast of news dealers and ribbonmakers (March 25th).

St. ANTHONY OF PADUA is invoked for the protection of asses and horses, and specially to find lost objects (June 13th).

St. APOLLONIA is invoked against toothache (February 9th).

The ASSUMPTION OF THE BLESSED VIRGIN is the feast of harness-makers and fish dealers (August 15th).

St. BALBINA is invoked against scrofulous diseases (March 31st).

St. BALTHASAR, patron of manufacturers of playing cards and sawmen, is also invoked against epilepsy (January 11th).

St. BARBARA, patroness of firemen, mathematicians, fireworks makers, artillery men, architects, smelters, saltpetre workers, brewers, armourers, hatters, tilers, masons, miners, and carpenters, is also invoked against lightning, sudden death, and final impenitence (December 4th).

St. BARTHOLOMEW is the patron of butchers, tanners, and bookbinders (August 24th).

St. BENEDICT is invoked against temptations of the devil, inflammatory diseases, erysipelas, fever, and kidney disease (March 21st).

St. BERNARD OF MENTHON was named patron of mountain climbers by Pius XI in 1923 (May 28th).

St. BLAISE, patron of woolweavers and carvers, builders and stonecutters, is also invoked against wild beasts, coughs, whooping cough, goitre, and throat diseases in general (February 3rd).

St. BRICE is invoked against diseases of the stomach (November 13th).

St. CAMILLUS DE LELLIS was named by Leo XIII, in 1886, as patron of the sick and of infirmarians (July 18th).

St. CATHERINE OF ALEXANDRIA is the patroness of philosophers, old maids, scholars, knife grinders, millers, wheelwrights, tanners, turners, and spinners (November 25th).

St. CATHERINE OF BOLOGNA is the patroness of painters (March 9th).

St. CATHERINE OF SIENA was given as patroness to the nurses of Italy by Pius XII in 1943 (April 30th).

St. CATHERINE OF SWEDEN is invoked against miscarriages in childbirth (March 24).

St. CECILIA is the patroness of musicians and makers of musical instruments (November 22nd).

St. CHRISTOPHER, patron of archers, market carriers, fullers, fruit dealers, and automobilists, is invoked against sudden death, storms, hail, toothache, and impenitence at death (July 25th).

St. CLARE is the patroness of embroidery workers, of gilders, and of washerwomen. She is invoked against diseases of the eye and for good weather (August 12th).

St. CLAUDIUS is the patron of turners and toymakers (June 6th).

St. CLEMENT OF ROME is the patron of boatmen; he is also prayed to for the cure of sick children (November 23rd).

St. CONCORDIA is the patroness of nursing mothers and children's nurses (August 13th).

St. COSMAS is the patron of doctors, surgeons, druggists, and midwives (September 27th).

Sts. CRISPIN and CRISPINIAN are the patrons of shoemakers, glove makers, and weavers (October 25th).

St. CUTHBERT, patron in England of shepherds and mariners (March 20th).

St. CYRIACUS is invoked against diseases of the eye (August 8th).

St. DIONYSIUS THE AREOPAGITE is invoked against headaches and against the devil (October 9th).

St. DOMINIC OF SORA is invoked against fever and snakes (January 22nd).

St. DYMPNA is prayed to for those who are insane or possessed by the devil (May 15th).

St. ELIGIUS or ELOI is the patron of metalworkers, blacksmiths, wheel-wrights, veterinarians, saddlers, cutlers, miners, locksmiths, clockmakers, carriage makers, toolmakers, cab drivers, farmers, jockeys, farm workers, and labourers. He is also invoked for the cure of sick horses (December 1st).

St. EMIDIUS is invoked against earthquakes (August 5th).

St. ERASMUS, patron of navigators, is invoked against storms, against colic, intestinal diseases of children, and during the pains of childbirth (June 2nd).

St. EULOGIUS, patron of carpenters (March 11th).

St. EUSTACHIUS is considered efficacious in fighting fires and protecting us from the fires of eternity (September 20th).

St. FELICITAS OF ROME is prayed to for male children (July 10th).

St. FELIX OF NOLA is invoked against perjury (January 14th).

St. FIACRE is the patron of gardeners, pewterers, boxmakers, hosiers, and tilemakers (August 30th).

St. FLORIAN is invoked against fire (May 4th).

The FOUR CROWNED MARTYRS have been taken as patrons by masons, sculptors, and stoneworkers (November 8th).

St. FRANCIS BORGIA is prayed to against earthquakes (October 10th).

St. FRANCIS DE SALES was given as patron to writers by Pius XI in 1923 (January 29th).

St. FRANCIS XAVIER is invoked against plague. In 1904 Pius X named him patron of the Propagation of the Faith and other similar works (December 3rd).

St. GENESIUS OF ROME, patron of clowns and comedians (August 25th).

St. GENEVIEVE is invoked against fever (January 3rd).

St. GEORGE is invoked against skin diseases (April 23rd).

St. GERTRUDE OF NIVELLES is invoked against fever, against mice and rats, especially field rats, for cats, and to obtain good lodgings when travelling (March 17th).

St. GILES or EGIDIUS, patron of cripples and spur makers, is invoked against cancer, sterility in women, the terrors of the night, and madness (September 1st).

St. GOMER is invoked against hernia. He is the patron of woodcutters, turners, glovemakers, cowherds, and those unhappily married (October 11th).

St. GREGORY THE GREAT is the patron of singers and scholars (March 12th).

St. GUY or VITUS is invoked for dogs and against rabies, also against sleeping sickness, epilepsy, and the dance which bears his name (June 15th).

St. HILARY is invoked against snakes (January 14th).

The HOLY INNOCENTS are the patrons of choirboys and foundlings (December 28th).

St. HONORÉ, patron of bakers (May 16th).

St. HUBERT is the patron of hunters, foresters, smelters, furriers, and makers of precision instruments. He is invoked against rabies and for the protection of dogs (November 3rd).

St. HUGH OF CLUNY is invoked against fever (April 29th).

St. IGNATIUS LOYOLA was named by Pius XI, in 1922, patron of those making the Spiritual Exercises (July 31st).

The IMMACULATE CONCEPTION was given as patroness to the soldiers of the United States by Pius XII in 1942 (December 8th). This date is also the feast of tapestry workers and upholsterers, clothworkers, and coopers.

St. IRENE, patroness of young girls (June 28th).

St. ISIDORE, patron of labourers (May 10th).

St. IVES is the patron of lawyers, jurists, advocates, notaries, bailiffs, and orphans (May 19th).

St. JEAN-BAPTISTE DE LA SALLE. Pope Pius XII has given him as patron to the educators of youth (May 15th).

St. JEAN-MARIE VIANNEY was named by Pius XI, in 1929, patron of parish priests (August 9th).

St. JEROME is the patron of students (September 30th).

St. JEROME EMILIANI, named as patron of orphans by Pius XI in 1928 (July 20th).

St. JOHN CHRYSOSTOM is invoked against epilepsy. In 1908 Pius X named him patron of preachers (January 27th).

St. JOHN OF GOD named as patron of the sick and the dying by Leo XIII (March 8th).

St. JOHN OF NEPOMUCENE is invoked for the protection of bridges; against indiscretions and calumnies; in order to make a good confession (May 16th).

St. JOHN THE BAPTIST, patron of bird dealers, of cutters and tailors, is also invoked against spasms, convulsions, epilepsy, hail; also prayed to for the protection of lambs (June 24th).

St. JOHN THE EVANGELIST is the patron of theologians. He is invoked against burns and poisons, and also for good friendships (December 27th).

St. JOSEPH, patron of carpenters, wheelwrights, cabinetmakers, and of a good death. He was given as patron to the universal Church by Pius IX in 1870, as patron of workmen by Benedict XV in 1920, as patron of those who combat atheistic Communism by Pius XI in 1937 (March 19th).

St. JULIAN is the patron of fiddlers, jugglers, clowns, shepherds, pilgrims, hotelkeepers, ferrymen, and travellers seeking good lodging (February 12th).

St. LAWRENCE is specially invoked against lumbago and fire, and for the protection of vineyards. He is also the patron of cooks and restaurateurs (August 10th).

St. LEONARD is invoked at childbirth. He is the patron of prisoners, of coppersmiths, blacksmiths, locksmiths, porters, coal miners, and in certain places, of greengrocers and coopers (November 6th).

St. LOUIS is the patron of builders, of button makers, embroidery workers and haberdashers, of distillers, hairdressers, and barbers (August 25th).

St. LUCY is invoked against eye diseases, dysentery, and in general against hæmorrhages (December 13th).

St. LUKE is the patron of doctors, painters, glassmakers, lacemakers, of artists in general, and particularly those who use colour and brush (October 18th).

St. MARGARET cures kidney diseases and comes to the aid of those in childbirth (July 20th).

St. MARK, patron of glaziers and lawyers, is particularly invoked against scrofulous diseases and final impenitence (April 25th).

St. MARTHA, patroness of innkeepers, hotelkeepers, and laundresses (July 29th).

St. MARTIN, patron of horsemen and tailors, is specially invoked for the protection of geese (November 11th).

Blessed MARTIN DE PORRES is the patron of mulattoes and is invoked against rats (November 3rd).

St. MARY MAGDALEN, patroness of perfumers, tanners, glovemakers, and repentant women and girls (July 22nd).

St. MARY OF EGYPT is also the patroness of women who have formerly lived in sin (April 2nd).

St. MATTHIAS, patron of carpenters, tailors, and repentant drunkards, is particularly invoked against smallpox (February 24th).

St. MAURICE is the patron of dyers and is invoked against gout (September 22nd).

St. MICHAEL, patron of coopers, hatmakers, swordsmen, haberdashers, and grocers, is often invoked for a good death. Pius XII named him as patron of policemen in 1950 (September 29th).

The NATIVITY OF THE BLESSED VIRGIN is the feast of drapers and needle makers, fish dealers, distillers, coffeehouse keepers, cooks, and restaurateurs, tilemakers and potters, pinmakers and workers in silk, gold, or silver (September 8th).

St. NICHOLAS, patron of scholars, boatmen, fishermen, dock workmen and sailors, coopers and brewers, travellers and pilgrims, and those who have unjustly lost a lawsuit; also invoked against robbers (December 6th).

St. NICHOLAS OF TOLENTINO is particularly invoked for the souls in purgatory (September 10th).

St. ODO is prayed to for rain (November 18th).

OUR LADY OF LORETO was named patron of aviators in 1920 by the Congregation of Rites (December 10th).

St. PANTALEON is one of the patrons of doctors and is invoked against consumption (July 27th).

St. PASCAL BAYLON was given as patron by Leo XIII, in 1897, to Eucharistic congresses and organizations (May 17th).

St. PAUL, patron of ropemakers, is invoked against hail and serpent bite (June 30th).

St. PETER is the patron of locksmiths and cobblers; in parts of France he is also the patron of harvesters; he is also prayed to for the success of affairs before the Roman court (June 29th).

St. PETER CLAVER was named by Leo XIII, in 1896, as patron of negro missions (September 9th).

St. QUENTIN is invoked against coughs (October 31st).

St. QUIRINUS or CYRINUS is invoked against evil spirits, in cases of possession or obsession (March 25th).

St. RAYMOND NONNATUS, patron of midwives, is invoked for women at childbirth and for little children (August 31st).

St. ROCH, patron of tilemakers and surgeons; he is invoked against plague, ills of the knees, and cattle diseases (August 16th).

St. ROMANUS is prayed to for madmen and those who have been drowned (February 28th).

St. SCHOLASTICA is invoked against storms (February 10th).

St. SEBALDUS is invoked against the cold (August 19th).

St. SERVATUS is invoked against rats, mice, diseases of the legs, and in general for the success of enterprises (May 13th).

St. SEVERUS, patron of drapers, wool manufacturers, weavers, and silk makers (February 1st).

St. SIMON, patron of curriers (October 28th).

St. STEPHEN is patron of smelters and stonecutters (December 26th).

St. SUITBERT is invoked against throat troubles (April 30th).

St. THERESA OF THE CHILD JESUS was named patroness of the missions by Pius XI in 1923 (October 3rd).

St. THIEMO, patron of engravers (September 28th).

St. THOMAS AQUINAS was given as patron by Leo XIII, in 1880, to Catholic schools (March 7th).

The TRANSFIGURATION OF OUR LORD is in certain countries the feast of pork butchers and cleaners (August 6th).

St. URSULA, patroness of the educators of young girls, is invoked for a good death (October 21st).

St. VAAST or GASTON is invoked for children who are late in learning to walk (February 6th).

St. VALENTINE, patron of engaged couples and those who wish to marry, is specially invoked against epilepsy, plague, and fainting diseases (February 14th).

St. VÉRAN is invoked for the help of those who are insane (September 11th).

St. VICTOR, patron of cabinetmakers, is invoked against lightning (July 21st).

St. VINCENT, patron of winegrowers (January 22nd).

St. VINCENT FERRER, patron of makers of tile and brick, pavement workers, and plumbers (April 5th).

St. WILLIBRORD is invoked against epilepsy and convulsions (November 7th).

St. WOLFGANG, patron of carpenters, is also invoked against paralysis and apoplexy (June 7th).

St. ZITA, patroness of maidservants and housekeepers (April 27th).

INDEX

Bartholomew the Leper, Bl.	*December 13*	BERNARDINE OF SIENA	*May 20*
Bartolomea Capitanio	*July 26*	Bernardino Realini	*July 2*
Bartolomeo degli Amidei	*February 12*	Bernard of Abbeville	*April 14*
Barulas	*November 18*	BERNARD OF CLAIRVAUX	*August 20*
Basilissa of Horren	*December 5*	Bernard of Corleone, Bl.	*January 12*
Basilissa of Rome	*April 15*	Bernard of Meissen. *See* Benno	
Basil of Ancyra	*March 22*	Bernard of Menthon	*May 28*
BASIL THE GREAT	*June 14*	Bernard of Toulouse, Bl.	*December 3*
Basinus	*March 4*	Bernard of Vienne	*January 23*
Basle	*November 26*	Berno, Bl.	*January 13*
Bassianus	*January 19*	Bertha de Marbais, Bl.	*July 18*
BATHILDE	*January 30*	Bertha of Avenay	*May 1*
BAUDARINUS (or BAUDRY)	*August 1*	Bertha of Biburg, Bl.	*August 6*
Bavo (or Allowin)	*October 1*	BERTHA OF BLAGNY	*July 4*
Bean	*December 16*	Berthold of Mt. Carmel	*March 29*
Beata (or Benedicta)	*June 29*	Bertilia of Marœil	*January 3*
Beatrix da Silva	*August 16*	BERTILLE OF CHELLES	*November 5*
BEATRIX D'ESTE, Bl.	*January 18*	BERTIN OF SITHIO	*September 5*
Beatrix d'Este, Bl.	*May 10*	Bertrand of Angoulême	*June 6*
Beatrix of Lens, Bl.	*January 19*	BERTRAND OF COMMINGES	*October 16*
Beatrix of Rome	*July 29*	Bertrand of Le Mans	*June 30*
Beatus	*February 19*	Bertuin of Malonne	*November 11*
BEDE THE VENERABLE	*May 27*	Bessarion	*June 17*
Begga	*December 17*	Bettelin	*September 9*
Begga of Egremont	*October 31*	BIBIANA (or VIVIAN)	*December 2*
Belina	*September 8*	BIBLIS	*June 2*
Benedetto dell' Antella	*February 12*	BLAISE	*February 3*
BENEDICT	*March 21*	Blanchard	*March 10*
Benedict. *See* Bonizet		BLANDINA	*June 2*
Benedicta. *See* Beata		Blane	*August 10*
Benedicta of Assisi, Bl.	*March 16*	Bonaventura Tornielli. Bl.	*March 31*
Benedicta of Rome	*January 4*	BONAVENTURE	*July 14*
Benedict Biscop	*January 12*	BONIFACE	*June 5*
Benedict Labre	*April 16*	BONIFACE OF CARTHAGE	*August 17*
Benedict of Aniane	*February 12*	Boniface of La Cambre. Bl.	*February 19*
Benedict of Milan	*March 11*	Boniface of Tarsus	*May 14*
Benedict the Moor	*April 4*	Bonizella Piccolomini Cacciaconti, Bl.	
Benvenuto	*March 22*		*May 6*
Bénézet	*April 14*	Bonizet (or Benedict)	*October 23*
BENIGNUS OF DIJON	*November 1*	Bonna of Pisa	*May 29*
Benignus of Vallombrosa	*July 17*	Bonna of Treviso	*September 12*
BENJAMIN THE DEACON	*March 31*	BONNE D'ARMAGNAC, Bl.	*October 26*
Benno (or Bernard) of Meissen	*June 16*	Boris (or Roman)	*July 24*
Berard	*January 16*	Bova	*April 24*
Berenice. *See* Veronica		Brendan of Birr	*November 29*
BERNADETTE	*April 16*	BRICE	*November 13*
Bernardina, Bl.	*September 21*	BRIDGET OF SWEDEN	*October 8*
Bernardine of Feltre, Bl.	*September 28*	Brieuc	*May 1*

Gaspar the Magi	*January* 6	GERTRUDE OF EISLEBEN	*November* 15
GASTON. *See* Vaast		Gertrude of Nivelles	*March* 17
GATIANUS	*December 18*	Gertrude van der Oosten	*January* 6
Gaubert. *See* Waldebert		Gervasius	*June* 19
Gaucherius	*April* 9	Gervinus	*March* 3
Gaudentius	*January 22*	Gery of Cambrai	*August* 11
Gauthier of Bruges, Bl.	*January 22*	Gery of Sens	*March 29*
Gauthier of Esterp	*May* 11	Gherardino di Sostegno	*February 12*
GELASIUS I, POPE	*November 21*	Ghislain	*October* 9
Gelasius II, Pope, Bl.	*January 29*	Gilberta (or Agilberta)	*August* 11
Gemma Galgani	*April* 11	Gilbert of Caithness	*April* 1
Generosus	*July* 17	Gilbert of Fontenelle	*November* 4
Genesius of Arles	*August 25*	Gilbert of Meaux	*February* 13
Genesius of Clermont	*June* 3	Gilbert of Neuffontaines	*June* 6
Genesius of Rome	*August 25*	GILBERT OF SEMPRINGHAM	*February* 4
GENEVIEVE	*January* 3	Gildas the Wise	*January 29*
Gengou Gangulphus	*May* 11	Giles of Assisi, Bl. *See* Egidius of Assisi	
Geoffrey de Loudoun, Bl.	*August* 3	Giles (or Egidius) of Languedoc	
GEOFFREY OF AMIENS	*November* 8		*September* 1
Geoffrey of Peronne, Bl.	*January 15*	GILES OF SANTAREM, Bl.	*May* 14
George of Antioch	*April* 19	Giles of Tyre, Bl.	*April 23*
GEORGE OF CORDOVA	*July 27*	Giovanna Maria, Bl.	*February 22*
GEORGE THE GREAT	*April 23*	Giovanni Manetti	*February 12*
GEORGIA (or GEORGETTE)	*February 15*	GISELA (or ISBERGE)	*May 21*
Gerald	*March 13*	Giuseppe Maria Tommasi, Bl.	*January* 1
Géran	*July 28*	Gleb (or David)	*July 24*
Gerard Cagnoli, Bl.	*January* 2	Goban	*June 20*
Gerard Majella	*October 16*	Gobert of Rheims	*November 23*
Gerard of Brogne	*October* 3	Gobert of Villers, Bl.	*August 28*
Gerard of Brou	*June* 1	Godard of Hildesheim	*May* 4
Gerard of Clairvaux, Bl.	*June 13*	Godard of Rouen	*June* 8
Gerard of Gallinaro	*August 11*	Godfrey ot Kappenberg, Bl.	*January 13*
GERARD OF GRANDE SAUVE	*April* 5	Gohard	*June 25*
Gerard of Joigny	*December* 7	Gomer	*October 11*
GERARD OF LUNEL	*May 25*	GONZALVO	*January 10*
Gerard of St. Albinus	*November* 4	Gordianus	*May 10*
Gerard of Toul	*April 23*	Gorkum, Holy Martyrs of	*July* 9
Gerard of Villamagna	*May 13*	Gottschalk and Companions	*June* 7
Gerlach	*January* 5	GRATIAN, Bl.	*December 22*
GERMAINE COUSIN	*June 15*	Gratus	*September* 7
Germain of Auxerre	*July 31*	Great Litanies	*April 25*
GERMAIN OF PARIS	*May 28*	Gregentius	*December 19*
German Gardiner, Bl.	*March* 7	Gregory Grassi	*July* 7
Germanus of Africa	*September* 6	Gregory Lopez, Bl.	*July 20*
Germer	*September 24*	GREGORY OF NAZIANZUS	*May* 9
Gerontius of Cervia	*May* 9	Gregory of Nicopolis	*March 16*
Gerontius of Milan	*May* 5	Gregory of Nyssa	*March* 9
		Gregory of Tours	*November 17*

Justina of Sardinia	*May 14*	Leontius of Phoenicia	*June 18*
Justus of Canterbury	*November 10*	Leontius of Saintes	*March 19*
Justus of Castile	*August 6*	LEONTIUS OF SEBASTE	*March 10*
JUSTUS OF DAMASCUS	*September 2*	Leontius the Younger	*July 11*
Justus of Jerusalem	*November 24*	LEO OF MOROCCO	*October 10*
Justus of St. Claudius	*July 6*	Leo of Sens	*April 22*
Justus of Vienne	*May 6*	Leopold	*November 15*
Jutta. *See* Judith		Leo IX, Pope	*April 19*
Juvenal Ancina, Bl.	*August 30*	LEO THE GREAT	*April 11*
Juvenal of Narni	*May 3*	Leovigild	*August 20*
Juventinus	*January 25*	Léry	*September 30*
		Liberatus, martyr of the East	*December 20*
Kilian	*July 8*	LIBERATUS OF BYZACENA	*August 17*
Kunigunde	*March 3*	Liborius	*July 23*
		Lidwina of Schiedam	*April 14*
Ladislaus or Gielnow, Bl.	*May 4*	Lietbertus	*June 23*
LADISLAUS (or LAZLO) OF POLAND	*June 27*	LILIOSA	*July 27*
Laetus	*September 6*	LINUS	*September 23*
Lambert of Lyons	*April 14*	Liphardus	*June 3*
LAMBERT OF MAESTRICHT	*September 17*	Liuthard	*February 24*
Landelin	*June 15*	Lizier	*August 27*
Landric	*April 17*	Lô	*September 22*
LANDRY OF PARIS	*June 10*	Lollian	*December 9*
Lanfranc, Bl.	*May 28*	Lomer	*January 19*
LARGUS	*August 8*	Longinus of Cappadocia	*March 15*
Laura	*October 19*	LONGINUS OF MARSEILLES	*July 21*
Laurentius	*October 8*	Lorenzo da Brindisi	*July 22*
LAWRENCE	*August 10*	Louis Bertrand	*October 9*
Lawrence Justinian	*September 5*	Louise Albertoni, Bl.	*January 31*
Lawrence Loricatus	*August 16*	LOUISE DE MARILLAC	*March 15*
Lazarus of Constantinople	*February 23*	Louise of Savoy, Bl.	*July 24*
Lazarus of Marseilles	*February 11*	Louis Marie Grignon of Montfort	*April 28*
LAZLO. *See* Ladislaus		Louis of Anjou	*August 19*
LEA	*March 22*	Louis of Cordova	*April 30*
LEANDER	*February 27*	LOUIS OF FRANCE	*August 25*
LEOBARDUS	*January 18*	Lourdes, Apparitions of	*February 11*
LEOCADIA	*December 9*	Lubentius	*October 13*
Leocrita	*March 15*	Lubin	*March 14*
LEODEGAR	*October 2*	Lucanus	*October 30*
Leonard of Avranches	*March 4*	Luchesius, Bl.	*April 28*
Leonard of Cava, Bl.	*August 18*	Lucia Filippini	*March 25*
LEONARD OF NOBLAT	*November 6*	Lucian of Antioch	*January 7*
Leonard of Port Maurice	*November 26*	Lucian of Beauvais	*January 8*
Leonard of Vandœuvre	*October 15*	Lucian of Tripoli	*December 24*
LEONIDAS OF ALEXANDRIA	*April 22*	Lucidius	*April 26*
Leonidas of Athens	*April 15*	Lucifer	*May 20*
Leontius of Alexandria	*September 12*	Lucilla	*October 31*
LEONTIUS OF CAESAREA	*January 13*	Lucina	*June 30*

Thais	October 8	Thiemo	September 21
Thea	December 19	THIERRY (or THEODORIC)	July 7
THECLA OF SELEUCIA	September 23	Thierry of Orléans	January 25
Thecla of Venice	September 3	Thierry of St. Hubert, Bl.	August 28
THECUSA	May 18	Thio. See Theodulf	
Themistocles	December 21	Thomas à Kempis	August 25
Theobald of Limousin	November 6	Thomas Aquinas	March 7
Theobald of Mondovì	June 1	THOMAS BECKET	December 29
Theodard	September 10	Thomasello, Bl.	March 17
THEODORA	April 28	Thomas Felton, Bl.	August 28
THEODORA. See Theodosia		Thomas Holford, Bl.	August 28
THEODORE OF AMASIA	February 7	THOMAS MORE	July 9
Theodore of Constantinople	December 27	Thomas of Hereford	October 2
Theodore of Libya	March 26	Thomas Sherwood, Bl	February 7
Theodore of Marseilles	February 3	THOMAS THE APOSTLE	December 21
Theodore of Pavia	May 20	Thomas Whitbread. Bl	June 20
Theodore of Rome	December 26	Tiberius	November 10
Theodore of Sikion	April 22	Tiburtius	April 14
Theodore of Studium	November 11	Timoleon (or Timotheus)	December 19
Theodore (or Theudart) of Vienne		TIMOTHY	January 24
	October 29	Titianus of Brescia	March 3
THEODORIC. See Thierry		Titianus of Lodi	May 4
THEODOSIA (or THEODORA)	April 2	Titus	January 4
THEODOSIUS THE CENOBITE	January 11	Torello of Poppi, Bl.	March 16
Theodotus	November 14	Totnan	July 8
Theodulf of Lobbes	June 24	Touchard	October 25
Theodulf (or Thiou) of Rheims	May 1	Transfiguration of Our Lord	August 6
Theodulus of Caesarea	February 17	Trond (or Trudo)	November 23
THEODULUS OF ROME	May 3	Trudpert	April 26
Theodulus of Thessalonica	April 4	TRYPHON	November 10
Theophanes of Constantinople	December 27	Turibius of Astorga	April 16
Theophanes the Chronographer	March 12	Turibius of Lima	March 23
THEOPHILUS OF ALEXANDRIA	December 20	Tygride, Bl	November 22
Theophilus of Antioch	October 13	Tyllo	January 7
Theophilus of Brescia	April 27		
Theophilus of Caesarea	March 5	UBALDUS	May 16
Theophilus of Constantinople	October 2	Uganda, Twenty-two Martyrs of	June 3
Theophilus of Corte	May 19	ULRICH OF AUGSBURG	July 4
Theophilus the Penitent	February 4	Ulrich of Lutzel, Bl.	April 11
Theotimus of Tripoli	December 24	Ulrich of Zell	July 10
THEOTIMUS THE PHILOSOPHER	April 20	Ultan	October 31
Theotonio	February 18	Urban of Langres	April 2
THERESA OF THE CHILD JESUS	October 3	Urban of Nicomedia	September 5
Thérèse Fantou, Bl.	June 26	Urban of Saragossa	April 16
Theudart. See Theodore		URBAN I, POPE	May 25
Thibaut of Provins	June 30	URBAN V, POPE, Bl.	December 19
Thibaut of Salanigo	July 1	Urbicius of Huesca	December 15
THIBAUT OF VIENNE	May 21	Urbicius of Meung-sur-Loire	June 3

Wendelin	*October 21*	Wolfgang	*June 7*
Wibert. *See* Guibert		Wolstan	*January 19*
Wilfrid of Northumbria	*October 12*	Wulfric, Bl.	*February 20*
Wilfrid of Sweden	*January 18*		
Wilfrid of York	*April 24*	Yolanda (or Helen) of Gnesen	*June 15*
Wilfrid the Younger	*April 29*	Yolanda of Marienthal, Bl.	*December 17*
William Dean, Bl.	*August 28*	Yrieix. *See* Aredius	
William Firmat	*April 24*	Yves Mayeuc	*September 20*
William Gunter, Bl.	*August 28*	YVETTE, Bl.	*January 13*
William of Bourges	*January 10*		
William of Dijon, Bl.	*January 1*	Zacharias the Prophet	*September 6*
William of Eskilsöe	*April 6*	ZACHARY	*November 5*
William of Gellone	*May 28*	Zachary, Pope	*March 15*
William of Maleval	*February 10*	ZENAIDA	*October 11*
WILLIAM OF MONTE VERGINE	*June 25*	Zenaida of Constantinople	*June 5*
William of Perth	*May 23*	Zenobius of Cilicia	*October 30*
William (or Anthelm) of Pontoise	*May 10*	Zenobius of Tripoli	*December 24*
William of Saint-Brieuc	*July 29*	Zenobius of Tyre	*October 29*
William of York	*June 8*	ZENO OF ALEXANDRIA	*December 20*
William Waring, Bl.	*June 20*	Zeno of Carthage	*April 10*
Willibald	*July 7*	Zeno of Verona	*April 12*
Willibrord	*November 7*	ZEPHYRINUS	*August 26*
Winebald	*December 18*	ZITA	*April 27*
Winnoc	*November 6*	Zoe of Pamphylia	*May 2*
WINWALLUS	*March 3*	ZOE OF ROME	*July 5*
Wiron. *See* Guiron		Zoilus	*June 27*
Widukind, Bl.	*January 7*	Zosimus of Palestine	*April 4*
Wolbod	*April 21*	Zosimus of Rome	*December 26*